Property of
Eld. H. J. Capman

Hymns for The Living Age

Edited by H. Augustine Smith

New York: The Century Co.

229

Acknowledgment

To the many authors of hymns, liturgic verse and prayers, and to composers of tunes whose material is used herein, we record our sincere thanks. Every effort has been made to ascertain the owners of copyright and to give due credit. Since this has not always been possible proper acknowledgment will be made as soon as possible after notification.

THE CENTURY CO.

Contents

Enter into His Gates with Thanksgiving and into His Courts with praise. Be Thankful unto Him and Bless His Name.

Services
for
Congregational Worship

Responsive Readings from the Psalter, the Prophets,
the Gospels and Epistles

Calls to Worship, Prayers, Confessions, Offertory
Sentences, Benedictions

Selected and Arranged by

Henry Hallam Saunderson
Osbert Wrightman Warmingham
Ernest Bourner Allen
Harry F. Ward
H. Augustine Smith

✠

Index of Subjects

SERVICES FOR CONGREGATIONAL WORSHIP

LIST OF BIBLICAL PASSAGES

7

Services for Congregational Worship

1.

Come, Let Us Worship

Oh come, let us sing unto the Lord, let us make a joyful noise to the rock of our salvation.

Let us come before his presence with thanksgiving; let us make a joyful noise unto him with psalms.

For the Lord is a great God, and a great King above all gods.

In his hand are the deep places of the earth; the strength of the mountains is his also.

The sea is his, and he made it; and his hands formed the dry land.

Oh come, let us worship and bow down; let us kneel before the Lord our Maker.

For he is our God, and we are the people of his pasture and the sheep of his hand.

Today, oh that ye would hear his voice! Make a joyful noise unto the Lord, all ye lands.

Serve the Lord with gladness, come before his presence with singing.

Know ye that the Lord, he is God: it is he that hath made us, and we are his; we are his people, and the sheep of his pasture.

Enter into his gates with thanksgiving, and into his courts with praise:

Give thanks unto him, and bless his name, for the Lord is good, his loving kindness endureth forever, and his faithfulness unto all generations.

I was glad when they said unto me: Let us go into the house of the Lord.

Our feet are standing within thy gates, O Jerusalem. Jerusalem, thou art builded as a city that is compact together;

Whither the tribes go up, even the tribes of the Lord, for an ordinance for Israel, to give thanks unto the name of the Lord.

For there are set thrones for judgment, the thrones of the house of David.

Pray for the peace of Jerusalem: they shall prosper that love thee.

Peace be within thy walls, and prosperity within thy palaces.

For my brethren and companions' sakes, I will now say: Peace be within thee.

For the sake of the house of the Lord our God, I will seek thy good.

I will lift up mine eyes unto the hills: from whence shall my help come? My help cometh from the Lord who made heaven and earth.

He will not suffer thy foot to be moved: he that keepeth thee will not slumber. Behold, he that keepeth Israel will neither slumber nor sleep.

The Lord is thy keeper, the Lord is thy shade upon thy right hand. The sun shall not smite thee by day nor the moon by night.

[OVER]

The Lord will keep thee from all evil; he will keep thy soul. The Lord will keep thy going out and thy coming in, from this time forth and for evermore.

It is a good thing to give thanks unto the Lord, and to sing praises unto thy name, O Most High;

To show forth thy loving kindness in the morning, and thy faithfulness every night.

For thou, Lord, hast made me glad through thy work; I will triumph in the work of thy hands. How great are thy works, O Lord! Thy thoughts are very deep.

All nations whom thou hast made shall come and worship before thee, O Lord; and they shall glorify thy name, for thou art great, and doest wondrous things: thou art God alone.

2.

The Stars in Their Courses

Thy years, O God, are throughout all generations. Of old didst thou lay the foundations of the earth; and the heavens are the work of thy hands.

They shall perish, but thou shalt endure; yea, all of them shall wax old like a garment; as a vesture shalt thou change them, and they shall be changed; but thou art the same, and thy years shall have no end.

Whereupon were the foundations of the earth fastened? or who laid the corner-stone thereof,

When the morning stars sang together, and all the sons of God shouted for joy?

Canst thou bind the sweet influences of the Pleiades, or loose the bands of Orion? Canst thou lead forth the signs of the Zodiac in their

season? Or canst thou guide the Great Bear with her train?

Knowest thou the ordinances of the heavens? Canst thou establish the dominion thereof in the earth?

He healeth the broken in heart, and bindeth up their wounds.

He counteth the number of the stars, he calleth them all by their names.

O Lord, thou hast searched me, and known me. Thou knowest my downsitting and mine uprising; thou understandest my thought afar off.

Thou searchest out my path, and my lying down, and art acquainted with all my ways.

For there is not a word in my tongue, but, lo, O Lord, thou knowest it altogether. Thou hath beset me behind and before, and laid thine hand upon me.

Such knowledge is too wonderful for me; it is high, I cannot attain unto it.

Whither shall I go from thy Spirit? Or whither shall I flee from thy presence?

If I ascend up into heaven thou art there. If I make my bed in the grave, behold thou art there.

If I take the wings of the morning, and dwell in the uttermost parts of the sea;

Even there shall thy hand lead me, and thy right hand shall hold me.

If I say; Surely the darkness shall cover me, then the night shall be light about me.

Even the darkness hideth not from thee, but the night shineth as the day: the darkness and the light are both alike to thee.

When I consider thy heavens, the work of thy fingers, the moon and the stars which thou hast ordained;

What is man, that thou art mindful of him? And the son of man, that thou visitest him?

For thou hast made him but little lower than the angels, and crownest him with glory and honor.

Thou makest him to have dominion over the works of thy hands; thou hast put all things under his feet.

How precious also are thy thoughts unto me, O God! How great is the sum of them!

If I should count them, they are more in number than the sand: when I awake, I am still with thee.

Search me, O God, and know my heart. Try me, and know my thoughts;

And see if there be any wicked way in me, and lead me in the way everlasting.

3.

Thy Way is in the Deep

Where wast thou when I laid the foundations of the earth? Declare if thou hast understanding.

Who determined the measures thereof, if thou knowest? Or who stretched the line upon it?

Or who shut up the sea with doors, when it brake forth as if newly born;

When I made clouds the garment thereof, and thick darkness a swaddling-band for it,

And marked out for it my bound, and set bars and doors,

And said, Hitherto shalt thou come, but no further; and here shall thy proud waves be stayed.

Hast thou entered into the springs of the sea? Or hast thou walked in the recesses of the deep?

Have the gates of death been revealed unto thee? Or hast thou seen the gates of the shadow of death?

Hast thou comprehended the earth in its breadth? Declare if thou knowest it all.

Canst thou lift up thy voice to the clouds that abundance of waters may cover thee?

The earth is the Lord's and the fulness thereof; the world and they that dwell therein.

For he hath founded it upon the seas, and established it upon the floods.

By the word of the Lord were the heavens made, and all the host of them by the breath of his mouth;

He gathereth the waters of the sea together as a heap; he layeth up the deep in store-houses.

Let all the earth fear the Lord: let all the inhabitants of the world stand in awe of him.

For he spake, and it was done; he commanded and it stood fast.

Thy mercy, O Lord, is in the heavens; thy faithfulness reacheth unto the skies.

Thy righteousness is like the mountains of God; thy judgments are a great deep.

God is our refuge and strength, a very present help in trouble. Therefore will we not fear, though the earth do change,

And though the mountains be shaken into the heart of the seas; though the waters thereof roar and be troubled, though the mountains tremble with the swelling thereof.

Thou rulest the pride of the sea: when the waves thereof arise, thou stillest them.

[OVER]

Thy way was in the sea, and thy paths in the great waters, and thy footsteps were not known.

They that go down to the sea in ships, that do business in great waters;

These see the works of the Lord, and his wonders in the deep.

For he commandeth and raiseth the stormy wind, which lifteth up the waves thereof.

They mount up to the heavens, they go down again to the depths: their soul melteth away because of trouble.

Then they cry unto the Lord in their trouble, and he bringeth them out of their distresses.

He maketh the storm a calm, so that the waves thereof are still.

Then are they glad because they are quiet; so he bringeth them to their desired haven.

Oh that men would praise the Lord for his loving-kindness, and for his wonderful works to the children of men.

4.

The Majesty of the Lord

The Lord reigneth; he is clothed with majesty; the Lord is clothed with strength:

He hath girded himself therewith: the world also is established, that it cannot be moved.

Thy throne is established of old: thou art from everlasting.

The floods have lifted up, O Lord, the floods have lifted up their voice; the floods lift up their waves.

Above the voices of many waters, the mighty breakers of the sea, the Lord on high is mighty.

Thy testimonies are very sure: holiness becometh thy house, O Lord, for evermore.

Oh sing unto the Lord a new song, sing unto the Lord, all the earth.

Sing unto the Lord, bless his name; show forth his salvation from day to day.

Declare his glory among the nations, his marvelous works among all the peoples.

For great is the Lord, and greatly to be praised: he is to be feared above all gods.

For all the gods of the peoples are idols; but the Lord made the heavens

Honor and majesty are before him: strength and beauty are in his sanctuary.

Ascribe unto the Lord, ye kindreds of the people, ascribe unto the Lord glory and strength.

Ascribe unto the Lord the glory due unto his name: bring an offering, and come into his courts.

O worship the Lord in the beauty of holiness; tremble before him all the earth.

Say among the nations: The Lord reigneth. The world also is established that it cannot be moved: he will judge the peoples with equity.

Let the heavens be glad, and let the earth rejoice; let the sea roar, and the fulness thereof;

Let the field exult, and all that is therein; then shall all the trees of the wood sing for joy, before the Lord;

For he cometh, for he cometh to judge the earth: he will judge the world in righteousness, and the peoples with his truth.

The Lord reigneth; let the earth rejoice; let the multitude of isles be glad.

Clouds and darkness are round about him: righteousness and justice are the foundation of his throne.

A fire goeth before him. His lightnings lightened the world: the earth saw and trembled.

The mountains melted like wax at the presence of the Lord, at the presence of the Lord of the whole earth.

The heavens declare his righteousness, and all the peoples have seen his glory.

Light is sown for the righteous, and gladness for the upright in heart.

Be glad in the Lord, ye righteous; and give thanks to his high memorial name.

5.

Thy Kingdom is Everlasting

I will extol thee, my God, O King; and I will bless thy name forever and ever.

Every day will I bless thee; and I will praise thy name forever and ever.

Great is the Lord, and greatly to be praised; and his greatness is unsearchable.

One generation shall laud thy works to another, and shall declare thy mighty acts.

Of the glorious majesty of thine honor, and of thy wondrous works, I will meditate.

And men shall speak of the might of thy terrible acts; and I will declare thy greatness.

They shall utter the memory of thy great goodness, and shall sing of thy righteousness.

The Lord is gracious, and merciful; slow to anger and of great lovingkindness.

The Lord is good to all; and his tender mercies are over all his works.

All thy works shall give thanks unto thee, O Lord; and thy saints shall bless thee.

They shall speak of the glory of thy kingdom, and talk of thy power;

To make known to the sons of men his mighty acts, and the glory of the majesty of his kingdom.

Thy kingdom is an everlasting kingdom, and thy dominion endureth throughout all generations.

The Lord upholdeth all that fall, and raiseth up all those that are bowed down.

The eyes of all wait for thee; and thou givest them their food in due season.

Thou openest thy hand, and satisfieth the desire of every living thing.

The Lord is righteous in all his ways, and gracious in all his works.

The Lord is nigh unto all them that call upon him, to all that call upon him in truth.

He will fulfil the desire of them that fear him; he also will hear their cry and save them.

The Lord preserveth all them that love him. My mouth shall speak the praise of the Lord; and let all flesh bless his holy name forever and ever.

Thy throne, O God, is forever and ever: a sceptre of equity is the sceptre of thy kingdom.

I will make thy name to be remembered in all generations: therefore shall the people give thee thanks forever and ever.

Praise ye the Lord; praise the Lord, O my soul. While I live will I praise the Lord: I will sing praises unto my God while I have any being.

13

[OVER]

Put not your trust in princes, nor in the son of man, in whom there is no help. His breath goeth forth; he returneth to his earth.

The Lord loveth the righteous, but the way of the wicked he turneth upside down.

The Lord will reign forever, thy God, O Zion, unto all generations. Praise ye the Lord.

6.

The Religion of the Spirit

(*God Speaks and Man Answers*)

The mighty one, even God the Lord, hath spoken and called the earth from the rising of the sun unto the going down thereof.

Out of Zion, the perfection of beauty, God hath shined forth. Our God cometh, and doth not keep silence: He calleth to the heavens above, and to the earth, that he may judge his people:

Gather my saints together unto me, those that have made a covenant with me by sacrifice.

And the heavens shall declare his righteousness; for God is judge himself.

Hear, O my people, and I will speak; O Israel, and I will testify unto thee: I am God, even thy God.

I will not reprove thee for thy sacrifices; and thy burnt-offerings are continually before me.

I will take no bullock out of thy house, nor he-goats out of thy folds.

For every beast of the forest is mine, and the cattle upon a thousand hills.

I know all the birds of the mountains; and the wild beasts of the field are mine.

If I were hungry, I would not tell thee; for the world is mine, and the fulness thereof.

Will I eat the flesh of bulls, or drink the blood of goats?

Offer unto God the sacrifice of thanksgiving; and pay thy vows unto the Most High.

And call upon me in the day of trouble: I will deliver thee, and thou shalt glorify me.

Whoso offereth the sacrifice of thanksgiving glorifieth me; and to him that ordereth his way aright will I show the salvation of God.

Have mercy upon me, O God, according to thy lovingkindness: according to the multitude of thy tender mercies blot out my transgressions.

Wash me thoroughly from mine iniquity, and cleanse me from my sin. For I know my transgressions, and my sin is ever before me.

Against thee, thee only, have I sinned, and done that which is evil in thy sight; that thou mayest be justified when thou speakest, and be clear when thou judgest.

Behold thou desirest truth in the inward parts; and in the hidden part thou wilt make me to know wisdom.

Purify me with hyssop, and I shall be clean: wash me and I shall be whiter than snow.

Hide thy face from my sins, and blot out all mine iniquities.

Create in me a clean heart, O God; and renew a right spirit within me.

Cast me not away from thy presence; and take not thy holy Spirit from me.

Restore unto me the joy of thy salvation; and uphold me with a willing spirit. Then will I teach transgressors thy ways; and sinners shall be converted unto thee.

Deliver me from bloodguiltiness, O God, thou God of my salvation; and my tongue shall sing aloud of thy righteousness.

O Lord, open thou my lips; and my mouth shall show forth thy praise. For thou delightest not in sacrifice, else would I give it:

Thou hast no pleasure in burnt-offering. The sacrifices of God are a broken spirit: a broken and a contrite heart, O God, thou wilt not despise.

7.

The Mercy of God

Hear my prayer, O Lord, and let my cry come unto thee. Hide not thy face from me in the day of my distress.

Incline thine ear unto me. In the day when I call answer me speedily.

Be merciful unto me, O God, be merciful unto me; for my soul taketh refuge in thee: yea, in the shadow of thy wings will I take refuge.

For thy lovingkindness is great unto the heavens, and thy truth unto the skies. Be thou exalted, O God, above the heavens; let thy glory be above all the earth.

I waited patiently for the Lord, and he inclined unto me, and heard my cry. He brought me up also out of a horrible pit, out of the miry clay;

And he set my feet upon a rock, and established my goings. And he hath put a new song into my mouth, even praise unto our God.

Sacrifice and offering thou hast no delight in; mine ears hast thou opened: burnt-offering and sin-offering hast thou not required.

Then said I: Lo, I am come; in the roll of the book it is written of me: I delight to do thy will, O my God; yea, thy law is within my heart.

I have proclaimed glad tidings of righteousness in the great assembly; Lo, I will not refrain my lips, O Lord, thou knowest.

Withhold not thou thy tender mercies from me, O Lord; let thy mercy and thy truth continually preserve me.

Sing praise unto the Lord, O ye saints of his. For his anger is but for a moment; his favor is for a lifetime.

Weeping may come in to lodge at even, but joy cometh in the morning.

How precious is thy lovingkindness, O God! The children of men take refuge under the shadow of thy wings.

They shall be abundantly satisfied with the goodness of thy house; and thou wilt make them drink of the river of thy pleasures.

For with thee is the fountain of life: in thy light shall we see light.

Oh continue thy lovingkindness unto them that know thee, and thy righteousness to the upright in heart.

Bless the Lord, O my soul; and all that is within me, bless his holy name.

Bless the Lord, O my soul, and forget not all his benefits: who forgiveth all thine iniquities; who healeth all thy diseases;

Who redeemeth thy life from destruction; who crowneth thee with lovingkindness and tender mercies;

Who satisfieth thy desire with good things, so that thy youth is renewed like the eagle.

The Lord is merciful and gracious, slow to anger and abundant in lovingkindness.

15

[OVER]

He will not always chide, neither will he keep his anger forever.

He hath not dealt with us after our sins, nor rewarded us after our iniquities.

For as the heavens are high above the earth, so great is his lovingkindness toward them that fear him.

As far as the east is from the west, so far hath he removed our transgressions from us.

Like as a father pitieth his children, so the Lord pitieth them that fear him. For he knoweth our frame; he remembereth that we are dust.

The lovingkindness of the Lord is from everlasting to everlasting upon them that fear him.

The Lord hath established his throne in the heavens, and his kingdom ruleth over all.

8.

All Thy Works Shall Praise Thee

The heavens declare the glory of God; and the firmament showeth his handiwork.

Day unto day uttereth speech, and night unto night showeth knowledge.

There is no speech nor language; and their voice is not heard.

But their line is gone out through all the earth, and their words to the end of the world.

In them hath he set a tabernacle for the sun, which is as a bridegroom coming out of his chamber, and rejoiceth as a strong man to run his course.

His going forth is from the end of the heavens, and his circuit unto the ends of it; and there is nothing hid from the heat thereof.

Many, O Lord, my God, are the wonderful works which thou hast done, and thy thoughts which are to us-ward:

They cannot be set in order unto thee. If I would declare and speak of them, they are more than can be numbered.

Praise ye the Lord; for it is good to sing praises unto our God, for it is pleasant and praise is comely.

Great is our Lord, and mighty in power; his understanding is infinite.

Who covereth the heavens with clouds, who prepareth rain for the earth, who maketh grass to grow upon the mountains.

He giveth to the beast his food, and to the young ravens which cry.

Praise the Lord, O Jerusalem, praise thy God, O Zion. For he hath strengthened the bars of thy gates; he hath blessed thy children within thee.

He maketh peace in thy borders; he filleth thee with the finest of the wheat.

He sendeth out his commandment upon earth; his word runneth very swiftly.

He giveth snow like wool; he scattereth the hoar-frost like ashes. He casteth forth his ice like morsels. Who can stand before his cold?

He sendeth out his word, and melteth them: he causeth his wind to blow and the waters flow.

Praise ye the Lord from the heavens. Praise him in the heights. Praise ye him all his angels: praise ye him all his host.

Praise ye him, sun and moon. Praise him all ye stars of light. Praise him, ye heavens of heavens, and ye waters that be above the heavens.

Let them praise the name of the Lord; for he commanded, and they were created. He hath also established them for ever and ever. He hath made a decree which shall not pass away.

Praise the Lord from the earth, ye sea-monsters and all deeps; fire and hail, snow and vapor, stormy wind fulfilling his word;

Mountains and all hills; fruitful trees and all cedars; beasts and all cattle; creeping things and flying birds.

Kings of the earth and all people; princes and all judges of the earth; both young men and maidens; old men and children.

Let them praise the name of the Lord; for his name alone is exalted. His glory is above the earth and the heavens.

9.

The Glory of Zion, City of God

Oh clap your hands, all ye people, shout unto God with the voice of triumph.

For the Lord Most High is a great King over all the earth. He subdueth peoples. He chooseth our inheritance for us, the glory of Jacob whom he loved.

God is gone up with a shout, the Lord with the sound of a trumpet. Sing praises to God; sing praises. Sing praises unto our King, sing praises.

For God is the King of all the earth: sing ye praises with understanding.

Lift up your heads, O ye gates; and be ye lifted up, ye everlasting doors, and the King of glory will come in.

Who is the King of glory? The Lord, strong and mighty, the Lord, mighty in battle.

Lift up your heads, O ye gates; yea, lift them up ye everlasting doors, and the King of glory will come in.

Who is this King of glory? The Lord of hosts, he is the King of glory.

God reigneth over the nations: God sitteth upon his holy throne.

The princes of the people are gathered together to be the people of the God of Abraham. For the shields of the earth belong unto God: he is greatly exalted.

Great is the Lord, and greatly to be praised, in the city of our God, in his holy mountain.

Beautiful in elevation, the joy of the whole earth, is mount Zion, on the sides of the north, the city of the great King.

God hath made himself known in her palaces for a refuge. For lo, the kings assembled themselves, they passed by together.

They saw it, then were they amazed; they were dismayed, they hasted away.

As we have heard, so have we seen in the city of the Lord of hosts, in the city of our God. God will establish it forever.

We have thought on thy loving-kindness, O God, in the midst of thy temple.

As is thy name, O God, so is thy praise unto the ends of the earth. Thy right hand is full of righteousness.

Let Mount Zion be glad, let the daughters of Judah rejoice, because of thy judgments.

Walk about Zion, and go round about her; number the towers thereof, mark ye well her bulwarks, consider her palaces:

That ye may tell it to the generation following. For this God is our God forever and ever: he will be our guide even unto death.

[OVER]

There is a river, the streams whereof make glad the city of God, the holy place of the tabernacles of the Most High.

God is in the midst of her; she shall not be moved: God will help her, and that right early.

Come, behold the works of the Lord. He maketh wars to cease unto the end of the earth. He breaketh the bow, and cutteth the spear in sunder. He burneth the chariots in the fire.

Be still and know that I am God. I will be exalted among the nations, I will be exalted in the earth. The Lord of hosts is with us; the God of Jacob is our refuge.

10.

Fret not Thyself

Fret not thyself because of evildoers, neither be thou envious against them that work unrighteousness.

For they shall soon be cut down like the grass, and wither as the green herb.

Trust in the Lord, and do good; dwell in the land, and feed on his faithfulness.

Delight thyself also in the Lord; and he will give thee the desires of thy heart.

Commit thy way unto the Lord; trust also in him, and he will bring it to pass.

And he will make thy righteousness to go forth as the light and thy justice as the noonday.

Rest in the Lord, and wait patiently for him: fret not thyself because of him who prospereth in his way, because of the man who bringeth wicked devices to pass.

Cease from anger, and forsake wrath. Fret not thyself: it tendeth only to evil-doing.

For evil-doers shall be cut off; but those that wait for the Lord, they shall inherit the land.

For yet a little while, and the wicked shall not be: yea, thou shalt diligently consider his place, and he shall not be.

But the meek shall inherit the land, and shall delight themselves in the abundance of peace.

Better is a little that the righteous hath than the abundance of many wicked.

The Lord knoweth the days of the perfect; and their inheritance shall be forever.

They shall not be put to shame in the time of evil; and in the days of famine they shall be satisfied.

A man's goings are established of the Lord, and he delighteth in his way.

Though he fall, he shall not be utterly cast down; for the Lord upholdeth him with his hand.

I have been young, and now am old; yet have I not seen the righteous forsaken, nor his seed begging bread.

All day long he dealeth graciously, and lendeth; and his seed is blessed.

Depart from evil, and do good, and dwell for evermore. For the Lord loveth justice, and forsaketh not his saints.

They are preserved forever: but the seed of the wicked shall be cut off. The righteous shall inherit the land, and dwell therein forever.

The mouth of the righteous talketh of wisdom, and his tongue speaketh justice.

The law of his God is in his heart; none of his steps shall slide. Wait for the Lord, and keep his way.

I have seen the wicked in great power, and spreading himself like a green tree in its native soil.

Yet he passed away, and, lo, he was not: yea, I sought him, but he could not be found.

Mark the perfect man, and behold the upright, for there is a happy end to the man of peace.

The salvation of the righteous is of the Lord. He is their stronghold in the time of trouble, because they have taken refuge in him.

11.

The House of the Interpreter

Surely God is good to Israel, even to such as are pure in heart. But as for me, my feet were almost gone; my steps had well nigh slipped.

For I was envious at the arrogant, when I saw the prosperity of the wicked. For there are no pangs in their death; but their strength is firm.

They are not in trouble as other men; neither are they plagued like other men. Therefore pride is as a chain about their neck. Violence covereth them as a garment.

They have more than heart could wish. They scoff, and in wickedness utter oppression: they speak loftily.

They have set their mouth against the heavens, and their tongue walketh through the earth. They say: How doth God know? And is there knowledge in the Most High?

Behold, these are the wicked; and, being always at ease, they increase in riches.

Surely in vain have I cleansed my heart, and washed my hands in innocency; for all day long have I been plagued, and chastened every morning.

When I thought how I might know this, it was too painful for me; until I went into the sanctuary of God, and considered their latter end.

Surely thou settest them in slippery places: thou castest them down to destruction. How are they become a desolation, in a moment!

As a dream when one awaketh, so, O Lord, when thou awakest, thou wilt despise their image.

For my soul was in a ferment, and I was pricked in my heart: so brutish was I, and ignorant. Nevertheless I am continually with thee.

Thou hast holden my right hand. Thou wilt guide me with thy counsel, and afterward receive me to glory.

Whom have I in heaven but thee? And there is none upon earth that I desire besides thee.

My flesh and my heart faileth; but God is the strength of my heart and my portion forever.

For, lo, they that are far from thee shall perish: but it is good for me to draw near to God:

I have made the Lord God my refuge, that I may tell of all his works.

Teach me thy way, O Lord; I will walk in thy truth: unite my heart to fear thy name.

I will praise thee, O Lord my God, with my whole heart; and I will glorify thy name for evermore.

For great is thy loving kindness toward me; and thou hast delivered my soul from the lowest pit.

Thou, O Lord, art a God merciful and gracious, slow to anger, and abundant in loving kindness and truth.

Oh turn unto me, and have mercy upon me; give thy strength unto thy servant, and save the son of thy handmaid.

Show me a token for good, that they who hate me may see it, and be put to shame, because thou, O Lord, hast helped me and comforted me.

12.

A Day in Thy Courts

How amiable are thy tabernacles, O Lord of hosts! My soul longeth, yea, even fainteth for the courts of the Lord; my heart and my flesh sing for joy unto the living God.

Yea, the sparrow hath found her a house, and the swallow a nest for herself, where she may lay her young, even thine altars, O Lord of hosts, my King and my God.

Blessed are they that dwell in thy house: they will be still praising thee.

Blessed is the man whose strength is in thee; in whose heart are the highways to Zion.

Passing through the valley of weeping they make it a place of springs; yea, the early rain covereth it with blessings.

They go from strength to strength; every one of them appeareth before God in Zion.

O Lord, God of hosts, hear my prayer; give ear, O God of Jacob.

Behold, O God our shield, and look upon the face of thine anointed.

For a day in thy courts is better than a thousand. I had rather be a door-keeper in the house of my God, than to dwell in the tents of wickedness.

For the Lord God is a sun and shield: the Lord will give grace and glory; no good thing will he withhold from them that walk uprightly.

O Lord of hosts, blessed is the man that trusteth in thee.

They that trust in the Lord are as Mount Zion, which cannot be moved, but abideth forever.

As the mountains are round about Jerusalem, so the Lord is round about his people from this time forth and for evermore.

For the sceptre of wickedness shall not rest upon the lot of the righteous; that the righteous put not forth their hands unto iniquity.

Do good, O Lord, unto those that are good, and to them that are upright in their hearts.

But as for such as turn aside unto their crooked ways, the Lord will lead them forth with the workers of iniquity. Peace be upon Israel.

When the Lord brought back those that returned to Zion, we were like unto them that dream.

Then was our mouth filled with laughter, and our tongue with singing:

Then said they among the nations; the Lord hath done great things for them.

The Lord hath done great things for us, whereof we are glad.

Turn again our captivity, O Lord, as the streams in the south. They that sow in tears shall reap in joy.

He that goeth forth and weepeth, bearing seed for sowing, shall doubtless come again with joy, bringing his sheaves with him.

Except the Lord build the house, they labor in vain that build it: except the Lord keep the city, the watchman waketh but in vain.

It is vain for you to rise up early, to take rest late, to eat the bread of toil, for so he giveth his beloved sleep.

13.

Praise Waiteth for Thee

Praise waiteth for thee, O God, in Zion; and unto thee shall the vow be performed.

O thou that hearest prayer, unto thee shall all flesh come. Iniquities prevail against me. As for our transgressions, thou wilt forgive them.

Blessed is the man whom thou choosest, and causest to approach unto thee, that he may dwell in thy courts.

We shall be satisfied with the goodness of thy house, thy holy temple.

By terrible things thou wilt answer us in righteousness, O God of our salvation,

Thou that art the confidence of all the ends of the earth, and of them that are afar off upon the sea.

Who by his strength setteth fast the mountains, being girded about with might;

Who stilleth the roaring of the seas, the roaring of their waves, and the tumult of the peoples.

They also that dwell in the uttermost parts are afraid at thy tokens. Thou makest the outgoings of the morning and evening to rejoice.

Thou visitest the earth, and waterest it, thou greatly enrichest it. The river of God is full of water.

Thou providest them grain, when thou hast so prepared the earth. Thou waterest its furrows abundantly.

Thou settlest the ridges thereof. Thou makest it soft with showers. Thou blessest the springing thereof.

Thou crownest the year with thy goodness, and thy paths drop fatness. They drop upon the pastures of the wilderness, and the hills are girded with joy.

The pastures are clothed with flocks; the valleys are covered over with grain; they shout for joy, they also sing.

Make a joyful noise unto God, all the earth. Sing forth the glory of his name; make his praise glorious.

All the earth shall worship thee, and shall sing unto thee; they shall sing to thy name.

He ruleth by his might forever. His eyes observe the nations: let not the rebellious exalt themselves.

For thou, O God, hast proved us. Thou hast tried us as silver is tried. Thou broughtest us into a wealthy place.

I will come into thy house. I will pay thee my vows which my lips uttered, and my mouth spake, when I was in distress.

Come, and hear, all ye that fear God, and I will declare what he hath done for my soul. I cried unto him with my mouth, and he was extolled with my tongue.

If I regard iniquity in my heart, the Lord will not hear me. But verily God hath heard; he hath attended to the voice of my prayer.

Blessed be God, who hath not turned away my prayer, nor his lovingkindness from me.

14.

Their Faces Were Radiant

Blessed is the man whose transgression is forgiven, whose sin is covered.

Blessed is the man unto whom the Lord imputeth not iniquity, and in whose spirit there is no guile.

I acknowledged my sin unto thee, and mine iniquity did I not hide.

I said: I will confess my transgression unto the Lord. And thou forgavest the iniquity of my sin.

For this let every one that is godly pray unto thee in a time when thou mayest be found.

Surely when the great waters overflow they shall not reach unto him.

Thou art my hiding-place; thou wilt preserve me from trouble; thou wilt compass me about with songs of deliverance.

I will instruct thee and teach thee in the way which thou shalt go.

I will counsel thee, with mine eye upon thee. Be glad in the Lord, and rejoice, ye righteous; and shout for joy, all ye that are upright in heart.

I will bless the Lord at all times: his praise shall continually be in my mouth.

My soul shall make her boast in the Lord; the meek shall hear thereof, and be glad.

Oh magnify the Lord with me, and let us exalt his name together. I sought the Lord, and he answered me, and delivered me from all my fears.

They looked unto him, and were radiant; and their faces shall never be confounded.

The angel of the Lord encampeth round about them that fear him, and delivereth them.

Oh taste and see that the Lord is good. Blessed is the man that taketh refuge in him.

Oh fear the Lord, ye his saints, for there is no want to them that fear him. The young lions do lack, and suffer hunger, but they that seek the Lord shall not want any good thing.

Come, ye children, hearken unto me. I will teach you the fear of the Lord. Keep thy tongue from evil, and thy lips from speaking guile.

Depart from evil and do good. Seek peace and pursue it. The eyes of the Lord are toward the righteous, and his ears are open unto their cry.

The righteous cried, and the Lord heard, and delivered them out of all their troubles.

The Lord is nigh unto them that are of a broken heart, and saveth such as are of a contrite spirit.

Many are the afflictions of the righteous, but the Lord delivereth him out of them all.

The Lord redeemeth the soul of his servants; and none of them that take refuge in him shall be condemned.

Oh how great is thy goodness which thou hast laid up for them that fear thee,

Which thou hast wrought for them that take refuge in thee before the sons of men.

In the covert of thy presence wilt thou hide them; thou wilt keep them secretly in a pavilion from the strife of tongues.

Oh love the Lord, all ye, his saints. Be strong, and let your heart take courage, all ye that hope in the Lord.

15.

Songs of Deliverance

Oh give thanks unto the Lord, for he is good; for his lovingkindness endureth forever.

Let the redeemed of the Lord say so, whom he hath redeemed from the hand of the adversary,

And gathered out of the lands, from the east and from the west, from the north and from the south.

They wandered in the wilderness in a desert way; they found no city of habitation. Hungry and thirsty their soul fainted in them.

Then they cried unto the Lord in their trouble, and he delivered them out of their distresses;

He led them also by a straight way, that they might go to a city of habitation.

Oh that men would praise the Lord for his lovingkindness, and for his wonderful works to the children of men!

For he satisfieth the longing soul, and the hungry soul he filleth with good.

Such as sat in darkness and in the shadow of death, being bound in affliction and iron,

Because they rebelled against the words of God, and contemned the counsel of the Most High:

Therefore he brought down their heart with labor; they fell down, and there was none to help.

Then they cried unto the Lord in their trouble, and he saved them out of their distresses.

He brought them out of darkness and the shadow of death, and brake their bonds in sunder.

For he hath broken the gates of brass, and cut the bars of iron in sunder.

Oh that men would praise the Lord for his lovingkindness, and for his wonderful works to the children of men!

And let them offer the sacrifices of thanksgiving, and declare his works with singing.

He turneth a wilderness into a pool of water, and a dry land into watersprings.

And there he maketh the hungry to dwell, that they may prepare a city of habitation;

And sow fields, and plant vineyards, and get them fruits of increase.

He blesseth them also, so that they are multiplied greatly; yet setteth he the needy on high from affliction, and maketh him families like a flock.

The upright shall see it, and be glad; and all iniquity shall stop her mouth.

Whoso is wise will give heed to these things; and they will consider the lovingkindness of the Lord.

Praise ye the Lord. Oh give thanks unto the Lord, for he is good; for his lovingkindness endureth forever.

Who can utter the mighty acts of the Lord, or show forth all his praise? Blessed are they that keep justice, and he that doeth righteousness at all times.

Save us, O Lord our God, and gather us from among the nations, to give thanks unto thy holy name, and to triumph in thy praise.

Blessed be the Lord, the God of Israel, from everlasting to everlasting. And let all the people say: Amen. Praise ye the Lord.

16.

The Folly of Trusting in Riches

Hear this, all ye peoples; give ear, all ye inhabitants of the world, both low and high, rich and poor together.

My mouth shall speak of wisdom, and the meditation of my heart shall be of understanding. I will incline mine ear to a parable.

Wherefore should I fear in the days of evil, when iniquity at my heels compasseth me about?

They that trust in their wealth, and boast themselves in the multitude of their riches;

23   [OVER]

None of them can by any means redeem his brother, nor give God a ransom for him; for the redemption of their life is costly, and it faileth forever.

Wise men die; the fool and the brutish alike perish, and leave their wealth to others.

Their inward thought is that their houses shall continue forever, and their dwelling-places to all generations. They call their lands after their own names.

But man, being in honor, abideth not. He is like the beasts that perish. This, their way, is their folly. Yet after them, men approve their sayings.

They are appointed as a flock for the grave. Death shall be their shepherd. Their beauty shall be for the grave to consume, that there be no habitation for it.

Be not thou afraid when one is made rich, when the glory of his house is increased: for when he dieth he shall carry nothing away. His glory shall not descend after him.

Though while he lived he blessed his soul,—and men praise thee, when thou doest well to thyself,—he shall go to the generation of his fathers.

They shall never see the light. Man that is in honor, and understandeth not, is like the beasts that perish.

Why boasteth thou thyself in mischief, O mighty man? The loving-kindness of God endureth continually.

Thy tongue deviseth very wickedness, like a sharp razor, working deceitfully. Thou lovest evil more than good, and lying rather than to speak righteousness.

Thou lovest all devouring words, O thou deceitful tongue. God will destroy thee forever.

He will take thee up, and pluck thee out of thy tent, and root thee out of the land of the living.

The righteous also shall see it and fear, saying: Lo, this is the man that made not God his strength, but trusted in the abundance of his riches, and strengthened himself in his wickedness.

But as for me, I trust in the loving-kindness of God, for ever and ever. I will give thanks for ever. And I will hope in thy name.

Save me, O God, by thy name, and judge me in thy might. Hear my prayer, O God; give ear to the words of my mouth.

Behold, God is my helper. I will give thanks unto thy name, O Lord, for it is good. For he hath delivered me out of all my trouble.

17.

A Soul in Anguish

Give ear to my prayer, O God; and hide not thyself from my supplication.

Attend unto me, and answer me: I am restless in my complaint, and moan, because of the voice of the enemy, because of the oppression of the wicked;

For they cast iniquity upon me, and in anger they persecute me.

My heart is sore pained within me: and the terrors of death are fallen upon me.

Fearfulness and trembling are come upon me, and horror hath overwhelmed me.

And I said, O that I had wings like a dove! Then would I fly away and be at rest.

Lo, then would I wander far off; I would lodge in the wilderness.

I would haste me to a shelter from the stormy wind and the tempest.

For it was not an enemy that reproached me; then I could have borne it.

Neither was it he that hated me that did magnify himself against me; then I would have hid myself from him.

But it was thou, a man mine equal, my companion, and my familiar friend.

We took sweet counsel together; we walked in the house of God with the throng.

He hath put forth his hands against such as were at peace with him; he hath profaned his covenant.

His mouth was smooth as butter; but his heart was war. His words were softer than oil, yet were they drawn swords.

As for me I will call upon God; and the Lord will save me. He hath redeemed my soul in peace from the battle that was against me.

Cast thy burden upon the Lord, and he will sustain thee: He will never suffer the righteous to be moved.

Unrighteous witnesses rise up; they ask me of things that I know not. They reward me evil for good, to the bereaving of my soul.

But as for me, when they were sick, my clothing was sackcloth. I afflicted my soul with fasting; and my prayer returned into mine own bosom.

I behaved myself as though it had been my friend or my brother. I bowed down mourning, as one that bewaileth his mother.

But in mine adversity they rejoiced, and gathered themselves together: the abjects gathered themselves together against me, and I knew it not.

Let not them that are mine enemies wrongfully rejoice over me; for they speak not peace. But they devise deceitful words against them that are quiet in the land.

Thou hast seen it, O Lord. Keep not silence. Stir up thyself and awake to the justice due unto me, even unto my cause.

All that hate me whisper against me; against me do they devise my hurt.

Yea, mine own familiar friend, in whom I trusted, who did eat of my bread, hath lifted up his heel against me.

But thou, O Lord, have mercy upon me, and raise me up. As for me, thou beholdest me in mine integrity, and settest me before thy face for ever.

Blessed be the Lord, the God of Israel, from everlasting to everlasting, Amen and Amen.

18.

Out of the Depths

I cry with my voice unto the Lord; with my voice unto the Lord do I make supplication.

I pour out my complaint before him; I show before him my trouble.

When my spirit was overwhelmed within me, thou knewest my path. In the way wherein I walk have they hidden a snare for me.

Look on my right hand, and see; for there is no man that knoweth me: refuge hath failed me; no man careth for my soul.

I cried unto thee, O Lord; I said: Thou art my refuge, my portion in the land of the living.

Attend unto my cry, for I am brought very low: deliver me from my

[OVER]

persecutors; for they are stronger than I.

Bring my soul out of prison, that I may give thanks unto thy name: the righteous shall compass me about; for thou wilt deal bountifully with me.

Out of the depths have I cried unto thee, O Lord. Lord, hear my voice: let thine ears be attentive to the voice of my supplications.

If thou, O Lord, shouldest mark iniquities, O Lord, who could stand?

But there is forgiveness with thee, that thou mayest be feared.

I wait for the Lord, my soul doth wait, and in his word do I hope.

My soul waiteth for the Lord more than watchmen wait for the morning; yea, more than watchmen for the morning.

O Israel, hope in the Lord; for with the Lord is lovingkindness, and with him is plenteous redemption. And he will redeem Israel from all his iniquities.

Innumerable evils have compassed me about; mine iniquities have overtaken me, so that I am not able to look up;

They are more than the hairs of my head; and my heart failed me. Be pleased, O Lord, to deliver me: make haste to help me, O Lord.

Let all those that seek thee rejoice and be glad in thee: let such as love thy salvation say continually: The Lord be magnified.

But I am poor and needy; yet the Lord thinketh upon me. Thou art my help and my deliverer; make no tarrying, O my God.

Lord, my heart is not haughty, nor mine eyes lofty; neither do I exercise myself in great matters, or in things too wonderful for me.

Surely I have stilled and quieted my soul. O Israel, hope in the Lord from this time forth and for evermore.

I will give thee thanks with my whole heart: I will worship toward thy holy temple, and give thanks unto thy name for thy lovingkindness and thy truth.

In the day that I called thou answeredst me; thou didst encourage me with strength in my soul.

For though the Lord is high, yet hath he respect unto the lowly; but the haughty he knoweth from afar.

Though I walk in the midst of trouble, thou wilt revive me; and thy right hand will save me.

The Lord will perfect that which concerneth me. Thy lovingkindness, O Lord, endureth forever; forsake not the works of thine own hands.

19.

The Rock that is Higher than I

Hear my cry, O God; attend unto my prayer. From the end of the earth will I call unto thee, when my heart fainteth.

Lead me to the rock that is higher than I. For thou hast been a refuge for me, a strong tower from the enemy.

I will dwell in thy tabernacle forever: I will take refuge in the covert of thy wings.

For thou, O God, hast heard my vows: thou hast given me the heritage of those that fear thy name.

O God, thou art my God; earnestly will I seek thee: my soul thirsteth for thee, my flesh longeth for thee, in a dry and weary land, where no water is.

So have I looked upon thee in the sanctuary, to see thy power and thy glory. **Because thy lovingkindness is better than life, my lips shall praise thee.**

So will I bless thee while I live: I will lift up my hands in thy name.

My soul shall be satisfied, and my mouth shall praise thee with joyful lips.

When I remember thee upon my bed, and meditate on thee in the night-watches.

For thou hast been my help, and in the shadow of thy wings will I rejoice.

As the hart panteth after the water brooks, so panteth my soul after thee, O God.

My soul thirsteth for God, for the living God: when shall I come and appear before God?

My tears have been my food day and night, while they continually say unto me: Where is thy God?

These things I remember and pour out my soul. How I went with the throng, and led them to the house of God, with the voice of joy and praise, a multitude keeping holyday!

Why art thou cast down, O my soul? And why art thou disquieted within me?

Hope thou in God; for I shall yet praise him for the help of his countenance.

Deep calleth unto deep at the noise of thy waterfalls: all thy waves and thy billows are gone over me.

Yet the Lord will command his lovingkindness in the daytime; and in the night his song shall be with me, even a prayer unto the God of my life.

Why art thou cast down, O my soul? and why art thou disquieted within me?

Hope thou in God; for I shall yet praise him, who is the help of my countenance and my God.

Judge me, O God, and plead my cause against an ungodly nation: O deliver me from the deceitful and unjust man.

Thou art the God of my strength. Why go I mourning because of the oppression of the enemy?

Oh send out thy light and thy truth; let them lead me. Let them bring me unto thy holy hill and to thy tabernacle.

Then will I go unto the altar of God, unto God my exceeding joy; and upon the harp will I praise thee, O God, my God.

20.

Penitence and Peace

O Lord, rebuke me not in thy wrath; neither chasten me in thy hot displeasure.

For thine arrows stick fast in me, and thy hand presseth me sore. There is no soundness in my flesh, because of thine indignation.

Neither is there any rest in my bones because of my sin. For mine iniquities are gone over my head: as a heavy burden they are too heavy for me.

I am pained and bowed down greatly; I go mourning all the day long. I have groaned by reason of the disquietness of my heart.

Lord, all my desire is before thee; and my groaning is not hid from thee.

My heart throbbeth, my strength faileth me; as for the light of mine eyes, it also is gone from me.

In thee, O Lord, do I hope; thou wilt answer, O Lord, my God.

OVER!

Forsake me not, O Lord. O my God, be not far from me. Make haste to help me, O Lord, my salvation.

Unto thee, O Lord, do I lift up my soul. O my God, in thee have I trusted, let me not be put to shame.

Yea, none that wait for thee shall be put to shame. Show me thy ways, O Lord; teach me thy paths.

Guide me in thy truth, and teach me; for thou art the God of my salvation. For thee do I wait all the day.

Remember, O Lord, thy tender mercies, and thy lovingkindnesses, for they have been ever of old.

Remember not the sins of my youth, nor my transgressions: according to thy lovingkindness remember thou me, for thy goodness sake, O Lord.

Good and upright is the Lord; therefore will he instruct sinners in the way. The meek will he guide in justice; and the meek will he teach his way.

All the paths of the Lord are lovingkindness and truth unto such as keep his covenant and his testimonies.

For thy name's sake, O Lord, pardon mine iniquity, for it is great.

What man is he that feareth the Lord? Him shall he instruct in the way that he shall choose.

His soul shall dwell at ease. The friendship of the Lord is with them that fear him; and he will show them his covenant.

Mine eyes are ever toward the Lord for he will pluck my feet out of the net.

Turn thee unto me, and have mercy upon me; for I am desolate and afflicted.

The troubles of my heart are enlarged: Oh bring thou me out of my distresses. Consider mine affliction and my pain; and forgive all my sins.

Oh keep my soul, and deliver me; let me not be put to shame, for I take refuge in thee. Let integrity and uprightness preserve me, for I wait for thee.

Consider and answer me, O Lord my God, lighten mine eyes, lest I sleep the sleep of death.

But I have trusted in thy lovingkindness; my heart shall rejoice in thy salvation. I will sing unto the Lord because he hath dealt bountifully with me.

21.

A Day of National Penitence

Give ear, O Shepherd of Israel. O Lord, God of hosts, how long wilt thou be angry against the prayer of thy people?

Thou hast fed them with the bread of tears, and given them tears to drink in large measure.

Remember not against us the iniquities of our forefathers: let thy tender mercies speedily meet us, for we are brought very low.

Help us, O God of our salvation, for the glory of thy name; and deliver us, and forgive our sins, for thy name's sake.

Let the sighing of the prisoner come before thee: according to the greatness of thy power, preserve thou those that are appointed to death.

So we thy people and sheep of thy pasture will give thanks forever; we will show forth thy praise to all generations.

Thou hast been angry; Oh restore us again. Thou hast made the land to tremble; thou hast rent it.

Thou hast showed thy people hard things. Thou hast given a banner to them that fear thee, that it may be displayed because of thy truth.

All this is come upon us; yet have we not forgotten thee, neither have we dealt falsely in thy covenant.

Our heart is not turned back, neither have our steps declined from thy way.

If we have forgotten the name of our God, or spread forth our hands to a strange god, will not God search this out? For he knoweth the secrets of the heart.

Our soul is bowed down to the dust: our body cleaveth unto the earth. Rise up for our help, and redeem us for thy lovingkindness sake.

Remember thy congregation, which thou hast gotten of old, which thou hast redeemed to be the tribe of thine inheritance.

Remember me, O Lord, with the favor that thou bearest unto thy people.

Oh visit me with thy salvation, that I may see the prosperity of thy chosen, that I may rejoice in the gladness of thy nation, that I may glory with thine inheritance.

We have sinned with our fathers, we have committed iniquity, we have done wickedly.

My days are like a shadow that declineth; and I am withered like grass.

But thou, O Lord, wilt abide for ever; and thy memorial name unto all generations.

Thou wilt arise and have mercy upon Zion, for it is time to have pity upon her.

For thy servants take pleasure in her stones, and have pity upon her dust.

God be merciful unto us, and bless us, and cause his face to shine upon us;

That thy way may be known upon earth, thy salvation among all nations.

Let the peoples praise thee, O God; let all the peoples praise thee.

Oh let the nations be glad and sing for joy; for thou wilt judge the peoples with equity, and govern the nations upon earth. God will bless us, and all the ends of the earth shall fear him.

22.

A Heart Without Fear

The Lord is my light and my salvation; whom shall I fear? The Lord is the strength of my life; of whom shall I be afraid?

When evil-doers came upon me to eat up my flesh, even mine adversaries and my foes, they stumbled and fell.

Though a host should encamp against me, my heart shall not fear: though war should rise against me, even then will I be confident.

One thing have I asked of the Lord, —that will I seek after: that I may dwell in the house of the Lord all the days of my life, to behold the beauty of the Lord and to inquire in his temple.

For in the day of trouble he will keep me secretly in his pavilion: in the covert of his tabernacle will he hide me; he will lift me up upon a rock.

And now shall my head be lifted up above mine enemies round about me; and I will offer in his tabernacle sacrifices of joy;

I will sing, yea, I will sing praises unto the Lord. Hear, O Lord, when I cry with my voice: have mercy also upon me, and answer me.

When thou saidst: Seek ye my face; my heart said unto thee: Thy face, O Lord, will I seek.

Hide not thy face from me; put not thy servant away in anger. Thou hast been my help; cast me not off, neither forsake me, O God of my salvation.

Teach me thy way, O Lord; and lead me in a plain path because of mine enemies.

I had fainted unless I had believed to see the goodness of the Lord in the land of the living.

Wait for the Lord. Be strong, and let thy heart take courage. Yea, wait thou for the Lord.

Blessed be the Lord, because he hath heard the voice of my supplications.

The Lord is my strength and my shield; my heart hath trusted in him, and I am helped. Therefore my heart greatly rejoiceth, and with my song will I praise him.

The Lord is their strength, and he is a stronghold of salvation to his anointed.

Save thy people, and bless thine inheritance. Be their shepherd also, and bear them up forever.

Rejoice in the Lord, O ye righteous. Praise is comely for the upright.

For the word of the Lord is right; and all his work is done in faithfulness.

He loveth righteousness and justice. The earth is full of the lovingkindness of the Lord. The Lord looketh from heaven; he beholdeth all the sons of men.

From the place of his habitation he looketh forth upon all the inhabitants of the earth. He fashioneth the hearts of them all; he considereth all their works.

Behold, the eye of the Lord is upon them that fear him, upon them that hope in his lovingkindness.

To deliver their soul from death, and to keep them alive in famine.

Our soul hath waited for the Lord: he is our help and our shield. For our heart shall rejoice in him, because we have trusted in his holy name.

Let thy lovingkindness, O Lord, be upon us, according as we hope in thee.

23.

The Secret Place of the Most High

Thou wilt keep him in perfect peace whose mind is stayed on thee, because he trusteth in thee.

The way of the just is uprightness: thou that art upright dost direct the path of the just.

My soul, wait thou in silence for God only; for my expectation is from him.

He only is my rock and my salvation: he is my high tower; I shall not be moved.

With God is my salvation and my glory: the rock of my strength, and my refuge, is in God. Trust in him at all times, ye people.

Pour out your heart before him: God is a refuge for us. God hath spoken once; yea, twice have I heard this, that power belongeth unto God.

He that dwelleth in the secret place of the Most High shall abide under the shadow of the Almighty.

I will say of the Lord: He is my refuge and my fortress; my God, in whom I trust.

For he will deliver thee from the snare of the fowler and from the deadly pestilence.

He will cover thee with his pinions, and under his wings shalt thou take refuge: his truth is a shield and buckler.

Thou shalt not be afraid for the terror by night, nor for the arrow that flieth by day;

For the pestilence that walketh in darkness, nor for the destruction that wasteth at noon day.

A thousand shall fall at thy side, and ten thousand at thy right hand, but fear shall not come nigh thee.

Only with thine eyes shalt thou behold, and see the reward of the wicked.

Because thou hast said: The Lord is my refuge! Thou hast made the Most High thy habitation.

There shall no evil befall thee, neither shall any plague come nigh thy tent.

For he will give his angels charge over thee to keep thee in all thy ways.

They shall bear thee up in their hands, lest thou dash thy foot against a stone.

Thou shalt tread upon the lion and adder: the young lion and the serpent shalt thou trample under foot.

Because he hath set his love upon me, therefore will I deliver him: I will set him on high, because he hath known my name.

He shall call upon me, and I will answer him; I will be with him in trouble: I will deliver him and honor him.

With long life will I satisfy him, and show him my salvation.

24.

The Man of Integrity

Blessed is the man that walketh not in the counsel of the wicked, nor standeth in the way of sinners, nor sitteth in the seat of scoffers:

But his delight is in the law of the Lord; and on his law doth he meditate day and night.

And he shall be like a tree planted by the streams of water, that bringeth forth its fruit in its season, whose leaf also doth not wither; and whatsoever he doeth shall prosper.

The wicked are not so, but are like the chaff which the wind driveth away.

Therefore the wicked shall not stand in the judgment, nor sinners in the congregation of the righteous.

For the Lord knoweth the way of the righteous; but the way of the wicked shall perish.

Judge me, O Lord, for I have walked in mine integrity: I have trusted also in the Lord without wavering.

Examine me, O Lord, and prove me; try my heart and my mind.

For thy lovingkindness is before mine eyes; and I have walked in thy truth.

I have not sat with men of falsehood; neither will I go in with dissemblers.

I hate the assembly of the evildoers, and will not sit with the wicked.

I will wash my hands in innocency: so will I compass thine altar, O Lord.

[OVER]

That I may make the voice of thanksgiving to be heard, and tell of all thy wondrous works.

O Lord, I love the habitation of thy house, and the place where thy glory dwelleth.

Gather not my soul with sinners, nor my life with men of blood.

In whose hands is wickedness, and their right hand is full of bribes.

But as for me, I will walk in mine integrity: redeem me and be merciful unto me.

My foot standeth in an even place: in the congregations will I bless the Lord.

The law of the Lord is perfect, restoring the soul: the testimony of the Lord is sure, making wise the simple.

The precepts of the Lord are right, rejoicing the heart; the commandment of the Lord is pure, enlightening the eyes.

The fear of the Lord is clean, enduring forever; the ordinances of the Lord are true, and righteous altogether.

More to be desired are they than gold, yea, than much fine gold; sweeter also than honey and the droppings of the honeycomb.

Moreover by them is thy servant warned: in keeping of them there is great reward.

Who can discern his errors? Clear thou me from hidden faults. Keep back thy servant also from sins of presumption;

Let them not have dominion over me: then shall I be upright and I shall be clear from great transgression.

Let the words of my mouth and the meditation of my heart be acceptable in thy sight, O Lord, my rock and my redeemer.

25.

Instruction in Wisdom

Blessed are they that are upright in the way, who walk in the law of the Lord.

Blessed are they that keep his testimonies, that seek him with the whole heart.

Thou hast commanded us thy precepts, that we should observe them diligently. Oh that my ways were established to observe thy statutes.

I will give thanks unto thee with uprightness of heart, when I learn thy righteous judgments.

Wherewith shall a young man cleanse his way? By taking heed thereto according to thy word.

With my whole heart have I sought thee. Oh let me not wander from thy commandments.

Thy word have I laid up in my heart, that I might not sin against thee. Blessed art thou, O Lord; teach me thy statutes.

I will meditate on thy precepts, and have respect unto thy ways. I will delight myself in thy statutes; I will not forget thy word.

Deal bountifully with thy servant, that I may live; so will I observe thy word.

Open thou mine eyes, that I may behold wondrous things out of thy law.

Make me to understand the way of thy precepts: so shall I meditate on thy wondrous works.

Strengthen thou me according to thy word. Remove from me the way of falsehood, and grant me thy law graciously.

Teach me, O Lord, the way of thy statutes, and I shall keep it unto the end.

Give me understanding, and I shall keep thy law; yea, I shall observe it with my whole heart.

Make me to go in the path of thy commandments, for therein do I delight. Incline my heart unto thy testimonies.

Turn away mine eyes from beholding vanity, and quicken me in thy ways. Confirm unto thy servant thy word.

Let thy lovingkindness also come unto me, O Lord, even thy salvation, according to thy word.

So shall I have an answer for him that reproacheth me, for I trust in thy word. So shall I observe thy law continually forever and ever.

I will also speak of thy testimonies before kings, and shall not be put to shame, and I will delight myself in thy commandments.

Thy statutes have been my songs in the house of my pilgrimage. I have remembered thy name, O Lord, in the night, and have observed thy law.

It is good for me that I have been afflicted; that I may learn thy statutes.

The law of thy mouth is better unto me than thousands of gold and silver.

Thy word is a lamp unto my feet, and light unto my path. Quicken me, O Lord, according to thy word.

Thy testimonies have I taken as a heritage forever; for they are the rejoicing of my heart.

I have inclined my heart to perform thy statutes forever, even unto the end.

Thy law do I love. Thou art my hiding-place and my shield; I hope in thy word. Thy righteousness is an everlasting righteousness, and thy law is truth.

26.

In the Evening of Life

In thee, O Lord, do I take refuge: let me never be put to shame.

Deliver me in thy righteousness, and rescue me: bow down thine ear unto me, and save me.

Be thou to me a rock of habitation, whereunto I may continually resort.

Thou hast given commandment to save me; for thou art my rock and my fortress.

Rescue me, O my God, out of the hand of the wicked, out of the hand of the unrighteous and cruel man.

For thou art my hope, O Lord, my God; thou art my trust from my youth. My praise shall be continually of thee.

I am as a wonder to many; but thou art my strong refuge. My mouth shall be filled with thy praise, and with thy honor all the day.

Cast me not off in the time of old age; forsake me not when my strength faileth. O God, be not far from me; O my God, make haste to help me.

But I will hope continually, and will praise thee yet more and more. My mouth shall tell of thy righteousness, and of thy salvation all the day.

I will come in the strength of the mighty acts of the Lord my God: I will make mention of thy righteousness, even of thine only.

O God, thou hast taught me from my youth; and hitherto have I declared thy wondrous works.

Yea, even when I am old and grayheaded, O God, forsake me not, until I have declared thy strength unto the

[OVER]

next generation, thy might to every one that is to come.

Thy righteousness also, O God, is very high; thou who hast done great things, O God, who is like unto thee?

Thou, who hast showed us many and sore troubles, wilt quicken us again, and wilt bring us up again from the depths of the earth.

Increase thou my greatness, and turn again and comfort me. I will also praise thee, even thy truth, O my God. Unto thee will I sing praises, O thou Holy One of Israel.

My lips shall shout for joy when I sing praises unto thee; and my soul, which thou hast redeemed. My tongue also shall talk of thy righteousness all the day long.

Make haste, O God, to deliver me; make haste to help me, O Lord.

Let all those that seek thee rejoice and be glad in thee: and let such as love thy salvation say continually: Let God be magnified.

But I am poor and needy; make haste unto me, O God.

Thou art my help and my deliverer; O Lord, make no tarrying.

27.

The Judge of all the Earth

O Lord, thou God to whom vengeance belongeth, thou God to whom vengeance belongeth, shine forth.

Lift up thyself, thou judge of the earth: render to the proud their desert.

O Lord, how long shall the wicked, how long shall the wicked triumph? They prate; they speak arrogantly. All the workers of iniquity boast themselves.

And they say: The Lord will not see. Neither will the God of Jacob consider.

Consider, ye brutish among the people, and ye fools: when will ye be wise? He that planted the ear, shall he not hear? He that formed the eye, shall he not see?

He that instructeth the nations, shall not he correct; even he that teacheth man knowledge? The Lord knoweth the thoughts of man.

Why standest thou afar off, O Lord? Why hidest thou thyself in times of trouble? In the pride of the wicked, the poor is hotly pursued.

The wicked, in the pride of his countenance, saith: He will not require it. All his thoughts are: There is no God.

He saith in his heart: I shall not be moved; to all generations I shall not be in adversity.

He saith in his heart: God hath forgotten, he hideth his face, he will never see it.

Arise, O Lord; O God, lift up thy hand: forget not the poor. Wherefore doth the wicked contemn God, and say in his heart: Thou wilt not require it?

Thou hast seen it, for thou beholdest mischief and spite to requite it with thy hand. O Lord, thou hast heard the desire of the meek: thou wilt prepare their heart, thou wilt cause thine ear to hear; to judge the fatherless and the oppressed.

The fool hath said in his heart; there is no God. They are corrupt, they have done abominable works.

The Lord looketh down from heaven upon the children of men, to see if there were any that did understand, that did seek after God.

The trangression of the wicked uttereth its word. There is no fear of God before his eyes.

For he flattereth himself, in his own eyes, that his iniquity will not be found out and be hated.

The eyes of the Lord are upon the ways of a man, and he seeth all his goings.

There is no darkness, nor thick gloom, where the workers of iniquity may hide themselves.

Am I a God at hand, saith the Lord, and not a God afar off? Can any hide himself in secret places so that I shall not see him? saith the Lord.

Do not I fill heaven and earth? saith the Lord. Is not my word like fire? saith the Lord; and like a hammer that breaketh the rock in pieces?

Wherefore hear the word of the Lord, ye scoffers. Because ye have said: We have made a covenant with death, and with the grave are we at agreement;

When the overflowing scourge shall pass through, it shall not come unto us; for we have made lies our refuge, and under falsehood have we hid ourselves;

The hail shall sweep away the refuge of lies, and the waters shall overflow the hiding-place.

And your covenant with death shall be annulled, and your agreement with the grave shall not stand.

For the bed is shorter than that a man can stretch himself on it; and the covering narrower than that he can wrap himself in it.

For the Lord will rise up, that he may do his work, his strange work; and bring to pass his act, his strange act.

28.

The Nation whose God is the Lord

We have heard with our ears, O God,—our fathers have told us, what works thou didst in their days, in the days of old.

Thou didst drive out the nations with thy hand; but them thou didst plant. Thou didst afflict the peoples; but them thou didst spread abroad.

For they got not the land in possession by their own sword, neither did their own arm save them;

But thy right hand, and thine arm, and the light of thy countenance, because thou wast favorable unto them.

Give ear, O my people to my law; incline your ears to the words of my mouth.

I will open my mouth in a parable; I will utter dark sayings of old,

Which we have heard and known and our fathers have told us; we will not hide them from their children,

Telling to the generation to come the praises of the Lord, and his strength, and his wondrous works, that he hath done.

For he established a testimony in Jacob, and appointed a law in Israel,

Which he commanded our fathers, that they should make them known to their children;

That the generation to come might know them, even the children that should be born; who should arise and tell them to their children,

That they might set their hope in God, and not forget the works of God, but keep his commandments.

Thou art holy, O thou that art enthroned upon the praises of Israel. Our fathers trusted in thee.

[OVER]

They trusted, and thou didst deliver them. They cried unto thee, and were delivered: they trusted in thee and were not put to shame.

When they were but a few in number, yea, very few, and sojourners in the land,

And they went about from nation to nation, from one kingdom to another people;

He suffered no man to do them wrong, yea, he reproved kings for their sakes,

Saying: Touch not mine anointed ones, and do my prophets no harm.

Turn us again, O God of hosts, and cause thy face to shine, and we shall be saved. Thou broughtest a vine out of Egypt: thou didst drive out the nations and plantedst it.

Thou preparedst room before it, and it took deep root, and filled the land. The mountains were covered with the shadow of it, and the boughs thereof were like goodly cedars.

It sent out its branches unto the sea, and its shoots unto the River. Turn again, we beseech thee, O God of hosts.

Look down from heaven, and behold, and visit this vine, and the stock which thy right hand planted, and the branch that thou madest strong for thyself.

So shall we not go back from thee. Quicken thou us, and we will call upon thy name.

Turn us again, O Lord, God of hosts; cause thy face to shine and we shall be saved.

The counsel of the Lord standeth forever, the thoughts of his heart to all generations.

Blessed is the nation whose God is the Lord; the people whom he hath chosen for his own inheritance.

29.

The Brevity of Human Life

I said: I will take heed to my ways that I sin not with my tongue: I will keep my mouth with a bridle while the wicked is before me.

I was dumb with silence. I held my peace, even from good. And my sorrow was stirred.

My heart was hot within me; while I was musing, the fire burned. Then spake I with my tongue:

Lord, make me to know mine end, and the measure of my days, what it is; let me know how frail I am.

Behold, thou hast made my days as handbreadths; and my life-time is as nothing before thee: surely every man at his best estate is altogether vanity.

Surely every man walketh in a vain show; surely they are disquieted in vain: he heapeth up riches, and knoweth not who shall gather them.

And now, Lord, what wait I for? My hope is in thee. Deliver me from all my transgressions: make me not the reproach of the foolish.

I was dumb, I opened not my mouth; because thou didst it. Remove thy stroke away from me: I am consumed by the blow of thy hand.

When thou, with rebukes, dost correct man for iniquity, thou makest his beauty to consume away like a moth. Surely every man is vanity.

Hear my prayer, O Lord, and give ear unto my cry; hold not thy peace at my tears.

For I am a stranger with thee, a sojourner, as all my fathers were.

Oh spare me, that I may recover strength, before I go hence and be no more.

As for man, his days are as grass; as a flower of the field, so he flourisheth.

For the wind passeth over it and it is gone; and the place thereof shall know it no more.

Man that is born of a woman is of few days, and full of trouble. He cometh forth like a flower, and is cut down: he fleeth also as a shadow, and continueth not.

Seeing his days are determined, the number of his months is with thee, and thou hast appointed his bounds that he cannot pass.

For there is hope of a tree, if it be cut down, that it will sprout again, and that the tender branch thereof will not cease.

If a man die, shall he live again? All the days of my warfare would I wait, till my release should come.

Remember now thy Creator in the days of thy youth, before the evil days come, and the years draw nigh, when thou shalt say: I have no pleasure in them;

Before the sun, and the light, and the moon, and the stars are darkened, and the clouds return after the rain;

In the day when the keepers of the house shall tremble, and the strong men shall bow themselves, and the grinders cease because they are few, and those that look out of the windows shall be darkened,

And the doors shall be shut in the street; when the sound of the grinding is low, and one shall rise up at the voice of a bird, and all the daughters of music shall be brought low.

Yea, they shall be afraid of that which is high, and terrors shall be in the way; and the almond-tree shall blossom, and the grasshopper shall be a burden:

And desire shall fail, because man goeth to his everlasting home, and the mourners go about the streets:

Before the silver cord is loosened, or the golden bowl is broken, or the pitcher is broken at the fountain, or the wheel broken at the cistern,

And the dust returneth to the earth as it was, and the spirit returneth unto God who gave it.

30.

Life Everlasting

Lord, thou hast been our dwelling place in all generations.

Before the mountains were brought forth, or ever thou hadst formed the earth and the world, even from everlasting to everlasting, thou art God.

For a thousand years in thy sight are but as yesterday when it is past, and as a watch in the night.

Thou carriest the years away as with a flood: they are as a sleep.

The days of our years are three-score years and ten, or even by reason of strength four-score years.

So teach us to number our days that we may get us a heart of wisdom.

O satisfy us in the morning with thy lovingkindness, that we may rejoice and be glad all our days.

Let thy work appear unto thy servants and thy glory unto their children.

And let the beauty of the Lord our God be upon us;

And establish thou the work of our hands upon us, yea, the work of our hands, establish thou it.

The Lord is my shepherd, I shall not want. He maketh me to lie down in green pastures, he leadeth

[OVER]

me beside the still waters, he restoreth my soul.

He guideth me in the paths of righteousness for his name's sake.

Yea, though I walk through the valley of the shadow of death, I will fear no evil;

For thou art with me; thy rod and thy staff, they comfort me. Thou preparest a table before me in the presence of mine enemies.

Thou hast anointed my head with oil. My cup runneth over.

Surely goodness and mercy shall follow me all the days of my life, and I shall dwell in the house of the Lord forever.

I have set the Lord always before me. Because he is at my right hand I shall not be moved.

Therefore my heart is glad, and my glory rejoiceth: my flesh also shall dwell in safety.

For thou wilt not leave my soul in the grave, neither wilt thou suffer thy beloved to see corruption.

Thou wilt show me the path of life: in thy presence is fulness of joy; at thy right hand there are pleasures forevermore.

My steps have held fast to thy paths, my feet have not slipped. I have called upon thee, for thou wilt answer me, O God:

Incline thine ear unto me, and hear my prayer. Show thy marvelous lovingkindness, O thou that savest, by thy right hand, them that take refuge in thee.

Keep me as the apple of the eye; hide me under the shadow of thy wings.

As for me I shall behold thy face in righteousness; I shall be satisfied when I awake with thy likeness.

31.

Thanksgiving and Praise

Bless the Lord, O my soul. O Lord, my God, thou art very great; thou art clothed with honor and majesty.

Who coverest thyself with light as with a garment: who stretchest out the heavens like a curtain;

Who layeth the beams of his chambers in the waters; who maketh the clouds his chariot; who walketh upon the wings of the wind;

Who maketh winds his messengers; flames of fire his ministers;

Who laid the foundations of the earth, that it should not be moved forever.

Thou coveredst it with the deep as with a vesture; the waters stood above the mountains.

At thy rebuke they fled; at the voice of thy thunder they hasted away;

The mountains rose, the valleys sank down unto the place which thou hadst founded for them.

Thou hast set a bound that they may not pass over; that they turn not again to cover the earth. He sendeth forth springs into the valleys;

They run among the mountains; they give drink to every beast of the field; the wild asses quench their thirst.

By them the birds of the heavens have their habitation; they sing among the branches.

He watereth the mountains from his chambers: the earth is filled with the fruit of thy works.

He causeth grass to grow for the cattle, and herb for the service of man; that he may bring forth food out of the earth.

He appointed the moon for seasons, the sun knoweth his going down. Thou makest darkness, and it is night, wherein all the beasts of the forest creep forth.

The young lions roar after their prey, and seek their food from God. The sun ariseth, they get them away, and lay them down in their dens.

Man goeth forth unto his work, and his labor until the evening. O Lord, how manifold are thy works! In wisdom hast thou made them all: the earth is full of thy riches.

Yonder is the sea, great and wide, wherein are things creeping innumerable, both small and great beasts. There go the ships.

These wait all for thee, that thou mayest give them their food in due season. Thou givest unto them, they gather;

Thou openest thine hand, they are satisfied with good. Thou hidest thy face, they are troubled; thou takest away their breath, they die, and return to their dust.

Thou sendest forth thy Spirit, they are created; thou renewest the face of the ground.

Let the glory of the Lord endure for ever; let the Lord rejoice in his works:

Who looketh on the earth, and it trembleth; he toucheth the mountains, and they smoke.

I will sing unto the Lord as long as I live: I will sing praise unto my God while I have any being.

Let my meditation be sweet unto him: I will rejoice in the Lord. Bless the Lord, O my soul. Praise ye the Lord.

32.

Thou Art The Messiah

The people that walked in darkness have seen a great light: they that dwelt in the land of the shadow of death, upon them hath the light shined.

For unto us a child is born, unto us a son is given; and the government shall be upon his shoulder:

And his name shall be called Wonderful, Counsellor, the Mighty God, Everlasting Father, Prince of Peace.

Of the increase of his government, and of peace, there shall be no end . . . from henceforth, even forever.

My soul doth magnify the Lord, and my spirit hath rejoiced in God my Saviour.

He that is mighty hath done to me great things: his mercy is unto generations and generations, on them that fear him.

He hath showed strength with his arm; he hath scattered the proud, in the imagination of their heart.

He hath exalted them of low degree. The hungry he hath filled with good things.

In the beginning was the Word, the Word was with God, and the Word was God.

He came unto his own, and they that were his own received him not. But as many as received him, to them gave he the right to become children of God, even to them that believe on his name.

And the Word became flesh, and dwelt among us, full of grace and truth.

Be not afraid; for behold I bring you good tidings of great joy, which shall be unto all the people:

[OVER]

For there is born to you this day, in the city of David, a Saviour, who is Christ the Lord.

Glory to God in the highest, and on earth peace among men in whom he is well-pleased!

33.

The Program of Ministry

The voice of one that crieth: Prepare ye in the wilderness the way of the Lord; make level in the desert a highway for our God.

Every valley shall be exalted, and every mountain and hill shall be made low;

And the uneven shall be made level, and the rough places plain;

And the glory of the Lord shall be revealed, and all flesh shall see it together.

And Jesus came to Nazareth, where he had been brought up: and he entered into the synagogue on the Sabbath day, as his custom was, and stood up to read.

And there was delivered unto him the book of the prophet Isaiah. And he opened the book, and found the place where it was written,

The Spirit of the Lord is upon me, because he anointed me to preach good tidings to the poor. He hath sent me to proclaim release to the captives, and recovering of sight to the blind,

To set at liberty them that are bruised, to proclaim the acceptable year of the Lord.

And he closed the book, and gave it back to the attendant, and sat down.

And the eyes of all in the synagogue were fastened on him. And he began to say unto them:

Today hath this scripture been fulfilled in your ears. And he came down to Capernaum, a city of Galilee.

And he was teaching them on the Sabbath day. And they were astonished at his teaching; for his word was with authority.

And when the sun was setting, all they that had any sick with divers diseases brought them unto him; and he laid his hands on every one of them, and healed them.

And demons also came out of many, crying out, and saying. Thou art the Son of God.

And when it was day, he came out and went into a desert place: and the multitudes sought after him, and came unto him, and would have stayed him, that he should not go from them.

But he said unto them: I must preach the good tidings of the Kingdom of God to the other cities also; for therefor was I sent.

34.

The Christ of Eternal Service

The Spirit of the Lord is upon me, because he anointed me to preach good tidings to the poor:

He hath sent me to proclaim release to the captives, and recovering of sight to the blind, to set at liberty them that are bruised, to proclaim the acceptable year of the Lord.

And John calling unto him two of his disciples sent them to the Lord, saying: Art thou he that cometh, or look we for another?

In that hour he cured many of diseases and plagues and evil spirits; and on many that were blind he bestowed sight.

And he answered and said unto them, go and tell John the things which ye have seen and heard;

The blind receive their sight, the lame walk, the lepers are cleansed, and the deaf hear, the dead are raised up, and the poor have good tidings preached to them.

And he said unto them: The Kings of the Gentiles have lordship over them, and they that have authority over them are called benefactors.

But ye shall not be so: but he that is the greater among you, let him become as the younger; and he that is chief, as he that doth serve.

Have this mind in you, which was also in Christ Jesus: who, existing in the form of God, counted not the being on an equality with God, a thing to be grasped,

But emptied himself, taking the form of a servant, being made in the likeness of men;

And being found in fashion as a man, he humbled himself, becoming obedient even unto death, yea, the death of the cross.

Wherefore also God highly exalted him, and gave unto him the name which is above every name;

That in the name of Jesus every knee should bow,

And that every tongue should confess that Jesus Christ is Lord, to the glory of God the Father.

35.

Justice and Freedom

Lord, who shall sojourn in thy tabernacles? Who shall dwell in thy holy hill?

He that walketh uprightly and worketh righteousness.

Who shall ascend into the hill of the Lord, and who shall stand in his holy place?

He that hath clean hands and a pure heart.

Hear the word of the Lord; give ear unto the law of our God! What unto me is the multitude of your sacrifices? saith the Lord.

Your new moons and your appointed feasts my soul hateth. And when ye spread forth your hands, I will hide mine eyes from you; yea, when ye make many prayers, I will not hear; your hands are full of blood.

Wash you, make you clean; put away the evil of your doings from before mine eyes.

Cease to do evil; learn to do well; seek justice, relieve the oppressed, judge the fatherless, plead for the widow.

Hate the evil and love the good and establish justice in the gate. But let justice roll down as waters, and righteousness as a mighty stream.

Wherewith shall I come before the Lord, and bow myself before the high God?

He hath showed thee, O man, what is good; and what doth the Lord require of thee:

But to do justly, and to love mercy, and to walk humbly with thy God?

Thus saith the Lord: For I desire goodness and not sacrifice; and the knowledge of God more than burnt offering.

Therefore, turn thou to thy God: keep kindness and justice, and wait for thy God continually.

Who is wise that he may understand these things? Prudent that he may know them?

[OVER]

For the ways of the Lord are right, and the just shall walk in them; but the transgressors shall fall therein.

Thus saith the Lord: Execute ye justice and righteousness, and deliver him that is robbed out of the hand of the oppressor: and do no wrong, do no violence, to the sojourner.

Woe unto him that buildeth his house by unrighteousness and his chambers by injustice; that useth his neighbor's service without wages and giveth him not his hire.

Did not thy father eat and drink, and do justice and righteousness? Then it was well with him.

He judged the cause of the poor and needy; then it was well. Was not this to know me? saith the Lord.

Thou shalt not oppress a hired servant that is poor and needy. Behold the hire of the laborers who mowed your field, which is of you kept back by fraud, crieth out: and the cries of them that reaped have entered into the ears of the Lord of Sabaoth.

Better a little with righteousness, than great revenues with injustice.

Jesus therefore said: If ye abide in my word, then are ye truly my disciples; and ye shall know the truth, and the truth shall make you free.

That the creation itself also shall be delivered from the bondage of corruption into the liberty of the glory of the children of God.

36.

Service and Brotherhood

And behold a certain lawyer stood up and made trial of him, saying; Teacher what shall I do to inherit eternal life?

And he said unto him: What is written in the law, how readest thou?

And he answering said: Thou shalt love the Lord thy God with all thy heart, and with all thy soul, and with all thy strength, and with all thy mind; and thy neighbor as thyself.

And he said unto him: Thou hast answered right; this do, and thou shalt live.

But Jesus called them unto him and said: Ye know that the rulers of the Gentiles lord it over them, and their great ones exercise authority over them. Not so shall it be among you.

But whosoever would become great among you shall be your minister and whosoever would be first among you shall be your servant: even as the Son of man came not to be ministered unto, but to minister, and to give his life a ransom for many.

Then spake Jesus to the multitude and to his disciples, saying: The scribes and Pharisees sit on Moses' seat.

All things therefore whatsoever they bid you, these do and observe: but do not ye after their works; for they say and do not.

Yea, they bind heavy burdens and grievous to be borne, and lay them on men's shoulders; but they themselves will not move them with their finger.

But all their works they do to be seen of men: they love the chief places at feasts and the chief seats in the synagogues, and the salutations in the marketplaces, and to be called of men Rabbi.

But be not ye called Rabbi: for one is your Teacher, and all ye are brethren. Neither be ye called masters: for one is your Master, even the Christ.

But he that is greatest among you shall be your servant.

42

And whosoever shall humble himself shall be exalted. Have this mind 'n you, which was also in Christ Jesus. Who, existing in the form of God, counted not the being on an equality with God a thing to be grasped.

But emptied himself, taking the form of a servant, being made in the likeness of men; and being found in fashion as a man, he humbled himself, becoming obedient even unto death, yea, the death of the cross.

So when he had washed their feet, and taken his garments and sat down again, he said unto them: Know ye what I have done to you?

You call me teacher and Lord: and ye say well, for so I am. If I then, the Lord and teacher, have washed your feet, ye also ought to wash one another's feet.

For I have given you an example that ye also should do as I have done to you.

Verily, verily, I say unto you, a servant is not greater than his Lord; neither one that is sent greater than he that sent him. If ye know these things, blessed are ye if ye do them.

For ye have heard, that it was said: Thou shalt love thy neighbor, and hate thine enemy;

But I say unto you: Love your enemies, and pray for them that persecute you; that ye may be sons of your Father who is in heaven: for he maketh his sun to rise on the evil and the good, and sendeth rain on the just and the unjust.

For if ye love them that love you what reward have you? Do not even the publicans the same?

And if ye salute your brethren only, what do ye more than others? Do not even the Gentiles the same?

Ye therefore shall be perfect, as your heavenly Father is perfect.

For ye are all sons of God through faith in Christ Jesus, and Christ is all and in all.

37.

Seek First His Kingdom

And it shall come to pass in the latter days, that the mountain of the Lord's house shall be established on the top of the mountains, and shall be exalted above the hill;

And all nations shall flow unto it; and many people shall say: Come ye, and let us go up to the mountain of the Lord, to the house of the God of Jacob.

And he will teach us of his ways, and we will walk in his paths: For out of Zion shall go forth the law, and the word of the Lord from Jerusalem.

And he will judge between the nations, and will decide concerning many peoples.

And they shall beat their swords into ploughshares and their spears into pruning-hooks; nation shall not lift up sword against nation, neither shall they learn war any more.

Then justice shall dwell in the wilderness and righteousness shall abide in the fruitful field.

And the work of righteousness shall be peace; and the effect of righteousness, quietness and confidence forever.

And my people shall abide in a peaceful habitation, and in safe dwellings, and in quiet resting-places.

Be not therefore anxious, saying what shall we eat, or what shall we drink, or wherewith shall we be clothed? For after all these things do the Gentiles seek;

[OVER]

For your heavenly Father knoweth that ye have need of all these things. But seek ye first his Kingdom and his Righteousness and all these things shall be added unto you.

To this end am I come into the world, that I should bear witness unto the truth. Every one that is of the truth heareth my voice.

If any man would come after me let him deny himself, and take up his cross and follow me.

For whosoever would save his life shall lose it: and whosoever shall lose his life for my sake shall find it.

For what shall a man be profited if he shall gain the whole world and forfeit his life, or what shall a man give in exchange for his life.

———

And I saw a new heaven and a new earth. For the first heaven and the first earth are passed away: and the sea is no more.

And I saw the holy city, the new Jerusalem, coming down out of heaven from God. And I heard a great voice out of the throne saying:

Behold the tabernacle of God is with men, and he shall dwell with them, and they shall be his peoples, and God himself shall be with them and be their God.

And he shall wipe away every tear from their eyes; and death shall be no more; neither shall there be mourning, nor crying, nor pain any more, the first things are passed away. And he that sitteth on the throne said: Behold I make all things new.

38.

The Appeal of Christ

Blessed are the poor in spirit: for theirs is the kingdom of heaven.

The foxes have holes, and the birds of the heaven have nests; but the Son of man hath not where to lay his head.

Blessed are they that mourn: for they shall be comforted.

If any man would come after me, let him deny himself, and take up his cross and follow me.

Blessed are the meek: for they shall inherit the earth.

Take my yoke upon you, and learn of me, for I am meek and lowly in heart: and ye shall find rest unto your souls.

Blessed are they that hunger and thirst after righteousness: for they shall be filled.

I have meat to eat that ye know not. My meat is to do the will of him that sent me, and to accomplish his work.

Blessed are the merciful: for they shall obtain mercy.

But go ye and learn what this meaneth, I desire mercy and not sacrifice: for I came not to call the righteous, but sinners.

Blessed are the pure in heart: for they shall see God.

I am the way, the truth, and the life: no man cometh unto the Father but by me. He that hath seen me hath seen the Father.

Blessed are the peacemakers: for they shall be called Sons of God.

Neither for these only do I pray, but for them also that believe on me through their word; that they may all be one.

Ye are the salt of the earth: ye are the light of the world.

Ye therefore shall be perfect, as your heavenly Father is perfect.

39.

Love and Gratitude

God so loved the world, that he gave his only begotten Son, that whosoever believeth on him should not perish, but have eternal life.

For God sent not the Son into the world to judge the world; but that the world should be saved through him.

Beloved, let us love one another: for love is of God; and every one that loveth is begotten of God, and knoweth God.

He that loveth not, knoweth not God; for God is love.

Herein was the love of God manifested in us, that God hath sent his only begotten Son into the world, that we might live through him.

Herein is love, not that we loved God but that he loved us, and sent his Son to be the propitiation for our sins.

Beloved, if God so loved us, we also ought to love one another.

No man hath beheld God at any time: if we love one another, God abideth in us, and his love is perfected in us.

Hereby we know that we abide in him, and he in us, because he hath given us of his Spirit.

Who shall separate us from the love of Christ? Shall tribulation, or anguish, or persecution, or famine, or nakedness, or peril, or sword?

Nay, in all these things we are more than conquerors through him that loved us.

For I am persuaded, that neither death, nor life, nor angels, nor principalities, nor things present, nor things to come, nor powers, nor height, nor depth, nor any other creature, shall be able to separate us from the love of God, which is in Christ Jesus, our Lord.

40

Despised and Rejected of Men

Then the soldiers of the governor took Jesus unto the palace, and gathered unto him the whole band.

He was despised and rejected of men: a man of sorrows and acquainted with grief.

And they stripped him, and put on him a scarlet robe: and they platted a crown of thorns and put it upon his head.

Surely he hath borne our griefs and carried our sorrows.

And they kneeled down before him, and mocked him. And they spat upon him and smote him.

He was wounded for our transgressions, he was bruised for our iniquities.

When the chief priests and the officers saw him, they cried out, saying: Crucify him, crucify him.

The chastisement of our peace was upon him; and with his stripes we are healed.

And all the people answered and said: His blood be on us and on our children.

All we like sheep have gone astray; we have turned every one to his own way; and the Lord hath laid on him the iniquity of us all.

And the governor asked him: Art thou the King of the Jews? And Jesus said unto him: Thou sayest. And when he was accused by the chief priests and elders, he answered nothing.

He was oppressed, yet when he was afflicted he opened not his mouth.

[OVER]

Then Pilate released unto them Barabbas; but Jesus he scourged and delivered to be crucified.

By oppression and judgment he was taken away. Yet he bare the sin of many, and made intercession for the transgressors.

They took Jesus therefore: and he went out, bearing the cross for himself.

And there followed him a great multitude of the people, and of women who bewailed and lamented him.

And when they came to the place which is called the Skull, there they crucified him.

And Jesus said: Father, forgive them; for they know not what they do.

And about the ninth hour he cried with a loud voice: My God, My God, why hast thou forsaken me?

And one of them ran, and took a sponge, and filled it with vinegar, and put it on a reed, and gave him to drink.

When therefore he had received the vinegar, he said: It is finished.

And when he had cried with a loud voice, he said: Father, into thy hands I commend my spirit.

41.

O, Death, Where is Thy Sting?

When the Sabbath was past, Mary Magdalene and Mary the mother of James, and Salome, brought spices, that they might come and anoint him.

And very early, on the first day of the week, they came to the tomb when the sun was risen.

And they were saying among themselves: Who shall roll us away the stone from the door of the tomb?

And looking up, they see that the stone is rolled back; for it was exceeding great.

And entering into the tomb, they saw a young man sitting on the right side, arrayed in a white robe; and they were amazed.

And he saith unto them: Be not amazed; ye seek Jesus, the Nazarene, who hath been crucified. He is risen; he is not here. Behold the place where they laid him!

But go, tell his disciples, and Peter: He goeth before you into Galilee: there shall ye see him, as he said unto you.

And they went out and fled from the tomb; for trembling and astonishment had come upon them.

Like as Christ was raised from the dead, through the glory of the Father, so we also might walk in newness of life:

Knowing this, that our old self was crucified with him, that the body of sin might be done away.

If then ye were raised together with Christ, seek the things that are above, where Christ is, seated on the right hand of God.

Set your mind on the things that are above, not on the things that are upon the earth.

For ye died, and your life is hid with Christ in God.

When Christ, who is our life, shall be manifested, then shall ye also with him be manifested in glory.

Put to death therefore your members which are upon the earth: fornication, uncleanness, passion, evil desire, and covetousness, which is idolatry.

Put on therefore, as God's elect, holy and beloved, a heart of compassion, kindness, lowliness, meekness, long suffering:

Forbearing one another, and forgiving each other, if any man have a complaint against any:

Even as the Lord forgave you, so also do ye.

Behold what manner of love the Father hath bestowed upon us, that we should be called children of God; and such we are.

Beloved, now are we children of God, and it is not yet made manifest what we shall be.

We know that, if he shall be manifested, we shall be like him; for we shall see him even as he is.

And every one that hath this hope set on him purifieth himself, even as he is pure.

42.

The Risen Christ

Now when Jesus was risen early on the first day of the week, he appeared first to Mary Magdalene.

She went and told them that had been with him, as they mourned and wept. And they, when they heard that he was alive, and had been seen of her, disbelieved.

And behold two of them were going that very day to a village named Emmaus, which was threescore furlongs from Jerusalem.

And they communed with each other of all these things which had happened.

And it came to pass, while they communed and questioned together, that Jesus himself drew near, and went with them.

But their eyes were holden that they should not know him. And he said unto them: What communications are these that ye have one with another as ye walk? And they stood still, looking sad.

And one of them, named Cleopas, answering said unto him: Dost thou alone sojourn in Jerusalem and not know the things which are come to pass there in these days?

And he said unto them: What things? And they said unto him: The things concerning Jesus the Nazarene, who was a prophet mighty in deed and word before God and all the people;

And how the chief priests and our rulers delivered him up to be condemned to death, and crucified him. But we hoped that it was he who should redeem Israel.

Moreover certain women of our company amazed us, having been early at the tomb; and when they found not his body, they came, saying, that they had also seen a vision of angels, who said that he was alive.

And he said unto them: O foolish men, and slow of heart to believe in all that the prophets have spoken! Behooved it not the Christ to suffer these things, and to enter into his glory?

And beginning from Moses and all the prophets, he interpreted to them in all the scriptures the things concerning himself.

And they drew nigh unto the village, whither they were going: and he made as though he would go further.

And they constrained him, saying: Abide with us; for it is toward evening, and the day is now far spent. And he went in to abide with them.

And it came to pass, when he had sat down with them to meat, he took bread and blessed; and breaking it he gave unto them.

And their eyes were opened, and they knew him; and he vanished out of their sight.

And they said one to another. Was not our heart burning within us,

47

(OVER)

while he spake to us in the way, while he opened to us the scriptures?

And they rose up that very hour, and returned to Jerusalem, and found the eleven gathered together, saying: The Lord is risen indeed! And they rehearsed the things that happened in the way, and how he was known of them in the breaking of bread.

43.

The Promise of Power

And being assembled together with them, Jesus charged them not to depart from Jerusalem but to wait for the promise of the Father.

They therefore, when they were come together, asked him, saying: Lord dost thou at this time restore the Kingdom to Israel?

And he said unto them: It is not for you to know times, and seasons, which the Father hath set within his own authority.

But ye shall receive power, when the Holy Spirit is come upon you: and ye shall be my witnesses both in Jerusalem, and in all Judea and Samaria, and unto the uttermost part of the earth.

And he led them out until they were over against Bethany: and he lifted his hands and blessed them.

And it came to pass, while he blessed them, he parted from them, and was carried up unto heaven; and a cloud received him out of their sight.

And while they were looking steadfastly into heaven as he went, behold two men stood by them in white apparel;

Who also said: Ye men of Galilee, why stand ye looking into heaven?

This Jesus, who was received up from you into heaven, shall so come in like manner as ye beheld him going into heaven.

Then returned they unto Jerusalem from the mount called Olivet.

And they went up into the upper chamber, where they were abiding; and all, with one accord, continued steadfastly in prayer.

And they went forth, and preached everywhere, the Lord working with them; and confirming the word by the signs that followed.

God, being rich in mercy, for his great love wherewith he loved us, even when we were dead through our trespasses, made us alive together with Christ.

And raised us up with him, and made us to sit with him in the heavenly places, in Christ Jesus: that in the ages to come he might show the exceeding riches of his grace, in kindness toward us, in Christ Jesus.

For by grace have ye been saved through faith; and that not of yourselves, it is the gift of God; not of works, that no man should glory.

For we are his workmanship, created in Christ Jesus for good works, which God afore prepared that we should walk in them.

44.

The Coming of the Spirit

Thus it is written, that the Christ should suffer and rise again from the dead, the third day; and that repentance and remission of sins should be preached in his name unto all the nations.

And Jesus said: Ye are witnesses of these things. And behold I send forth the promise of my Father upon you: but tarry ye in the city, until ye be clothed with power from on high.

48

And when the day of Pentecost was now come, they were all together in one place.

And suddenly there came from heaven a sound as of the rushing of a mighty wind, and it filled all the house where they were sitting.

And there appeared unto them tongues, parting asunder, like as of fire; and it sat upon each of them.

And they were all filled with the Holy Spirit, and began to speak with other tongues, as the Spirit gave them utterance.

Now there were dwelling at Jerusalem Jews, devout men, from every nation under heaven.

And when this sound was heard, the multitude came together, and were confounded, because that every man heard them speaking in his own language.

And they were all amazed and marvelled, saying; Behold, are not all these which speak Galileans?

And how hear we, every man in our own language wherein we were born? And they were all amazed, and were perplexed, saying one to another: What meaneth this?

But Peter standing up with the eleven, lifted up his voice and spake forth unto them, saying: This is that which hath been spoken through the prophet Joel:

And it shall be in the last days, saith God, I will pour forth of my Spirit upon all flesh: and your sons and your daughters shall prophesy, and your young men shall see visions, and your old men shall dream dreams:

Yea, and on my servants and on my handmaidens in those days, will I pour forth of my Spirit; and they shall prophesy.

And it shall be that whosoever shall call on the name of the Lord shall be saved.

Now when they heard this, they were pricked in their heart, and said unto Peter and the rest of the apostles: Brethren, what shall we do?

And Peter said unto them: Repent ye, and be baptized every one of you in the name of Jesus Christ unto the remission of your sins; and ye shall receive the gift of the Holy Spirit.

For to you is the promise, and to your children, and to all that are afar off, even as many as the Lord our God shall call unto him.

And with many other words he testified, and exhorted them, saying: Save yourself from this crooked generation.

Then they that received his word were baptized: and there were added unto them in that day about three thousand souls.

And they continued steadfastly in the apostles' teaching and fellowship, in the breaking of bread and the prayers.

45.

The Unity of the Spirit

I beseech you therefore, brethren, by the mercies of God, to present your bodies a living sacrifice, holy, acceptable to God, which is your spiritual service.

And be not fashioned according to this world: but be ye transformed by the renewing of your mind, that ye may prove what is the good and acceptable and perfect will of God.

For I say, through the grace that was given me, to every man that is among you, not to think of himself more highly than he ought to think;

[OVER]

But so to think as to think soberly, according as God hath dealt to each man a measure of faith.

For even as we have many members in one body, and all the members have not the same office:

So we, who are many, are one body in Christ, and severally members one of another.

And having gifts differing according to the grace that was given to us, whether prophecy, let us prophesy according to the proportion of our faith;

Or ministry, let us give ourselves to our ministry; or he that teacheth to his teaching;

Or he that exhorteth, to his exhorting: he that giveth, let him do it with liberality;

He that ruleth, with diligence; he that showeth mercy, with cheerfulness.

Now there are diversities of gifts, but the same Spirit. And there are diversities of ministrations, and the same Lord.

And there are diversities of workings, but the same God, who worketh all things in all. But to each one is given the manifestation of the Spirit to profit withal.

For as the body is one, and hath many members, and all the members of the body, being many, are one body; so also is Christ.

For in one Spirit were we all baptized into one body, whether Jews or Greeks, whether bond or free; and were all made to drink of one Spirit. For the body is not one member, but many.

And whether one member suffereth, all the members suffer with it; or one member is honored, all the members rejoice with it. Now ye are the body of Christ, and severally members thereof.

And God hath set some in the church, first apostles, secondly prophets, thirdly teachers, then miracles, then gifts of healings, helps, governments, divers kinds of tongues.

I therefore beseech you to walk worthily of the calling wherewith ye were called, with all lowliness, and meekness,

With long-suffering, forbearing one another in love; giving diligence to keep the unity of the Spirit in the bond of peace.

There is one body, and one Spirit, even as also ye were called in one hope of your calling;

One Lord, one faith, one baptism, one God and Father of all, who is over all, and through all, and in all.

But unto each one of us was the grace given according to the measure of the gift of Christ.

Wherefore he saith, when he ascended on high, he led captivity captive, and gave gifts unto men.

46.

The New Covenant

Behold the days come, saith the Lord, that I will make a new covenant with the house of Israel, and with the house of Judah:

Not according to the covenant that I made with their fathers in the day that I took them by the hand to bring them out of the land of Egypt;

Which covenant they brake, although I was a husband unto them, saith the Lord.

But this is the covenant that I will make with the house of Israel after those days, saith the Lord:

I will put my law in their inward parts, and in their heart will I write it; and I will be their God, and they shall be my people:

And they shall teach no more every man his neighbor, and every man his brother, saying: Know the Lord;

For they shall all know me from the least of them unto the greatest of them, saith the Lord:

For I will forgive their iniquity, and their sin will I remember no more.

This commandment which I command thee this day, it is not too hard for thee, neither is it far off.

It is not in heaven that thou shouldest say: Who shall go up for us to heaven, and bring it unto us, and make us to hear it, that we may do it?

Neither is it beyond the sea, that thou shouldest say: Who shall go over the sea for us, and bring it unto us, and make us to hear it, that we may do it?

But the word is very nigh unto thee, in thy mouth, and in thy heart, that thou mayest do it.

The works of the Lord are great, sought out of all them that have pleasure therein.

His work is honor and majesty; and his righteousness endureth forever. He hath made his wonderful works to be remembered:

The Lord is gracious and merciful. He will ever be mindful of his covenant.

He hath showed his people the power of his works. The works of his hands are truth and justice; all his precepts are sure.

They are established forever and ever; they are done in truth and uprightness.

He hath sent redemption unto his people; he hath commanded his covenant forever.

Our sufficiency is from God, who also made us sufficient as ministers of a new covenant; not of the letter, but of the spirit: for the letter killeth, but the spirit giveth life.

Until this very day, at the reading of the old covenant, the same veil remaineth.

Now the Lord is the Spirit, and where the Spirit of the Lord is, there is liberty.

But we all, with unveiled face, beholding as in a mirror the glory of the Lord, are transformed into the same image from glory to glory, even as from the Lord the Spirit.

Seeing it is God that said: Light shall shine out of darkness, who shined in our hearts, to give the light of the knowledge of the glory of God, in the face of Jesus Christ.

Wherefore we faint not; but though our outward man is decaying, yet our inward man is renewed day by day.

For our light affliction, which is for the moment, worketh for us more and more exceedingly an eternal weight of glory;

While we look not at the things which are seen, but at the things which are not seen: for the things which are seen are temporal; but the things which are not seen are eternal.

47.

The Testimony of Scripture

Having then a great high priest, who hath passed through the heavens, Jesus the Son of God, let us hold fast our confession.

For we have not a high priest that cannot be touched with the feeling of our infirmities;

[OVER]

But one that hath been, in all points, tempted like as we are, yet without sin.

Let us therefore draw near with boldness unto the throne of grace, that we may receive mercy, and may find grace to help us in time of need.

Now we that are strong ought to bear the infirmities of the weak, and not to please ourselves.

Let each one of us please his neighbor for that which is good, unto edifying. For Christ also pleased not himself; but, as it is written: The reproaches of them that reproached thee fell upon me.

For whatsoever things were written aforetime were written for our learning, that through patience and through comfort of the scriptures we might have hope.

Now the God of patience and of comfort grant you to be of the same mind one with another according to Christ Jesus.

God, having of old time spoken unto the fathers in the prophets by divers portions and in divers manners,

Hath at the end of these days spoken unto us in his Son, whom he appointed heir of all things.

Therefore we ought to give the more earnest heed to the things that were heard, lest haply we drift away from them.

For if the word, spoken through angels, proved steadfast and every transgression and disobedience received a just recompense of reward;

How shall we escape, if we neglect so great a salvation? which having at the first been spoken through the Lord, was confirmed unto us by them that heard;

God also bearing witness with them, both by signs and wonders, and by manifold powers, and by gifts of the Holy Spirit, according to his will.

Take heed, brethren, lest haply there shall be in any one of you an evil heart of unbelief, in falling away from the living God.

For we are become partakers of Christ, if we hold fast the beginning of our confidence firm unto the end.

But abide thou in the things which thou hast learned and hast been assured of, knowing of whom thou hast learned them;

And that from a babe thou hast known the sacred writings which are able to make thee wise unto salvation through faith which is in Christ Jesus.

Every scripture inspired of God is also profitable for teaching, for reproof, for correction, for instruction which is in righteousness;

That the man of God may be complete, furnished completely unto every good work.

I charge thee in the sight of God, and of Christ Jesus, who shall judge the living and the dead, and by his appearing and his kingdom:

Preach the word; be urgent in season, out of season; reprove, rebuke, exhort, with all longsuffering and teaching.

Of these things put them in remembrance, charging them in the sight of the Lord, that they strive not about words, to no profit, to the subverting of them that hear.

Give diligence to present thyself approved unto God, a workman that needeth not to be ashamed, handling aright the word of truth.

48.

Peace and Power Through Faith

By grace have ye been saved through faith; and that not of yourselves, it is the gift of God.

Being therefore justified by faith, we have peace with God through our Lord Jesus Christ;

Through whom also we have had our access by faith, into this grace wherein we stand;

And we rejoice in hope of the glory of God. And not only so, but we also rejoice in our tribulations:

Knowing that tribulation worketh steadfastness; and steadfastness, approvedness; and approvedness, hope:

And hope putteth not to shame; because the love of God hath been shed abroad in our hearts through the Holy Spirit which was given unto us.

For while we were yet weak, in due season Christ died for the ungodly.

God commendeth his own love toward us, in that while we were yet sinners, Christ died for us.

For this cause I bow my knees unto the Father, from whom every family in heaven and on earth is named,

That he would grant you, according to the riches of his glory, that ye may be strengthened with power through his spirit in the inward man:

That Christ may dwell in your hearts through faith; to the end that ye, being rooted and grounded in love,

May be strong to apprehend with all the saints what is the breadth and length and height and depth,

And to know the love of Christ which passeth knowledge, that ye may be filled unto all the fulness of God.

Peace I leave with you; my peace I give unto you: not as the world giveth give I unto you.

Unto him that is able to do exceeding abundantly above all that we ask or think,

Unto him be the glory in the church, and in Christ Jesus unto generations, forever and ever. Amen.

49.

Illumination and Guidance

It is expedient for you that I go away; for if I go not away, the Comforter will not come unto you; but if I go, I will send him unto you.

When he, the Spirit of truth is come, he shall guide you into all truth.

He shall glorify me: for he shall take of mine, and shall declare it unto you.

Now the Lord is the Spirit: and where the Spirit of the Lord is, there is liberty.

Walk by the Spirit, and ye shall not fulfil the lust of the flesh. For the flesh lusteth against the Spirit, and the Spirit against the flesh; for these are contrary the one to the other; that ye may not do the things that ye would.

Now the works of the flesh are manifest, which are these: fornication, uncleanness, lasciviousness, idolatry, sorcery, enmities, strife, jealousies, wrath, factions, divisions, parties, envyings, drunkenness, revellings, and such like.

Of which I forewarn you even as I did forewarn you, that they who practice such things, shall not inherit the kingdom of God.

But the fruit of the Spirit is love, joy, peace, longsuffering, kindness, goodness, faithfulness, meekness, self control; against such there is no law.

[OVER]

And they that are of Christ Jesus have crucified the flesh with the passions and the lusts thereof.

If we live by the Spirit, by the Spirit let us walk. For as many as are led by the Spirit of God these are sons of God.

For ye received not the spirit of bondage again unto fear; but ye received the spirit of adoption, whereby we cry Abba, Father.

The Spirit himself beareth witness with our spirit, that we are children of God: and if children, then heirs; heirs of God, and joint-heirs with Christ; if so be that we suffer with him, that we may be also glorified with him.

50.

Confidence in Conflict

Count it all joy, my brethren, when ye fall into manifold temptations; knowing that the proving of your faith worketh patience;

And let patience have its perfect work, that ye may be perfect and entire, lacking in nothing.

If the world hateth you, ye know that it hath hated me before it hated you.

If ye were of the world, the world would love its own: but because ye are not of the world, but I chose you out of the world, therefore the world hateth you.

Remember the word that I said unto you: a servant is not greater than his lord.

If they persecuted me, they will also persecute you; if they kept my word, they will keep yours also.

But all these things will they do unto you for my name's sake, because they know not him that sent me.

In the world ye have tribulation: but be of good cheer; I have overcome the world.

Be strong in the Lord, and in the strength of his might. Put on the whole armor of God, that ye may be able to stand against the wiles of the devil.

For our wrestling is not against flesh and blood, but against the principalities, against the powers, against the world rulers of this darkness, against the spiritual hosts of wickedness in the heavenly places.

Wherefore take up the whole armor of God, that ye may be able to withstand in the evil day, and having done all, to stand.

Stand, therefore, having girded your loins with truth, and having put on the breastplate of righteousness, and having shod your feet with the preparation of the gospel of peace,

Withal taking up the shield of faith wherewith ye shall be able to quench all the fiery darts of the evil one;

And take the helmet of salvation, and the sword of the Spirit, which is the Word of God: with all prayer and supplication praying at all seasons in the Spirit.

For our light affliction, which is for the moment, worketh for us more and more exceedingly an eternal weight of glory.

While we look not at the things which are seen, but at the things which are not seen: for the things which are seen are temporal; but the things which are not seen are eternal.

51.

Salvation and Sonship

This is the message which we have heard from him and announce unto

you, that God is light, and in him **is** no darkness at all.

If we say that we have fellowship with him and walk in darkness, we lie, and do not the truth:

But if we walk in the light, as he is in the light, we have fellowship one with another, and the blood of Jesus his Son cleanseth us from all sin.

If we say that we have no sin, we deceive ourselves, and the truth is not in us.

If we confess our sins, he is faithful and righteous to forgive us our sins, and to cleanse us from all unrighteousness.

If we say that we have not sinned we make him a liar and his word is not in us.

And ye know that he was manifested to take away sins: and in him is no sin.

Whosoever abideth in him sinneth not: whosoever sinneth hath not seen him, neither knoweth him.

My little children, let no man lead you astray: he that doeth righteousness is righteous, even as he is righteous: he that doeth sin is of the devil; for the devil sinneth from the beginning.

Whosoever is begotten of God doeth no sin, because his seed abideth in him: and he cannot sin because he is begotten of God.

Verily, verily, I say unto thee, except one be born anew, he cannot see the kingdom of God.

That which is born of the flesh is flesh; and that which is born of the Spirit is spirit.

The wind bloweth where it will, and thou hearest the voice thereof, but knowest not whence it cometh, and whither it goeth: so is every one that is born of the Spirit.

As many as received him, to them gave he the right to become children of God, even to them that believe on his name.

Who were born, not of blood, nor of the will of the flesh, nor of the will of man but of God.

As many as are led by the Spirit of God, these are sons of God.

For ye received not the spirit of bondage again unto fear; but ye received the spirit of adoption, whereby we cry: Abba Father.

The Spirit beareth witness with our spirit, that we are the children of God: and if children, then heirs; heirs of God, and joint-heirs with Christ.

52.
Foreign Missions

Not unto us, O Lord, not unto us, but unto thy name give glory, for thy lovingkindness, and for thy truth's sake.

Wherefore should the nations say: Where is now their God? But our God is in the heavens.

Their idols are silver and gold, the work of men's hands. They have mouths but they speak not.

Eyes have they, but they see not; they have ears, but they hear not; noses have they, but they smell not.

They have hands, but they handle not; feet have they, but they walk not; neither speak they through their throat.

They that make them shall be like unto them; yea, every one that trusteth in them.

They that fashion a graven image are all of them vanity; and the things that they delight in shall not profit; and their own witnesses see not, nor know.

[OVER]

Who hath fashioned a god, or molten an image that is profitable for nothing? Behold, all his fellows shall be put to shame.

The smith maketh an axe, and worketh in the coals, and fashioneth it with hammers, and worketh it with his strong arm:

Yea, he is hungry, and his strength faileth; he drinketh no water, and is faint.

The carpenter stretcheth out a line; he marketh it out with a pencil; he shapeth it with planes, and he marketh it out with the compasses,

And shapeth it after the figure of a man, according to the beauty of a man, to dwell in a house.

He planteth a fir-tree, and the rain doth nourish it. Then shall it be for a man to burn; and he taketh thereof, and warmeth himself;

Yea, he kindleth it, and baketh bread: yea, he maketh a god and worshippeth it; he maketh it a graven image and falleth down thereto.

He maketh a god, even his graven image; he falleth down unto it and worshippeth, and prayeth unto it, and saith: Deliver me, for thou art my god!

They know not, neither do they consider: for he hath shut his eyes that they cannot see; and their hearts, that they cannot understand.

He feedeth on ashes; a deceived heart hath turned him aside. And he cannot deliver his soul, nor say: Is there not a lie in my right hand?

The same Lord is Lord over all, and is rich unto all that call upon him: for whosoever shall call upon the name of the Lord shall be saved.

How then shall they call on him in whom they have not believed? And how shall they believe in him whom they have not heard?

And how shall they hear without a preacher? And how shall they preach except they be sent?

Even as it is written: How beautiful are the feet of them that bring glad tidings of good things!

So belief cometh of hearing, and hearing by the word of Christ. But I say: Did they not hear? Yea, verily: Their sound went out into all the earth, and their words unto the ends of the world.

Go ye therefore, and make disciples of all the nations, baptizing them into the name of the Father and of the Son and of the Holy Spirit;

Teaching them to observe all things whatsoever I command you: and lo, I am with you always, even unto the end of the world.

Order of Worship

ORGAN PRELUDE

CHOIR PROCESSIONAL HYMN

CALL TO WORSHIP (Sentences by the Minister)

DOXOLOGY OR DOXOLOGIC HYMN (all uniting)

INVOCATION

THE LORD'S PRAYER (all uniting)

CHOIR ANTHEM

RESPONSIVE READING (all uniting)

GLORIA PATRI (all uniting)

SCRIPTURE LESSON

PASTORAL PRAYER

CHOIR OR ORGAN RESPONSE

CHOIR ANTHEM OR SOLO

OFFERTORY (including Offertory Sentences, Prayer, and Conse
cration of Offering)

CONGREGATIONAL HYMN (all uniting)

SERMON

CONGREGATIONAL HYMN (all uniting)

PRAYER AND BENEDICTION

SILENT PRAYER

ORGAN POSTLUDE

Communion Service

Minister:

And when the hour was come Jesus sat down and his disciples with him. And he said unto them: With desire have I desired to eat this passover with you before I suffer. For I say unto you: I will not eat it henceforth, until it be fulfilled in the kingdom of God.

Hymn (all uniting) No. 136:

> Break thou the bread of life,
> Dear Lord, to me,
> As thou didst break the loaves
> Beside the sea;
> Beyond the sacred page
> I seek thee, Lord;
> My spirit pants for thee,
> O living Word!

Minister:

Greater love hath no man than this, that a man lay down his life for his friends. Ye are my friends, if ye do whatsoever I command you. Henceforth I call you not servants; for the servant knoweth not what his lord doeth; but I have called you friends, for all things that I have heard of my Father, I have made known unto you.

Hymn:

> Bless thou the truth, dear Lord,
> To me, to me,
> As thou didst bless the bread
> By Galilee;
> Then shall all bondage cease,
> All fetters fall;
> And I shall find my peace,
> My all in all.

Prayers (all uniting):

Almighty God, unto whom all hearts are open, all desires known, and from whom no secrets are hid; cleanse the thoughts of our hearts by the inspiration of thy Holy Spirit, that we may perfectly love thee, and worthily magnify thy holy name; through Christ our Lord.   Amen.

O God, our heavenly Father, grant that this service may be profitable to all who partake of it, for the sanctification of body and soul, for fruitfulness in good works, and for the establishing of thy holy Church.   Amen.

O Lamb of God, who takest away the sin of the world; have mercy upon us.
                    Amen.

Hymn No. 220:

> My faith looks up to thee,
> Thou Lamb of Calvary,
> Saviour divine;
> Now hear me while I pray;
> Take all my guilt away,
> O let me from this day
> Be wholly thine.

58

The Invitation of the Church to the Communion

Hymn:

> May thy rich grace impart
> Strength to my fainting heart,
> My zeal inspire:
> As thou hast died for me,
> O may my love to thee,
> Pure, warm, and changeless be,
> A living fire.

The Distribution of the Bread

For I have received of the Lord that which also I delivered unto you: That the Lord Jesus the same night in which he was betrayed took bread: and when he had given thanks, he brake it, and said: Take, eat; this is my body, which is broken for you: this do in remembrance of me.

The Prayer of Thanksgiving—The Administration of the Cup

After the same manner also he took the cup, when he had supped, saying: This cup is the New Testament in my blood: this do ye, as oft as ye drink it, in remembrance of me. For as often as ye eat this bread, and drink this cup, ye do show the Lord's death till he come.

Hymn (all uniting) No. 458

> A parting hymn we sing
> Around thy table, Lord;
> Again our grateful tribute bring,
> Our solemn vows record.
>
> In self-forgetting love
> Be our communion shown,
> Until we join the church above,
> And know as we are known. Amen.

Benediction

Baptism

BAPTISM was instituted by our Lord Jesus Christ, who came from Galilee to the Jordan unto John to be baptized of him.

And Jesus, when he was baptized, went up straightway from the water; and lo, the heavens were opened unto him, and he saw the Spirit of God descending as a dove, and coming upon him; and lo, a voice out of the heavens saying: This is my beloved Son, in whom I am well pleased.

Hymn, Soldiers of Christ, Arise, No. 322

Prayer—

Almighty and immortal God, the aid of all that need, the helper of all that flee to thee for succor, the life of them that believe, and the resurrection of the dead: we call upon thee for *these persons*, that *they*, coming to thy holy baptism, may also be filled with thy Holy Spirit. Receive *them*, O Lord, as thou hast promised by thy well-beloved Son, saying: Ask, and ye shall receive; seek, and ye shall find; knock, and it shall be opened unto you. So give now unto us that ask; let us that seek, find; open the gate unto us that knock; that *these persons* may enjoy the everlasting benediction of thy heavenly washing, and may come to the eternal kingdom which thou hast promised, by Christ our Lord. Amen.

Jesus answered: Verily, verily, I say unto thee: Except one be born of the water and the Spirit he cannot enter into the kingdom of God.

Repent and be baptized every one of you in the name of Jesus Christ unto the remission of your sins, and ye shall receive the gift of the Holy Spirit.

He that believeth and is baptized shall be saved.

The Rite of Baptism

Hymn, O Jesus, I have promised, No. 300

Closing Sentences:

There is one body and one spirit; even as ye were called in one hope of your calling, one Lord, one faith, one baptism, one God and Father of all who is above all, and through all, and in all.

Go ye therefore and make disciples of all the nations, baptizing them into the name of the Father and of the Son and of the Holy Spirit.

Defend, O Lord, this thy Servant, with thy heavenly grace; that *he* may continue thine for ever; and daily increase in thy Holy Spirit more and more, until *he* come unto thy everlasting kingdom. Amen.

The Commandments

GOD spake all these words, saying: I am the LORD thy God, which have brought thee out of the land of Egypt, out of the house of bondage.

I. Thou shalt have no other gods before me.

II. Thou shalt not make unto thee any graven image, or any likeness of any thing that is in heaven above, or that is in the earth beneath, or that is in the water under the earth: thou shalt not bow down thyself to them, nor serve them: for I the LORD thy God am a jealous God, visiting the iniquity of the fathers upon the children unto the third and fourth generation of them that hate me; and showing mercy unto thousands of them that love me, and keep my commandments.

III. Thou shalt not take the name of the LORD thy God in vain; for the LORD will not hold him guiltless that taketh his name in vain.

IV. Remember the Sabbath-day, to keep it holy. Six days shalt thou labor, and do all thy work: but the seventh day is the Sabbath of the LORD thy God; in it thou shalt not do any work, thou, nor thy son, nor thy daughter, thy man-servant, nor thy maid-servant, nor thy cattle, nor thy stranger that is within thy gates; for in six days the LORD made heaven and earth, the sea, and all that in them is, and rested the seventh day: wherefore the LORD blessed the Sabbath-day, and hallowed it.

    V.   Honor thy father and thy mother: that thy days may be long upon the land which the LORD thy God giveth thee.

    VI.   Thou shalt not kill.

    VII.   Thou shalt not commit adultery.

    VIII.   Thou shalt not steal.

    IX.   Thou shalt not bear false witness against thy neighbor.

    X.   Thou shalt not covet thy neighbor's house, thou shalt not covet thy neighbor's wife, nor his man-servant, nor his maid-servant, nor his ox, nor his ass, nor any thing that is thy neighbor's.

HEAR also the words of our Lord Jesus, how he saith: Thou shalt love the Lord thy God with all thy heart, and with all thy soul, and with all thy mind. This is the first and great commandment. And the second is like unto it: Thou shalt love thy neighbor as thyself. On these two commandments hang all the law and the prophets.

The Beatitudes

Blessed are the poor in spirit:
For theirs is the kingdom of heaven.
Blessed are they that mourn:
For they shall be comforted.
Blessed are the meek:
For they shall inherit the earth.
Blessed are they that hunger and thirst after righteousness:
For they shall be filled.
Blessed are the merciful:
For they shall obtain mercy.
Blessed are the pure in heart:
For they shall see God.
Blessed are the peacemakers:
For they shall be called sons of God.
Blessed are they that have been persecuted for righteous-
    ness' sake:
For theirs is the kingdom of heaven.
Blessed are ye when men shall reproach you, and persecute
    you, and say all manner of evil against you falsely, for
    my sake.
Rejoice, and be exceeding glad; for great is your reward in
    heaven:
For so persecuted they the prophets that were before you.

The Apostles' Creed

I BELIEVE in GOD THE FATHER Almighty, Maker of heaven and earth, and in Jesus Christ his only Son our Lord: who was conceived by the Holy Ghost, born of the Virgin Mary: suffered under Pontius Pilate, was crucified, dead, and buried: the third day he rose again from the dead: he ascended into heaven, and sitteth on the right hand of God the Father Almighty: from thence he shall come to judge the quick and the dead.

I believe in the HOLY GHOST: the Holy Catholic Church: the Communion of Saints: the Forgiveness of sins: the Resurrection of the dead: and the life Everlasting. Amen.

A Scripture Confession of Faith

TO us there is: One God, the Father, of whom are all things, and we unto him; and one Lord Jesus Christ, through whom are all things, and we through him; who was manifested in the flesh, justified in the spirit, seen of angels, preached among the nations, believed on in the world, received up in glory; and one Spirit of truth, proceeding from the Father, bearing witness of Christ, guiding us into all truth, declaring unto us the things that are to come, bearing witness with our spirit that we are children of God, having fruit in all goodness, righteousness and truth. Amen.

Calls to Worship

SURELY the Lord is in this place. This is none other than the house of God, and this is the gate of heaven.

The hour cometh, and now is, when the true worshippers shall worship the Father in spirit and in truth; for the Father seeketh such to worship him.

God is a spirit, and they that worship him must worship him in spirit and in truth.

O magnify the Lord with me, and let us exalt his name together; for with him is the fountain of life, and in his light shall we see light.

Know ye that the Lord he is God; it is he that hath made us, and not we ourselves; we are his people, and the sheep of his pasture. Enter into his gates with thanksgiving, and into his courts with praise.

Who shall ascend into the hill of the Lord? or who shall stand in his holy place? He that hath clean hands and a pure heart; who hath not lifted up his soul unto vanity, nor sworn deceitfully. He shall receive the blessing of the Lord, and righteousness from the God of his salvation.

Let us search and try our ways, and turn again to the Lord. Let us lift up our hearts with our hands unto God in the heavens.

Serve the Lord with gladness; come before his presence with a song. Know ye that the Lord he is God: it is he that hath made us and not we ourselves; we are his people and the sheep of his pasture.

My voice shalt thou hear in the morning, O Lord; in the morning will I direct my prayer unto thee, and will look up.

What shall I render unto the Lord for all his benefits toward me? I will take the cup of salvation, and call upon the name of the Lord: I will pay my vows unto the Lord, yea, in the presence of all his people, in the courts of the Lord's house, in the midst of thee, O Jerusalem. Praise ye the Lord.

O go your way into his gates with thanksgiving, and into his courts with praise. Be thankful unto him, and speak good of his name. For the Lord is good; his kindness endureth forever, and his faithfulness unto all generations.

The Lord is my light and my salvation; whom shall I fear? The Lord is the strength of my life; of whom shall I be afraid? One thing have I desired of the Lord, that will I seek after; that I may dwell in the house of the Lord all the days of my life, to gaze upon the beauty of the Lord, and to inquire in his temple.

O that we may be filled with the goodness of thy house, the holiness of thy temple.

Hope in the Lord; for with the Lord there is mercy, and with him is plenteous redemption. Humble yourselves under the mighty hand of God, and he shall lift you up. Draw nigh unto God, and he will draw nigh unto you.

O that men would praise the Lord for his goodness, and for his wonderful works to the children of men.

Lift up your hearts.
We lift them up unto the Lord.
O Lord, open thou our eyes.
That we may behold wondrous things out of thy law.
O Lord, open thou our lips.
And our mouth shall show forth thy praise.
Praise ye the Lord.
The Lord's name be praised.

Evening

Lord, lift thou up the light of thy countenance upon us. O send out thy light and thy truth; let them lead me: let them bring me unto thy holy hill, and to thy tabernacles.

From the rising of the sun to the going down of the same, the Lord's name is to be praised. Let our prayers be set forth as incense before him, and the lifting up of our hands as the evening sacrifice.

Peace, peace, to him that is afar off, and peace to him that is near, saith the Lord. Peace to all who enter here; peace to every one abiding here.

The day goeth away, and the shadows of the evening are stretched out; but it shall come to pass, that at evening time there shall be light. Abide with us, for it is toward evening, and the day is far spent.

Let the words of my mouth and the meditation of my heart be acceptable in thy sight, O Lord, my strength and my Redeemer.

Offertory

Remember the words of the Lord Jesus, how he himself said: It is more blessed to give than to receive.

Freely ye have received, freely give. Every man according as he hath purposed in his heart, so let him give: not grudgingly or of necessity, for God loveth a cheerful giver.

Honor the Lord with thy substance, and with the first fruits of all thine increase. Give unto the Most High according as he hath enriched thee, and, as thou hast gotten, give with a generous hand.

Upon the first day of the week let each one of you lay by him in store as God hath prospered him. Every man shall give as he is able, according to the blessing of the Lord thy God which he hath given thee.

All things come of thee, O Lord, and of thine own have we given thee.

And this commandment have we from him that he who loveth God love his brother also.

But whoso hath this world's goods, and seeth his brother have need, and shutteth up his compassion from him; how dwelleth the love of God in him? Have this mind in you which was also in Christ Jesus?

Even so let your light shine before men, that they may see your good works and glorify your Father which is in heaven.

Benedictions

The peace of God which passeth all understanding, keep your hearts and minds in the knowledge and love of God, and of his Son, Jesus Christ our Lord; and the blessing of God Almighty, the Father, the Son, and the Holy Spirit, be amongst you and remain with you always. Amen.

Now the God of peace, who brought again from the dead our Lord Jesus, that great Shepherd of the sheep, make you perfect in every good work to do his will, working in you that which is well pleasing in his sight, through Jesus Christ; to whom be the glory forever and ever. Amen.

Now unto him that is able to keep us from falling, and to present us faultless before the presence of his glory with exceeding joy, to the only wise God, our Saviour, be glory and majesty, dominion and power, both now and ever. Amen.

The grace of our Lord Jesus Christ, the love of God, and the communion of the Holy Spirit, be with you all. Amen.

The Lord bless you and keep you: the Lord make his face to shine upon you and be gracious unto you: the Lord lift up his countenance upon you and give you peace. Amen.

Advent

Prepare ye the way of the Lord, make straight in the desert a highway for our God.

Christmas

Arise, shine! for thy light is come, and the glory of the Lord is risen upon thee; and Gentiles shall come to thy light, and kings to the brightness of thy rising.

Lent

The sacrifices of God are a broken spirit: a broken and a contrite heart, O God, thou wilt not despise.

Seek ye the Lord while he may be found; call ye upon him while he is near. Let the wicked forsake his way, and the unrighteous man his thought; and let him return unto the Lord, and he will have mercy upon him; and to our God, for he will abundantly pardon.

Good Friday

Is it nothing to you, all ye that pass by? Behold, and see if there be any sorrow like unto my sorrow.

Easter

When this mortal shall have put on immortality, then shall be brought to pass the saying that is written: death is swallowed up in victory. O death, where is thy sting? O grave, where is thy victory?

Prayers

The Lord's Prayer

OUR Father who art in heaven, hallowed be thy name; thy kingdom come, thy will be done on earth as it is in heaven; give us this day our daily bread; and forgive us our debts, as we forgive our debtors; and lead us not into temptation, but deliver us from evil; for thine is the kingdom, and the power, and the glory, forever. Amen.

Morning

Eternal God, who hast neither dawn nor evening, yet sendest us alternate mercies of the darkness and the day, there is no light but thine, without or within. As thou liftest the curtains of night from our abodes, take also the veil from all our hearts. Rise with thy morning upon our souls; quicken all our labor and our prayer; and, though all else declines, let the noontide of thy grace and peace remain. May we walk, while it is yet day in the steps of him, who with fewest hours, finished thy divinest work. Amen.

Evening

We beseech thee, Lord, to behold us with favor, folk of many families and nations gathered together in the peace of this roof, weak men and women subsisting under the covert of thy patience. Be patient still; suffer us yet a while longer—with our broken purposes of good, with our idle endeavors against evil, suffer us a while longer to endure and (if it may be) help us to do better. Bless to us our extraordinary mercies; if the day come when these must be taken, brace us to play the man under affliction. Be with our friends, be with ourselves. Go with each of us to rest; if any awake, temper to them the dark hours of watching; and when the day returns, return to us, our sun and comforter, and call us up with morning faces and with morning hearts, eager to labor, eager to be happy if happiness shall be our portion, and if the day be marked for sorrow, strong to endure it. Amen.

The New Year

Ever-living God, by whose mercy we have come to the gateway of another year; grant that we may enter it with humble and grateful hearts; and confirm our resolution, we beseech thee, to walk more closely in thy way, and labor more faithfully in thy service, according to the teaching and example of thy Son our Lord. Let not the errors and offences of the past cling to us, but pardon us and set us free, that with a purer purpose and a better hope, we may renew our vows in thy presence, and set forth under the guidance of thy Spirit, to travel in that path which shineth more and more unto the perfect day of thy heavenly kingdom. Amen.

Good Friday

O Lamb of God who takest away the sin of the world, our hearts are bowed in reverence and humility before the wonder of thy cross. Thou hast borne our griefs and carried our sorrows. With thy stripes we are healed, and the Lord hath laid on thee the iniquity of us all. By thy temptation and obedience, the betrayal and forsaking, the scourge and piercing thorns, the cruel wounding of the nails, the taunts and burning thirst, the lingering anguish of the cross which thou hast willingly endured for our salvation, grant us thy pardon and thy peace. Through dying thou hast conquered death, and risen again that we may share thy life forevermore. Let thy glory shine amid the trials of the earth. Quicken our faith and make our love effective for thy service. Draw us to thyself in true repentance and unfeigned humility, and may our lives bear witness to thy love through all our years. Amen.

Easter

O God, who for our redemption didst give thine only-begotten Son to the death of the cross. and by his glorious resurrection hast delivered us from the power of our enemy; grant us so to die daily from sin, that we may evermore live with him in the joy of his resurrection; through the same Christ our Lord. Amen.

Thanksgiving

Almighty God, our heavenly Father, from whom cometh every good and perfect gift; we call to remembrance thy loving kindness and thy tender mercies which have been ever of old, and with grateful hearts we lift up to thee the voice of our thanksgiving. For the life thou hast given us, and the world in which we live: We praise Thee, O God. For the order and constancy of nature; for the beauty and bounty of the world: We praise Thee, O God. For all the comforts and gladness of life; for our homes and all our home-blessings; for our friends and all the pure pleasures of social intercourse; for the love, sympathy and good-will of men: We praise Thee, O God. For the gift of thy Son, Jesus Christ, and all the helps and hopes which are ours as his disciples; for the presence and inspiration of thy Holy Spirit, and for all the ministers of thy truth and grace: We praise Thee, O God.

And now, O Lord, having praised thee with our lips; grant that we may also praise thee in consecrated and faithful lives; through Jesus Christ our Lord. Amen.

Prayers

Christmas

Holy Father, the Giver of every good and perfect gift; we thank thee for the sweet human significance of the festival which we are now celebrating. We thank thee for home and childhood, and for all our dear human fellowships and friendships. Forgive our enemies, if we have any, and help us to forgive them. Take from us all narrow and bitter thoughts and feelings; our vanity and pride, and all dislike, doubt and jealousy of others, that this day we may enter the kingdom as little children. Soften and fill our hearts with love and gratitude, with tenderness and peace. Consecrate our joy; help us to serve thee with mirth, and whether we eat or drink, or whatsoever we do, may we do all to thy glory. Amen.

Heaven on Earth

O God of patience and consolation, give us such good-will, we beseech thee, that with free hearts we may love and serve thee and our brethren. And, having thus the mind of Christ, may begin heaven on earth, and exercise ourselves therein till that day when heaven, where love abideth, shall seem no strange habitation to us. For Jesus Christ's sake. Amen.

For Wisdom

Almighty God our heavenly Father, without whose help labor is useless, without whose light search is vain, invigorate our studies and direct our enquiries, that by due diligence and right discernment, we may establish ourselves and others in thy holy faith. Take not, O Lord, thy Holy Spirit from us; let not evil thoughts have dominion in our minds. Let us not linger in ignorance, but enlighten and support us, for the sake of Jesus Christ our Lord. Amen.

For a Useful, Noble Life

Eternal God, who committest to us the swift and solemn trust of life; since we know not what a day may bring forth, but only that the hour for serving thee is always present; may we wake to the instant claims of thy holy will. Lay to rest, by the persuasion of thy spirit, the resistance of our passion, indolence or fear. Consecrate with thy presence the way our feet may go; that the humblest work may shine, and the roughest places be made plain. Lift us above unrighteous anger and mistrust into faith and hope and charity by a simple and steadfast reliance on thy sure will. In all things draw us to the mind of Christ, that thy lost image may be traced again in us, and that thou mayest own us at one with him and thee, to the glory of thy holy name. Amen.

Cleansed Hearts

O Lord, our God, great, eternal, wonderful in glory, who keepest covenant and promise for those that love thee with their whole heart, who art life of all, the help of those that flee unto thee, the hope of those who cry unto thee; cleanse us from our sins and from every thought displeasing to thy goodness, that with a pure heart and a clean mind, with perfect love and calm hope, we may venture confidently and fearlessly to pray unto thee; through Jesus Christ our Lord. Amen.

Gratitude

Our Father, we thank thee that thy mercies are still upon us, and that thy love wraps us round about. We bless thee for the joy of existence, and for every good and beautiful thing thou hast put into our lives. Thou hast set beauty in all the world about us, and thou dost seek us through every sense we have. We know that thou art merciful, for there has never been a moment of our lives in which thou hast dealt with us according to our sins. We bless thee for the exceeding riches of thy grace, and thy kindness towards us. Continue to be with us all our lives and keep us in thy grace, so that we may be freed from the evils which beset our pathway. Through Jesus Christ our Lord. Amen.

For the Abounding Life

Father of us all, we thank thee for life and that we live now; that our eyes have been opened to the beauties of to-day; that our hands have been filled with the tasks of the present. Nor do we despise the past, into whose labors we have entered; its errors warn us, its successes inform us, its sacrifices inspire us, and to its brave souls we are forever debtors. We are thankful for the moral leadership of the world, for the women and the men who are the road-breakers of liberty, for those prophets of the humanities who hear first the call of life, to whom bodies are more than gold, and the soul of a little child of greater value than the buildings of a city. We are thankful for the friends whose faith in us makes us better than we are; for the children who call us by the holiest name men may ever know; for the tasks we are unworthy of, but rejoice in; and for Jesus of Nazareth, thy Son and our only Saviour, in whose name are all our prayers and supplications. Amen.

For Schools and Colleges

O God, who art the Light and Truth, open now our minds that we may think thy thoughts after thee. Cleanse thine own temple of all that hinders thy presence—of all pride of intellect, all fear of human scorn, all prejudice against men or nations, all selfishness and love of ease—and make us to prefer truth, whatever the consequences it may bring. May we follow truth even when it hurts us, when it reproves us, when it convicts us of sin, and may we reject all the pleasant falsehoods that would blind our eyes and paralyze our efforts.

We thank thee for the quiet courage of the Nazarene, who in an obscure province, surrounded by poverty and formalism, lived undiscouraged and unafraid, and died that he might bear witness to the truth. Make us to follow him, through the house of worship and the place of study, through both the green pastures and the valley of the shadow, until we shall some day meet him and be with him forever. Amen.

For the Community

O God, grant us a vision of our city, fair as she might be; a city of justice, where none shall prey on others; a city of plenty, where vice and poverty shall cease to fester; a city of brotherhood, where all success shall be founded on service, and honor shall be given to nobleness alone; a city of peace, where order shall not rest on force, but on the love of all for the city, the great mother of common life and weal. Hear thou, O Lord, the silent prayer of all our hearts as we each pledge our time and strength and thought to speed the day of her coming beauty and righteousness. Amen.

For Business Life

O God, we pray thee for those who are pressed by the cares and beset by the temptations of business life. We acknowledge before thee our common guilt for the hardness and deceitfulness of industry and trade. May thy spirit which is ceaselessly pleading within us, prevail at last to bring our business life under Christ's law of service, so that all who share in the processes of factory and trade may become conscious of a divine calling and may consciously devote their strength to the common good? Amen.

For Deliverance from National Sins

Lord God Almighty, defend our land, we beseech thee, from the secret power and the open shame of great national sins. From all dishonesty and civic corruption; from all vainglory and selfish luxury; from all cruelty and the spirit of violence; from covetousness which is idolatry; from impurity which defiles the temple of the Holy Spirit; and from intemperance which is the mother of many crimes and sorrows; good Lord, deliver and save us, and our children, and our children's children, in the land which thou hast blessed with the light of pure religion; through Jesus Christ, our only Saviour and King. Amen.

Commemoration

Let us be here dedicated to the great task remaining before us: that from these honored dead we take increased devotion to that cause for which they gave the last full measure of devotion.

Let us here highly resolve that these dead shall not have died in vain; that this nation, under God, shall have a new birth of freedom; and that government of the people, by the people, for the people, shall not perish from the earth. Amen.

For New Life in Our Churches

O God, our Shepherd, give to the church a new vision and a new charity, new wisdom and fresh understanding, the revival of her brightness and the renewal of her unity; that the eternal message of thy Son, undefiled by the traditions of men, may be hailed as the good news of the new age; through him who maketh all things new, Jesus Christ our Lord. Amen.

For a Better World

O Christ, thou hast bidden us pray for the coming of thy Father's Kingdom, in which his righteous will shall be done on earth. We have treasured thy words, but we have forgotten their meaning, and thy great hope has grown dim in thy Church. We bless thee for the inspired souls of all ages who saw afar the shining city of God, and by faith left the profit of the present to follow their vision. We rejoice that to-day their hope is becoming the clear faith of millions. Help us, O Lord, in the courage of faith to seize what has now come so near, that the glad day of God may dawn at last. As we have mastered nature that we might gain wealth, help us now to master the social relations of mankind that we may gain justice and a world of brothers.

Make us determined to live by truth and not by lies, to found our common life on the eternal foundations of righteousness and love, and no longer to prop the tottering house of wrong by legalized cruelty and force. Help us to make the welfare of all the supreme law of our land, that so our commonwealth may be built strong and secure on the love of all its citizens. Our Master, once more we make thy faith our prayer: Thy kingdom come. Thy will be done on earth. Amen.

For the Unity of God's People

O God, who hast made of one blood all the nations of mankind, so that all are children and members one of another, how is it that we are so slow to trace the family likeness, so reluctant to claim our common kinship? We pray, thee, O our God, to make the peoples one.

We pray for the church of Christ so broken, scattered and dismembered, that none would think we followed all one Lord and held a common faith. Purge away the vanity, intolerance, and unforgiving spirit which has kept us far apart. May the seamless robe not be utterly rent nor the body any longer broken.

We pray that since man's need is one, we all may find the one way to thee, the one God. Forbid that in our highest things we should find fellowship impossible. May the spirit of Christ break down all barriers and answer the desire of all nations.

We pray for a union so deep and universal that it shall gather all within one fold: those who pray and those who cannot; those whose faith is firm, and those whose doubt is slow to clear. May we never be content with aught that excludes another from the fullness of thy grace, a single soul from the welcome of thy heart. Amen.

Authorship of Prayers

Morning Prayer	Hunter's "Devotional Services"
Evening Prayer	Robert Louis Stevenson
The New Year	Book of Common Worship
Good Friday	I. O. Rankin
Christmas	Hunter's "Devotional Services"
Heaven on Earth	Christina Rossetti
For Wisdom	Samuel Johnson
For a Useful, Noble Life	James Martineau
Cleansed Hearts	Coptic Liturgy of St. Basil (Fourth Century)
Thanksgiving	D. T. McGill
The Abounding Life	Daniel A. Poling
The Community	Walter Rauschenbusch
Schools and Colleges	W. H. P. Faunce
For Business Life	Walter Rauschenbusch
For Deliverance from National Sin	The Book of Common Worship
Commemoration	Abraham Lincoln
For New Life in Our Churches	Percy Dearmer
For a Better World	Walter Rauschenbusch
For the Unity of God's People	W. E. Orchard

Used by Permission.

The Hymns

Oh! Let the Nations be glad, and sing for joy.

Hymns for the Living Age

1

ITALIAN HYMN. 6. 6. 4. 6. 6. 6. 4.

ANONYMOUS

FELICE DE GIARDINI, 1769

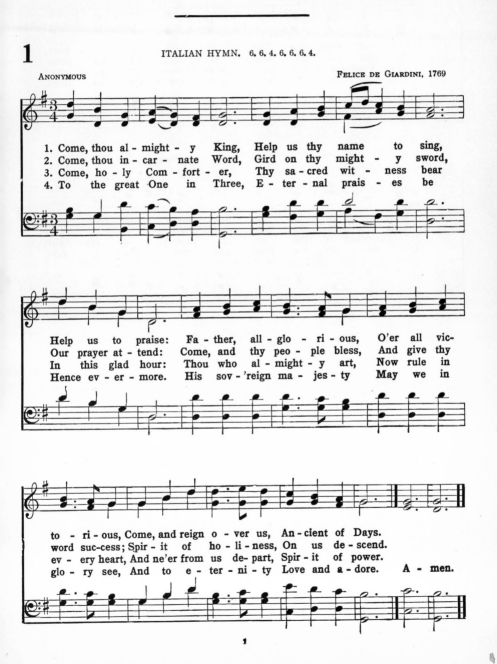

1. Come, thou al - might - y King, Help us thy name to sing,
2. Come, thou in - car - nate Word, Gird on thy might - y sword,
3. Come, ho - ly Com - fort - er, Thy sa - cred wit - ness bear
4. To the great One in Three, E - ter - nal prais - es be

Help us to praise: Fa - ther, all - glo - ri - ous, O'er all vic-
Our prayer at - tend: Come, and thy peo - ple bless, And give thy
In this glad hour: Thou who al - might - y art, Now rule in
Hence ev - er - more. His sov - 'reign ma - jes - ty May we in

to - ri - ous, Come, and reign o - ver us, An - cient of Days.
word suc - cess; Spir - it of ho - li - ness, On us de - scend.
ev - ery heart, And ne'er from us de - part, Spir - it of power.
glo - ry see, And to e - ter - ni - ty Love and a - dore. A - men.

2

LYONS. 10. 10. 11. 11.

Robert Grant, 1833

J. Michael Haydn, 1770

1. O wor - ship the King, all glo - rious a - bove,
2. O tell of his might, O sing of his grace,
3. Thy boun - ti - ful care what tongue can re - cite?
4. Frail chil - dren of dust, and fee - ble as frail,

O grate - ful - ly sing his power and his love;
Whose robe is the light, whose can - o - py space;
It breathes in the air, it shines in the light;
In thee do we trust, nor find thee to fail;

Our Shield and De - fend - er, the An - cient of Days,
His char - iots of wrath the deep thun - der - clouds form,
It streams from the hills, it de - scends to the plain,
Thy mer - cies how ten - der, how firm to the end,

Pa - vil - ioned in splen - dor, and gird - ed with praise.
And dark is his path on the wings of the storm.
And sweet - ly dis - tils in the dew and the rain.
Our Ma - ker, De - fend - er, Re - deem - er, and Friend! A - men.

Call to Worship

3

HANOVER. 10. 10. 11. 11.

CHARLES WESLEY, 1744

WILLIAM CROFT, 1708

1. Ye ser - vants of God, your Mas - ter pro - claim,
2. God rul - eth on high, al - might - y to save;
3. Sal - va - tion to God, who sits on the throne!
4. Then let us a - dore, and give him his right,

And pub - lish a - broad his won - der - ful name;
And still he is nigh— his pres - ence we have.
Let all cry a - loud, and hon - or the Son.
All glo - ry and power, and wis - dom and might,

The name all vic - to - rious, of Je - sus ex - tol;
The great con - gre - ga - tion his tri - umph shall sing,
Of Je - sus the prais - es the an - gels pro - claim,
All hon - or and bless - ing, with an - gels a - bove,

His king - dom is glo - rious, and rules o - ver all.
A - scrib - ing sal - va - tion to Je - sus, our King.
Fall down on their fa - ces and wor - ship the Lamb.
And thanks nev - er ceas - ing, and in - fi - nite love. A - men.

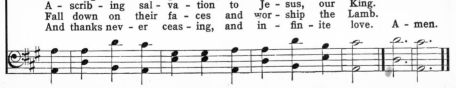

4

ST. ASAPH. 8. 7. 8. 7. D.

ANON, 1801 and EDWARD OSLER, 1836

WILLIAM S. BAMBRIDGE, 1872

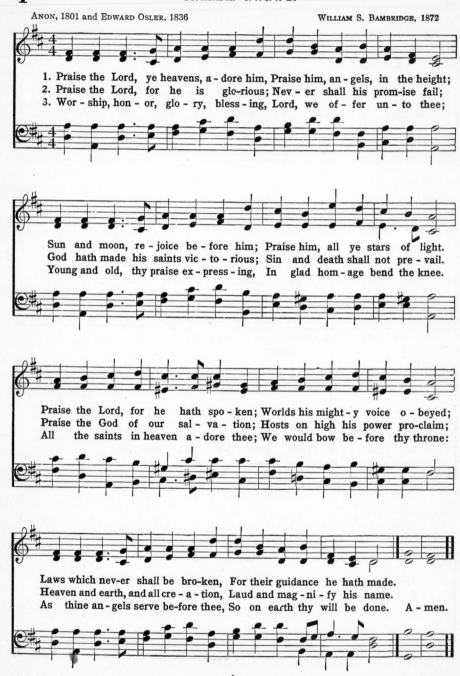

1. Praise the Lord, ye heavens, a - dore him, Praise him, an - gels, in the height;
2. Praise the Lord, for he is glo-rious; Nev - er shall his prom-ise fail;
3. Wor - ship, hon - or, glo - ry, bless - ing, Lord, we of - fer un - to thee;

Sun and moon, re - joice be - fore him; Praise him, all ye stars of light.
God hath made his saints vic - to - rious; Sin and death shall not pre - vail.
Young and old, thy praise ex - press - ing, In glad hom - age bend the knee.

Praise the Lord, for he hath spo - ken; Worlds his might - y voice o - beyed;
Praise the God of our sal - va - tion; Hosts on high his power pro - claim;
All the saints in heaven a - dore thee; We would bow be - fore thy throne:

Laws which nev-er shall be bro - ken, For their guidance he hath made.
Heaven and earth, and all cre - a - tion, Laud and mag - ni - fy his name.
As thine an - gels serve be - fore thee, So on earth thy will be done. A - men.

Call to Worship

FABEN. 8. 7. 8. 7. D.

RICHARD MANT, 1837

JOHN H. WILLCOX, 1849

1. Round the Lord in glo-ry seat-ed, Cher-u-bim and ser-a-phim
2. Heaven is still with glo-ry ring-ing, Earth takes up the an-gels' cry,
3. 'Lord, thy glo-ry fills the heav-en, Earth is with thy full-ness stored,

Filled his tem-ple, and re-peat-ed Each to each th'al-ter-nate hymn:
'Ho-ly, ho-ly, ho-ly,' sing-ing, 'Lord of hosts, the Lord Most High.'
Un-to thee be glo-ry giv-en, Ho-ly, ho-ly, ho-ly Lord.'

'Lord, thy glo-ry fills the heav-en, Earth is with thy full-ness stored;
With his ser-aph train be-fore him, With his ho-ly church be-low,
Thus thy glo-rious name con-fess-ing, With thine an-gel hosts we cry,

Un-to thee be glo-ry giv-en, Ho-ly, ho-ly, ho-ly Lord.'
Thus u-nite we to a-dore him, Bid we thus our an-them flow:
'Ho-ly, ho-ly, ho-ly,' bless-ing Thee, the Lord of hosts Most High. A-men.

6

HYMN TO JOY. 8. 7. 8. 7. D.

HENRY VAN DYKE, 1908

Arranged from BEETHOVEN, 1826,
by EDWARD HODGES

1. Joy - ful, joy - ful, we a - dore thee, God of glo - ry, Lord of love;
2. All thy works with joy sur-round thee, Earth and heaven re - flect thy rays,
3. Thou art giv - ing and for - giv - ing, Ev - er bless - ing, ev - er blest,
4. Mor-tals, join the might-y cho - rus, Which the morn-ing stars be - gan;

Hearts un -fold like flowers be - fore thee, Hail thee as the sun a - bove.
Stars and an - gels sing a - round thee, Cen - ter of un - bro - ken praise;
Well-spring of the joy of liv - ing, O - cean - depth of hap - py rest!
Fa - ther - love is reign - ing o'er us, Broth - er - love binds man to man.

Melt the clouds of sin and sad-ness; Drive the dark of doubt a - way;
Field and for - est, vale and moun-tain, Blossoming mead-ow, flash - ing sea,
Thou our Fa - ther, Christ our Broth- er,—All who live in love are thine:
Ev - er sing - ing march we on - ward, Vic - tors in the midst of strife;

Giv - er of im - mor - tal glad-ness, Fill us with the light of day!
Chant-ing bird and flow-ing foun-tain, Call us to re - joice in thee.
Teach us how to love each oth - er, Lift us to the Joy Di - vine.
Joy - ful mu - sic lifts us sun-ward In the tri-umph song of life. A - men.

ANGEL VOICES. P. M.

Francis Pott, 1861   Arthur S. Sullivan, 1872

1. An - gel voic - es, ev - er sing - ing Round thy
2. Yea, we know thy love re - joic - es O'er each
3. Here, great God, to - day we of - fer Of thine
4. Hon - or, glo - ry, might, and mer - it, Thine shall

throne of light, An - gel harps, for ev - er ring - ing,
work of thine; Thou didst ears and hands and voic - es
own to thee; And for thine ac - cept - ance prof - fer,
ev - er be, Fa - ther, Son, and Ho - ly Spir - it,

Rest not day nor night; Thou - sands on - ly live to
For thy praise com - bine; Craft - men's art and mu - sic's
All un - worth - i - ly, Hearts and minds, and hands and
Bless - ed Trin - i - ty: Of the best that thou hast

bless thee, And con - fess thee Lord of might.
meas - ure For thy pleas - ure Didst de - sign.
voic - es, In our choic - est Mel - o - dy.
giv - en Earth and heav - en Ren - der thee. A - men.

8

KREMSER. 12. 11. 12. 11.

JULIA BULKLEY CADY, (1882 ——)

Old Netherlands Melody, 1625

1. We praise thee, O God, our Re-deem-er, Cre-a-tor,
2. We wor-ship thee, God of our fa-thers, we bless thee;
3. With voic-es u-ni-ted our prais-es we of-fer,

In grate-ful de-vo-tion our trib-ute we bring.
Through life's storm and tem-pest our Guide hast thou been.
To thee, great Je-ho-vah, glad an-thems we raise.

We lay it be-fore thee, we kneel and a-dore thee,
When per-ils o'er-take us, es-cape thou wilt make us,
Thy strong arm will guide us, our God is be-side us,

We bless thy ho-ly name, glad prais-es we sing.
And with thy help, O Lord, our bat-tles we win.
To thee, our great Re-deem-er, for-ev-er be praise. A-men.

Call to Worship

LONGWOOD. 10. 10. 10. 10.

9

Lucy E. G. Whitmore, 1824

Joseph Barnby, 1872

1. Fa - ther, a - gain in Je - sus' name we meet,
2. O, we would bless thee for thy cease - less care,
3. A - las, un - worth - y of thy bound - less love,
4. O, by that name in which all ful - ness dwells,

And bow in pen - i - tence be - neath thy feet,
And all thy work from day to day de - clare:
Too oft with care - less feet from thee we rove!
O, by that love which ev - ery love ex - cels,

A - gain to thee our fil - ial voic - es raise,
Is not our life with hour - ly mer - cies crowned?
But now, en - cour - aged by thy voice, we come,
O, by that blood so free - ly shed for sin,

To sue for mer - cy, and to sing thy praise.
Does not thine arm en - cir - cle us a - round?
Re - turn - ing wan - derers to a Fa - ther's home.
O - pen blest mer - cy's gate, and take us in! A - men.

10

MANOAH. C. M.

Isaac Watts. 1707

Arranged from
Gioacchino A. Rossini, 1851

1. Be - gin, my tongue, some heavenly theme, And speak some boundless thing,
2. Tell of his wond-rous faith - ful - ness, And sound his power a - broad;
3. His ver - y word of grace is strong As that which built the skies;
4. O might I hear thy heaven-ly tongue But whis - per 'Thou art mine,'

The might - y works, or mightier name, Of our e - ter - nal King.
Sing the sweet promise of his grace, The love and truth of God.
The voice that rolls the stars a - long Speaks all the prom-is-es.
Those gentle words should raise my song To notes al-most di-vine. A - men.

11

OLD HUNDREDTH. L. M.

Isaac Watts, 1719

Louis Bourgeois, 1551

1. From all that dwell be - low the skies, Let the Cre - a - tor's praise a - rise:
2. E - ter - nal are thy mer - cies, Lord; E - ter - nal truth at - tends thy word;

Let the Re-deem-er's name be sung Thro' ev-ery land, by ev-ery tongue.
Thy praise shall sound from shore to shore Till suns shall rise and set no more. A-men.

12

OLD HUNDREDTH. L. M.

Praise God from whom all blessings flow;
Praise him, all creatures here below;
Praise him above, ye heavenly host;
Praise Father, Son and Holy Ghost. Amen.

Thomas Ken. 1695

Call to Worship

13

PARK STREET. L. M.

ISAAC WATTS, 1719

FREDERICK M. A. VENUA, 1810

1. Be - fore Je - ho - vah's aw - ful throne, Ye na - tions bow with
2. His sov-ereign power, with - out our aid, Made us of clay, and
3. We are his peo - ple, we his care, Our souls, and all our
4. We'll crowd thy gates with thank - ful songs, High as the heavens our
5. Wide as the world is thy com - mand, Vast as e - ter - ni -

sa - cred joy; Know that the Lord is God a - lone; He can cre -
formed us men; And when like wandering sheep we strayed, He brought us
mor - tal frame; What last - ing hon - ors shall we rear, Al - might - y
voic - es raise; And earth, with her ten thou-sand tongues, Shall fill thy
ty thy love; Firm as a rock thy truth must stand, When roll-ing

ate, and he de - stroy, He can cre - ate, and he de - stroy.
to his fold a - gain, He brought us to his fold a - gain.
Mak - er, to thy name? Al-might-y Mak - er, to thy name?
courts with sound-ing praise, Shall fill thy courts with sound-ing praise.
years shall cease to move, When roll-ing years shall cease to move. A - men.

14

OLD HUNDREDTH. L. M.

1. All people that on earth do dwell,
   Sing to the Lord with cheerful voice;
   Him serve with fear, his praise forth tell,
   Come ye before him and rejoice.

2. The Lord ye know is God indeed,
   Without our aid he did us make;
   We are his folk, he doth us feed,
   And for his sheep he doth us take.

3 O enter then his gates with praise,
   Approach with joy his courts unto;
   Praise, laud, and bless his name always,
   For it is seemly so to do.

4 For why? the Lord our God is good,
   His mercy is for ever sure;
   His truth at all times firmly stood,
   And shall from age to age endure.

WILLIAM KETHE. 1561

11

15

ST. THOMAS. S. M.

ISAAC WATTS, 1709.

AARON WILLIAMS, 1763

1. Come, we who love the Lord, And let our joys be known; Join
2. Let those re - fuse to sing Who nev - er knew our God; But
3. The men of grace have found Glo - ry be - gun be - low; Ce -
4. The hill of Zi - on yields A thou - sand sa - cred sweets Be -
5. Then let our songs a - bound, And ev - ery tear be dry; We're

in a song of sweet ac - cord, And thus sur-round the throne.
chil - dren of the heaven - ly King Should speak their joys a-broad.
les - tial fruits on earth - ly ground From faith and hope may grow.
fore we reach the heaven-ly fields, Or walk the gold - en streets.
marching thro' Em-man-uel's ground To fair - er worlds on high. A-men.

16

ST. BEES. 7. 7. 7. 7.

WILLIAM HAMMOND, 1745

JOHN B. DYKES, 1862

1. Lord, we come be - fore thee now, At thy feet we hum - bly bow;
2. Lord, on thee our souls de - pend; In com - pas - sion now de-scend,
3. Send some mes - sage from thy word That may joy and peace af-ford;
4. Com - fort those who weep and mourn, Let the time of joy re - turn;
5. Grant that those who seek may find Thee a God sin - cere and kind;

O do not our suit dis-dain, Shall we seek thee, Lord, in vain?
Fill our hearts with thy rich grace, Tune our lips to sing thy praise.
Let thy spir - it now im - part Full sal - va - tion to each heart.
Those that are cast down, lift up Strong in faith, in love and hope.
Heal the sick, the cap - tive free, Let us all re - joice in thee. A-men.

12

17

DUKE STREET. L. M.

John Needham (—— 1786)

John Hatton, about 1793

1. A-wake, my tongue, thy trib-ute bring To him who gave thee pow'r to sing;
2. How vast his knowl-edge, how pro-found! A deep where all our tho'ts are drowned;
3. Thro' each bright world a-bove, be-hold Ten thousand, thousand charms un-fold:
4. But in re-demp-tion, O what grace! Its won-ders, O what tho't can trace!

Praise him who is all praise a-bove, The source of wis-dom and of love.
The stars he num-bers, and their names He gives to all those heav'n-ly flames.
Earth, air and might-y seas com-bine To speak his wis-dom all di-vine.
Here, wis-dom shines for-ev-er bright; Praise him, my soul, with sweet de-light. A-men.

18

MORNING HYMN. L. M.

Thomas Ken, 1695

Francois H. Barthelemon, 1789

1. A-wake, my soul, and with the sun Thy dai-ly stage of du-ty run;
2. Shine on me, Lord! new life im-part, Fresh ar-dors kin-dle in my heart:
3. In con-ver-sa-tion be sin-cere, Keep con-science as the noon-day clear,
4. Di-rect, con-trol, sug-gest this day All I de-sign, or do, or say,—
5. Lord, I my vows to thee re-new: Dis-perse my sins as morn-ing dew,

Shake off dull sloth, and joy-ful rise To pay thy morn-ing sac-ri-fice.
One ray of thine all-quickening light Dis-pels the sloth and clouds of night.
Think how all-see-ing God, thy ways And all thy se-cret thoughts sur-veys.
That all my pow'rs, with all their might, In thy sole glo-ry may u-nite.
Guard my first springs of tho't and will, And with thy-self my spir-it fill. **A-men.**

19

NICÆA. 11. 12. 12. 10.

REGINALD HEBER, 1826

JOHN B. DYKES, 1861

1. Ho - ly, ho - ly, ho - ly! Lord God Al - might - y!
2. Ho - ly, ho - ly, ho - ly! all the saints a - dore thee,
3. Ho - ly, ho - ly, ho - ly! tho' the dark - ness hide thee,
4. Ho - ly, ho - ly, ho - ly! Lord God Al - might - y!

Ear - ly in the morn - ing our song shall rise to thee;
Cast - ing down their gold - en crowns a - round the glass - y sea;
Though the eye of sin - ful man thy glo - ry may not see,
All thy works shall praise thy name, in earth, and sky, and sea;

Ho - ly, ho - ly, ho - ly, mer - ci - ful and might - y!
Cher - u - bim and ser - a - phim fall - ing down be - fore thee,
On - ly thou art ho - ly, there is none be - side thee,
Ho - ly, ho - ly, ho - ly, mer - ci - ful and might - y!

God in Three Per - sons, bless - ed Trin - i - ty!
Which wert, and art, and ev - er - more shalt be.
Per - fect in power, in love, and pur - i - ty.
God in Three Per - sons, bless - ed Trin - i - ty! A - men.

20

LAUDES DOMINI. 6. 6. 6. 6. 6. 6.

German, 19th Century
Translated by EDWARD CASWALL, 1853

JOSEPH BARNBY, 1868

1. When morn-ing gilds the skies, My heart a-wak-ing cries,
2. When-e'er the sweet church bell Peals o-ver hill and dell,
3. When e-vil thoughts mo-lest, With this I shield my breast,
4. The night be-comes as day, When from the heart we say,

May Je-sus Christ be praised! A-like at work and prayer,
May Je-sus Christ be praised! O hark to what it sings,
May Je-sus Christ be praised! Does sad-ness fill my mind?
May Je-sus Christ be praised! The powers of dark-ness fear,

To Je-sus I re-pair; May Je-sus Christ be praised!
As joy-ous-ly it rings, May Je-sus Christ be praised!
A so-lace here I find, May Je-sus Christ be praised!
When this sweet chant they hear, May Je-sus Christ be praised! A-men.

5 In heaven's eternal bliss
   The loveliest strain is this,
      May Jesus Christ be praised!
Let earth, and sea, and sky
From depth to height reply
      May Jesus Christ be praised!

6 Be this, while life is mine,
   My canticle divine,
      May Jesus Christ be praised!
Be this the eternal song,
Through all the ages long,
      May Jesus Christ be praised!

21

WINDSOR. 11. 10. 11. 10.

HARRIET BEECHER STOWE, 1855

JOSEPH BARNBY, 1838–1896

1. Still, still with thee, when pur - ple morn - ing break - eth,
2. A - lone with thee, a - mid the mys - tic shad - ows,
3. Still, still with thee; as to each new - born morn - ing
4. When sinks the soul, sub - dued by toil, to slum - ber,
5. So shall it be at last, in that bright morn - ing,

When the bird wak - eth, and the shad - ows flee;
The sol - emn hush of na - ture new - ly born;
A fresh and sol - emn splen - dor still is given,
Its clos - ing eye looks up to thee in prayer;
When the soul wak - eth, and life's shad - ows flee:

Fair - er than morn - ing, love - lier than the day - light,
A - lone with thee in breath - less ad - o - ra - tion,
So doth this bless - ed con - scious - ness, a - wak - ing,
Sweet the re - pose be - neath thy wings o'er - shad - ing,
O in that hour, fair - er than day - light dawn - ing,

Dawns the sweet con - scious - ness, I am with thee.
In the calm dew and fresh - ness of the morn.
Breathe, each day, near - ness un - to thee and heaven.
But sweet - er still to wake and find thee there.
Shall rise the glo - rious thought, I am with thee. A - men.

22

GOUNOD. 7. 7. 7. 7. 7. 7.

CHARLES WESLEY, 1740

CHARLES F. GOUNOD, 1872

1. Christ, whose glo - ry fills the skies, Christ the true, the
2. Dark and cheer - less is the morn Un - ac - com - pan -
3. Vis - it, then, this soul of mine; Pierce the gloom of

on - ly Light, Sun of Right - eous - ness, a - rise,
ied by thee, Joy - less is the day's re - turn
sin and grief; Fill me, Ra - dian - cy Di - vine;

Tri - umph o'er the shades of night; Day - spring from on
Till thy mer - cy's beams I see; Till they in - ward
Scat - ter all my un - be - lief; More and more thy -

high, be near; Day - star, in my heart ap - pear.
light im - part, Glad my eyes and warm my heart.
self dis - play, Shin - ing to the per - fect day. A - men.

23

HAYDN. 8. 4. 7. 8. 4. 7.

FRIEDRICH R. L. VON CANITZ, 1654–1699
Translated by HENRY JAMES BUCKOLL, 1841

Arranged from
FRANZ JOSEPH HAYDN, 1791

1. Come, my soul, thou must be wak-ing; Now is break-ing O'er the earth an-oth-er day. Come to him who made this splen-dor, See thou ren-der All thy fee-ble strength can pay.

2. Glad-ly hail the sun re-turn-ing; Read-y burn-ing Be the in-cense of thy powers; For the night is safe-ly end-ed: God hath tend-ed With his care thy help-less hours.

3. Pray that he may pros-per ev-er Each en-deav-or, When thine aim is good and true; But that he may ev-er thwart thee, And con-vert thee, When thou e-vil wouldst pur-sue.

4. On-ly God's free gifts a-buse not, Light re-fuse not, But his Spir-it's voice o-bey; Thou with him shalt dwell, be-hold-ing Light en-fold-ing All things in un-cloud-ed day. A-men.

24

KELSO. 7. 7. 7. 7. 7. 7.

GREVILLE PHILLIMORE, 1863

EDWARD J. HOPKINS, 1872

1. Ev - ery morn - ing mer - cies new Fall as fresh as morn - ing dew; Ev - ery morn - ing let us pay Trib - ute with the ear - ly day: For thy mer - cies, Lord, are sure; Thy com - pas - sion doth en - dure.

2. Still the great - ness of thy love Dai - ly doth our sins re - move; Dai - ly, far as east from west, Lifts the bur - den from the breast; Gives un - bought to those who pray Strength to stand in e - vil day.

3. Let our prayers each morn pre - vail, That these gifts may nev - er fail; And, as we con - fess the sin And the tempt - er's power with - in, Ev - ery morn - ing, Feed us with the bread of life.

4. As the morn - ing light re - turns, As the sun with splen - dor burns, Teach us still to turn to thee, Ev - er - bless - ed Trin - i - ty, With our hands our hearts to raise, In un - fail - ing prayer and praise. A - men.

25

HOPE. L. M.

CAROLINE ATHERTON MASON, 1823–1890

HERBERT S. IRONS, 1834–1905

1. O God, I thank thee for each sight Of beau-ty that thy hand doth give; For sun-ny skies and air and light; O God, I thank thee that I live.
2. That life I con-se-crate to thee, And ev-er, as the day is born, On wings of joy my soul would flee, And thank thee for an-oth-er morn;
3. An-oth-er day in which to cast Some si-lent deed of love a-broad, That, greatening as it jour-neys past, May do some earn-est work for God.
4. An-oth-er day to do, to dare, To use a-new my grow-ing strength, To arm my soul with faith and prayer, And so reach heaven and thee at length. A-men.

26

GREENWOOD. S. M.

CHARLES H. SPURGEON, 1834–1892

JOSEPH E. SWEETZER, 1849

1. Sweet-ly the ho-ly hymn Breaks on the morn-ing air;
2. While flowers are wet with dews, Dew of our souls de-scend;
3. Up-on the bat-tle-field, Be-fore the fight be-gins,
4. Ere yet our ves-sel sails Up-on the streams of day,

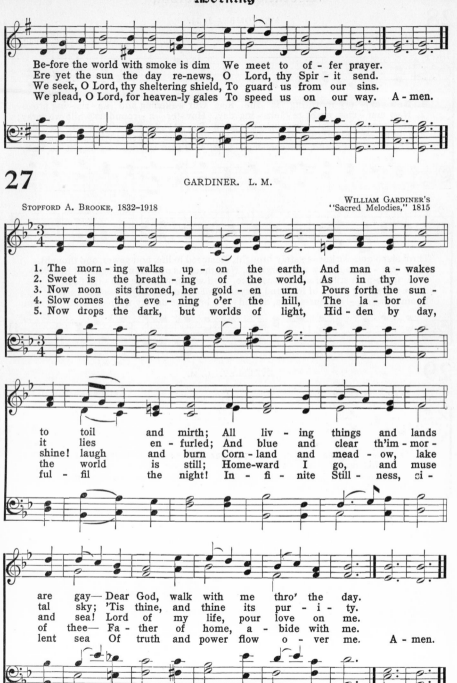

Be-fore the world with smoke is dim We meet to of - fer prayer.
Ere yet the sun the day re-news, O Lord, thy Spir - it send.
We seek, O Lord, thy sheltering shield, To guard us from our sins.
We plead, O Lord, for heaven-ly gales To speed us on our way. A - men.

27

GARDINER. L. M.

STOPFORD A. BROOKE, 1832–1918

WILLIAM GARDINER'S
"Sacred Melodies," 1815

1. The morn - ing walks up - on the earth, And man a - wakes
2. Sweet is the breath - ing of the world, As in thy love
3. Now noon sits throned, her gold - en urn Pours forth the sun -
4. Slow comes the eve - ning o'er the hill, The la - bor of
5. Now drops the dark, but worlds of light, Hid - den by day,

to toil and mirth; All liv - ing things and lands
it lies en - furled; And blue and clear th'im - mor -
shine! laugh and burn Corn - land and mead - ow, lake
the world is still; Home-ward I go, and muse
ful - fil the night! In - fi - nite Still - ness, si -

are gay— Dear God, walk with me thro' the day.
tal sky; 'Tis thine, and thine its pur - i - ty.
and sea! Lord of my life, pour love on me.
of thee— Fa - ther of home, a - bide with me.
lent sea Of truth and power flow o - ver me. A - men.

21

28

MELCOMBE. L. M.

JOHN KEBLE, 1822

SAMUEL WEBBE, 1792

1. New ev - ery morn-ing is the love Our wakening and up-ris-ing prove—
2. New mer - cies, each re-turn-ing day, Hov-er a-round us while we pray;
3. If on our dai-ly course our mind Be set to hal-low all we find,
4. Old friends, old scenes, will love-lier be, As more of heaven in each we see:
5. The tri-vial round, the com-mon task, Will furn-ish all we ought to ask,—

Thro' sleep and darkness safely brought, Restored to life, and power, and thought.
New per - ils past, new sins forgiven, New thoughts of God, new hopes of heaven.
New treas-ures still, of count-less price, God will provide for sac-ri-fice.
Some soften-ing gleam of love and prayer Shall dawn on every cross and care.
Room to de - ny our-selves, a road To bring us dai-ly near-er God. A-men.

29

EVERSLEY. C. M.

F. A. PERCY, 1896

ARTHUR COTTMAN, 1875

1. O Fa - ther, hear my morn-ing prayer, Thine aid im-part to me, That
2. May this de-sire my spir-it rule, And, as the mo-ments fly, Some-
3. Some grace that seeks my heart to win, With shin-ing vic-tory meet; Some
4. That so through-out the com-ing day The hours shall car-ry me A

I may make my life to - day Ac-cept-a-ble to thee.
thing of good be born in me, Some-thing of e-vil die.
sin that strives for mas-ter-y Find o-ver-throw com-plete;
lit - tle far-ther from the world, A lit-tle near-er thee. A-men.

Evening

30

SEYMOUR. 7. 7. 7. 7.

GEORGE W. DOANE, 1824

Arranged from
CARL M. VON WEBER, 1826

1. Soft - ly now the light of day Fades up - on my sight a - way:
2. Thou, whose all - per - vad - ing eye Naught es - capes, with - out, with - in,
3. Soon, for me, the light of day Shall for - ev - er pass a - way:
4. Thou who, sin - less, yet hast known All of man's in - fir - mi - ty,

Free from care, from la - bor free, Lord, we would commune with thee.
Par - don each in - fir - mi - ty, O - pen fault, and se - cret sin.
Then, from sin and sor - row free, Take me, Lord, to dwell with thee.
Then, from thine e - ter - nal throne, Je - sus, look with pity - ing eye. A - men.

31

EVENING PRAYER. 8. 7. 8. 7.

JAMES EDMESTON, 1820

GEORGE C. STEBBINS, 1878

1. Sav - iour breathe an eve - ning bless - ing, Ere re - pose our spir - its seal;
2. Though the night be dark and drear - y, Dark - ness can - not hide from thee;
3. Though de - struc - tion walk a - round us, Though the ar - row past us fly,
4. Should swift death this night o'er - take us, And our couch be - come our tomb,

Sin and want we come con - fess - ing; Thou canst save, and thou canst heal.
Thou art he who, nev - er wea - ry, Watchest where thy peo - ple be.
An - gel - guards from thee surround us, We are safe if thou art nigh.
May the morn in heaven a - wake us, Clad in light and deathless bloom. A - men.

32

CHAUTAUQUA. 7. 7. 7. 7. 4. With Refrain

Mary A. Lathbury, 1877

William F. Sherwin, 1877

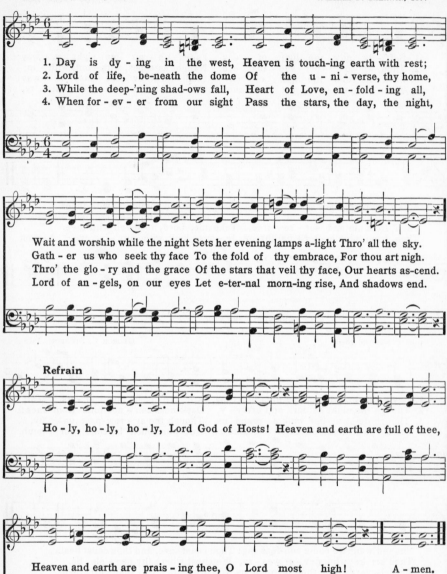

1. Day is dy-ing in the west, Heaven is touch-ing earth with rest;
2. Lord of life, be-neath the dome Of the u-ni-verse, thy home,
3. While the deep-'ning shad-ows fall, Heart of Love, en-fold-ing all,
4. When for-ev-er from our sight Pass the stars, the day, the night,

Wait and worship while the night Sets her evening lamps a-light Thro' all the sky.
Gath-er us who seek thy face To the fold of thy embrace, For thou art nigh.
Thro' the glo-ry and the grace Of the stars that veil thy face, Our hearts as-cend.
Lord of an-gels, on our eyes Let e-ter-nal morn-ing rise, And shadows end.

Refrain

Ho-ly, ho-ly, ho-ly, Lord God of Hosts! Heaven and earth are full of thee,

Heaven and earth are prais-ing thee, O Lord most high! A-men.

33

ST. CLEMENT. 9. 8. 9. 8.

JOHN ELLERTON, 1870

CLEMENT C. SCHOLEFIELD, 1874

1. The day thou gav - est, Lord, is end - ed,
2. We thank thee that thy church un - sleep - ing,
3. As o'er each con - ti - nent and is - land
4. The sun that bids us rest is wak - ing
5. So be it, Lord; thy throne shall nev - er,

The dark - ness falls at thy be - hest;
While earth rolls on - ward in - to light,
The dawn leads on an - oth - er day,
Our breth - ren 'neath the west - ern sky,
Like earth's proud em - pires, pass a - way;

To thee our morn - ing hymns as - cend - ed,
Thro' all the world her watch is keep - ing,
The voice of prayer is nev - er si - lent,
And hour by hour fresh lips are mak - ing
Thy king - dom stands, and grows for - ev - er

Thy praise shall sanc - ti - fy our rest.
And rests not now by day or night.
Nor dies the strain of praise a - way.
Thy won - drous do - ings heard on high.
Till all thy crea - tures own thy sway. A - men.

34 ST. LEONARD. C. M. D.

Adelaide A. Procter, 1862   Henry Hiles, 1868

1. The shad-ows of the eve-ning hours Fall from the dark-'ning sky;
2. The sor-rows of thy ser-vants, Lord, O do not thou de-spise,
3. Let peace, O Lord, thy peace, O God, Up-on our souls de-scend;

Up-on the fra-grance of the flowers The dews of eve-ning lie:
But let the in-cense of our prayers Be-fore thy mer-cy rise:
From mid-night fears and per-ils thou Our trem-bling hearts de-fend;

Be-fore thy throne, O Lord of heaven, We kneel at close of day;
The bright-ness of the com-ing night Up-on the dark-ness rolls;
Give us a res-pite from our toil, Calm and sub-due our woes;

Look on thy chil-dren from on high, And hear us while we pray.
With hopes of fu-ture glo-ry chase The shad-ows from our souls.
Through the long day we la-bor, Lord, O give us now re-pose. A-men.

Evening

35

Ambrose N. Blatchford, 1878

Frederick C. Maker (1844–)

1. Peace - ful - ly round us the shad - ows are fall - ing,
2. Hushed are the sheep - bells a - far on the moor - land,
3. Soft - ly may wear - y ones rest from their du - ty,
4. Lord of the night, let thine an - gels de - fend us;

Glad be our prais - es and trust - ful our prayer:
O'er the still mead - ows the night breez - es sweep,
Bright be the dreams of the troub - led and worn,
Sun - shine and gloom are a - like un - to thee:

Hear us, O Lord, on thy prov - i - dence call - ing,
Faint fall the foot - steps in cit - y and ham - let,
While thro' the shade beam the stars in their beau - ty,
Lord of the day, let thy Spir - it at - tend us,

Light - en our dark - ness, and ban - ish our care.
Safe - ly the chil - dren are fold - ed in sleep.
Watch - ing the world till the break - ing of morn.
Bless us and keep us, wher - ev - er we be. A - men.

36

ABENDS. L. M.

Samuel Longfellow, 1859

Herbert S. Oakeley, 1874

1. A - gain, as eve - ning's shad - ow falls, We gath - er
2. May strug - gling hearts that seek re - lease Here find the
3. O God, our Light! to thee we bow; With - in all
4. Life's tu - mult we must meet a - gain, We can - not

in these hal - lowed walls; And ves - per hymn and ves - per
rest of God's own peace; And, strengthened here by hymn and
shad - ows stand - est thou; Give deep - er calm than night can
at the shrine re - main; But, in the spir - it's se - cret

prayer Rise min - gling on the ho - ly air.
prayer, Lay down the bur - den and the care.
bring; Give sweet - er songs than lips can sing.
cell, May hymn and prayer for - ev - er dwell! A - men.

37

GARDEN CITY. S. M.

John Ellerton, 1868

Horatio W. Parker, 1890

1. Our day of praise is done, The eve - ning shad - ows fall, But
2. A - round the throne on high, Where night can nev - er be, The
3. Yet, Lord, to thy dear will, If thou at - tune the heart, We
4. 'Tis thine each soul to calm, Each way - ward thought re - claim, And

Copyright by Horatio W. Parker

28

Evening

pass not from us with the sun, True Light that lightenest all.
white-robed harp-ers of the sky Bring cease-less hymns to thee.
in thine an-gels' mu-sic still May bear our low-er part.
make our dai-ly life a psalm Of glo-ry to thy name. A-men.

38

ANGELUS. L. M.

HENRY TWELLS, 1868

GEORG JOSEPH, 1657

1. At e-ven, ere the sun was set, The sick,
2. Once more 'tis e-ven-tide, and we, Op-pressed
3. O Sav-iour Christ, our woes dis-pel; For some
4. And none, O Lord, have per-fect rest, For none

O Lord, a-round thee lay; O, in what di-vers pains
with var-ious ills, draw near: What if thy form we can-
are sick, and some are sad, And some have nev-er loved
are whol-ly free from sin; And they who fain would serve

they met! O, with what joy they went a-way!
not see? We know and feel that thou art here.
thee well, And some have lost the love they had.
thee best Are con-scious most of wrong with-in. A-men.

5 O Saviour Christ, thou too art man;
  Thou hast been troubled, tempted, tried;
Thy kind but searching glance can scan
  The very wounds that shame would hide.

6 Thy touch has still its ancient power,
  No word from thee can fruitless fall;
Hear, in this solemn evening hour,
  And in thy mercy heal us all.

39

EVENTIDE. 10. 10. 10. 10.

Henry F. Lyte, 1847

William H. Monk, 1861

1. A - bide with me! fast falls the e - ven - tide;
2. Swift to its close ebbs out life's lit - tle day;
3. I need thy pres - ence ev - ery pass - ing hour;
4. I fear no foe, with thee at hand to bless;
5. Hold thou thy cross be - fore my clos - ing eyes,

The dark - ness deep - ens; Lord, with me a - bide!
Earth's joys grow dim, its glo - ries pass a - way;
What but thy grace can foil the temp - ter's power?
Ills have no weight, and tears no bit - ter - ness:
Shine through the gloom, and point me to the skies:

When oth - er help - ers fail, and com - forts flee,
Change and de - cay in all a - round I see;
Who like thy - self my guide and stay can be?
Where is death's sting? where, grave, thy vic - to - ry?
Heaven's morn - ing breaks, and earth's vain shad - ows flee;

Help of the help - less, O a - bide with me!
O thou who chang - est not, a - bide with me!
Through cloud and sun - shine, O a - bide with me!
I tri - umph still if thou a - bide with me!
In life and death, O Lord, a - bide with me! A - men.

Evening

AR HYD Y NOS. 8. 4. 8. 4. 8. 8. 8. 4.

REGINALD HEBER, 1783–1826; WILLIAM MERCER, 1864;
RICHARD WHATELY, 1838

Welsh Traditional, 1784
Harmonized by L. O. EMERSON, 1906

1. God, that mad-est earth and heav-en, Dark-ness and light;
2. And when morn a-gain shall call us To run life's way,
3. Guard us wak-ing, guard us sleep-ing; And, when we die,

Who the day for toil hast giv-en, For rest the night;
May we still, what-e'er be-fall us, Thy will o-bey.
May we in thy might-y keep-ing All peace-ful lie.

May thine an-gel-guards de-fend us, Slum-ber sweet thy mer-cy send us;
From the power of e-vil hide us, In the nar-row path-way guide us,
When the last dread call shall wake us, Do not thou, our Lord, for-sake us,

Ho-ly dreams and hopes at-tend us, This live-long night.
Nor thy smile be e'er de-nied us The live-long day.
But to reign in glo-ry take us, With thee on high. A-men.

41

EVENING LIGHT. 7. 6. 7. 6. D. With Refrain

CALVIN W. LAUFER, 1922   CALVIN W. LAUFER, 1922

1. When comes the gold-en sun-set That trails God's way on high,
2. So God re-veals at sun-set The grand-eur of his throne,
3. Then come, blest hour of sun-set, A-long the gold-en way,

And with its ra-diant splen-dor Il-lumes the eve-ning sky,
The deep-er, full-er glo-ry Re-served to be our own;
And thrill us with the splen-dors That fill life's per-fect day.

How are the hills and val-leys A-glow with crim-son rays,
And in that hour's un-fold-ing For-got are fear and pain
God is the end of liv-ing, He sat-is-fies the soul,

While na-ture's deep-toned or-gan Lifts heav-en-ward its praise:
In love's a-bound-ing sol-ace, In heav-en's great re-frain:
And they who seek his glo-ry Will find in him their goal.

Evening

Refrain

'Ho - ly, ho - ly!' An - gel voic - es sing it; 'Ho - ly, ho - ly!'

Cloud-y pin - ions wing it; 'Ho - ly, ho - ly!' Gleam-ing tow - ers

ring it; 'Ho - ly, ho - ly, is the Lord most high!' A - men.

42   GORTON. S. M.

Arranged from
BEETHOVEN, 1770–1827

Lord, keep us safe this night, Se - cure from all our fears; May

an - gels guard us while we sleep, Till morn-ing light ap - pears. A - men.

43

HURSLEY. L. M.

John Keble, 1820

Peter Ritter, 1792
Arranged by William H. Monk, 1861

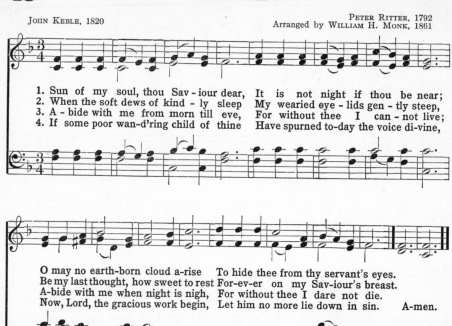

1. Sun of my soul, thou Sav-iour dear, It is not night if thou be near;
2. When the soft dews of kind-ly sleep My wearied eye-lids gen-tly steep,
3. A-bide with me from morn till eve, For without thee I can-not live;
4. If some poor wan-d'ring child of thine Have spurned to-day the voice di-vine,

O may no earth-born cloud a-rise To hide thee from thy servant's eyes.
Be my last thought, how sweet to rest For-ev-er on my Sav-iour's breast.
A-bide with me when night is nigh, For without thee I dare not die.
Now, Lord, the gracious work begin, Let him no more lie down in sin.   A-men.

5 Watch by the sick, enrich the poor
    With blessings from thy boundless store;
    Be every mourner's sleep to-night,
    Like infants' slumbers, pure and light:

6 Come near and bless us when we wake,
    Ere through the world our way we take,
    Till in the ocean of thy love
    We lose ourselves in heaven above.

44

MERRIAL. 6. 5. 6. 5.

Sabine Baring-Gould, 1865

Joseph Barnby, 1868

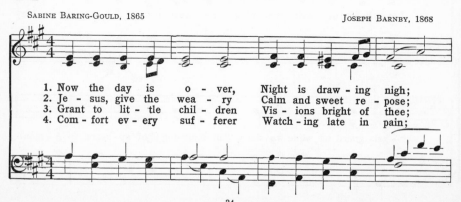

1. Now the day is o - ver, Night is draw-ing nigh;
2. Je - sus, give the wea - ry Calm and sweet re - pose;
3. Grant to lit - tle chil - dren Vis - ions bright of thee;
4. Com - fort ev - ery suf - ferer Watch-ing late in pain;

Evening

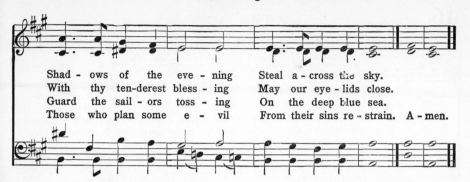

Shad - ows of the eve - ning Steal a - cross the sky.
With thy ten-derest bless - ing May our eye - lids close.
Guard the sail - ors toss - ing On the deep blue sea.
Those who plan some e - vil From their sins re - strain. A - men.

5 Through the long night-watches
  May thine angels spread
  Their white wings above me,
  Watching round my bed.

6 When the morning wakens,
  Then may I arise
  Pure and fresh and sinless
  In thy holy eyes.

45

TALLIS' EVENING HYMN. L. M.

THOMAS KEN, 1695

Arranged from
THOMAS TALLIS, 1567

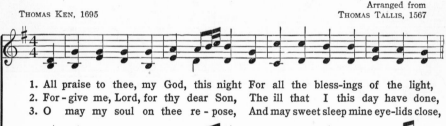

1. All praise to thee, my God, this night For all the bless-ings of the light,
2. For-give me, Lord, for thy dear Son, The ill that I this day have done,
3. O may my soul on thee re - pose, And may sweet sleep mine eye-lids close,

Keep me, O keep me, King of kings, Be-neath thy own al - might - y wings.
That with the world, myself, and thee, I, ere I sleep, at peace may be.
Sleep that may me more vigorous make To serve my God when I a-wake! A-men.

46

BIRKDALE. 10. 10. 10. 6.

HARRIET McEWEN KIMBALL, 1866

JOSEPH BARNBY, 1883

1. The day is end - ed. Ere I sink to sleep
2. With lov - ing kind - ness cur - tain thou my bed,
3. At peace with all the world, dear Lord, and thee,

My wear - y spir - it seeks re - pose in thine;
And cool in rest my burn - ing pil - grim feet,
No fears my soul's un - waver - ing faith can shake;

Fa - ther, for - give my tres - pass - es, and keep
Thy par - don be the pil - low for my head;
All's well, which - ev - er side the grave for me

This lit - tle life of mine.
So shall my rest be sweet.
The morn - ing light may break. A - men.

Close of Worship

BENEDICTION. 10. 10. 10. 10.

JOHN ELLERTON, 1866   EDWARD J. HOPKINS, 1867

1. Sav - iour, a - gain to thy dear name we raise,
2. Grant us thy peace up - on our home - ward way;
3. Grant us thy peace, Lord, through the com - ing night;
4. Grant us thy peace through - out our earth - ly life,

With one ac - cord, our part - ing hymn of praise;
With thee be - gan, with thee shall end the day:
Turn thou for us its dark - ness in - to light;
Our balm in sor - row, and our stay in strife;

We stand to bless thee ere our wor - ship cease;
Guard thou the lips from sin, the hearts from shame,
From harm and dan - ger keep thy chil - dren free,
Then, when thy voice shall bid our con - flict cease,

Then, low - ly kneel - ing, wait thy word of peace.
That in this house have called up - on thy name.
For dark and light are both a - like to thee.
Call us, O Lord, to thine e - ter - nal peace. A - men.

48

SICILIAN MARINERS. 8. 7. 8. 7. 4. 7.

JOHN FAWCETT, 1773

Sicilian Melody, 1794

1. Lord, dis-miss us with thy bless-ing; Fill our hearts with
2. Thanks we give and ad - o - ra - tion For thy gos - pel's

joy and peace; Let us each, thy love pos - sess - ing,
joy - ful sound: May the fruits of thy sal - va - tion

Tri - umph in re - deem - ing grace: O re - fresh us,
In our hearts and lives a - bound: Ev - er faith - ful,

O re - fresh us, Trav - eling thro' this wil - der - ness.
Ev - er faith - ful To the truth may we be found. A - men.

Close of Worship

HERMAS 6. 5. 6. 5. D. With Refrain

JOHN S. B. MONSELL, 1863

FRANCES R. HAVERGAL, 1871

1. On our way re-joic-ing As we homeward move, Hearken to our prais-es,
2. If with hon-est-heart-ed Love for God and man, Day by day thou find us
3. On our way re-joic-ing Glad-ly let us go; Vic-tor is our Lead-er,
4. Un-to God the Fa-ther Joy-ful songs we sing; Un-to God the Sav-iour

O thou God of love! Is there grief or sad-ness? Thine it can-not be;
Do-ing all we can, Thou who giv'st the seed-time Wilt give large in-crease,
Van-quished is the foe; Christ with-out, our safe-ty; Christ with-in, our joy;
Thankful hearts we bring; Un-to God the Spir-it Bow we and a-dore;

Refrain

Is our sky be-cloud-ed? Clouds are not from thee.
Crown the head with blessings, Fill the heart with peace.
Who, if we be faith-ful, Can our hope de-stroy?
On our way re-joic-ing Now and ev-er-more.

On our way re-joic-ing

As we homeward move, Hearken to our prais-es, O thou God of love! A-men.

50

BEATITUDO. C. M.

JOHN ELLERTON, 1876

JOHN B. DYKES, 1875

1. The Lord be with us as we bend His bless-ings to re-ceive;
2. The Lord be with us as we walk A-long our home-ward road;
3. The Lord be with us till the night En-fold our day of rest;
4. The Lord be with us through the hours Of slum-ber calm and deep,

His gift of peace on us de-scend Be-fore his courts we leave.
In si-lent thought or friend-ly talk, Our hearts be near to God.
Be he of ev-ery heart the light, Of ev-ery home the guest.
Pro-tect our homes, re-new our powers, And guard his peo-ple's sleep. A-men.

51

DORRNANCE. 8. 7. 8. 7.

JOHN NEWTON, 1779

ISAAC B. WOODBURY, 1848

1. May the grace of Christ our Sav-iour, And the Fa-ther's boundless love,
2. Thus may we a-bide in un-ion With each oth-er and the Lord,

With the Ho-ly Spir-it's fa-vor, Rest up-on us from a-bove.
And pos-sess, in sweet com-mu-nion, Joys which earth cannot afford. A-men.

The Lord's Day

52

SABBATH. 7. 7. 7. 7. 7. 7.

John Newton, 1774

Lowell Mason, 1824

1. Safe - ly through an - oth - er week, God has brought us on our way;
2. While we pray for pardon-ing grace, Through the dear Re - deem-er's name,
3. Here we come thy name to praise: May we feel thy pres - ence near;

Let us now a bless-ing seek, Wait-ing in his courts to - day:
Show thy rec - on - cil - ed face, Take a - way our sin and shame:
May thy glo - ry meet our eyes, While we in thy house ap - pear:

Day of all the week the best, Em - blem of e - ter - nal rest;
From our world - ly cares set free, May we rest this day in thee;
Here af - ford us, Lord, a taste Of our ev - er - last - ing feast;

Day of all the week the best, Em-blem of e - ter - nal rest.
From our world - ly cares set free, May we rest this day in thee.
Here af - ford us, Lord, a taste Of our ev - er - last - ing feast. A - men.

53

MENDEBRAS. 7. 6. 7. 6. D.

CHRISTOPHER WORDSWORTH, 1862

Arranged by
LOWELL MASON, 1839

1. O day of rest and glad-ness, O day of joy and light,
2. On thee at the cre - a - tion The light first had its birth;
3. To - day on wea - ry na - tions The heaven-ly man - na falls;
4. New gra - ces ev - er gain-ing From this our day of rest,

O balm of care and sad - ness, Most beau - ti - ful, most bright:
On thee, for our sal - va - tion, Christ rose from depths of earth;
To ho - ly con - vo - ca - tions The sil - ver trum - pet calls,
We reach the rest re - main - ing To spir - its of the blest;

On thee the high and low - ly, Bend - ing be - fore the throne,
On thee, our Lord, vic - to - rious, The Spir - it sent from heaven;
Where gos - pel light is glow - ing With pure and ra - diant beams,
To Ho - ly Ghost be prais - es, To Fa - ther and to Son;

Sing 'Ho - ly, ho - ly, ho - ly,' To the great Three in One.
And thus on thee, most glo-rious, A tri - ple light was given.
And liv - ing wa - ter flow - ing With soul - re - fresh-ing streams.
The Church her voice up - rais - es To thee, blest Three in One. A - men.

54

AURELIA. 7. 6. 7. 6. D.

ADA C. CROSS, 1866

SAMUEL S. WESLEY, 1864

1. The dawn of God's dear Sab-bath Breaks o'er the earth a-gain,
2. Lord, we would bring for of-fering Though marred with earth-ly soil,
3. And we would bring our bur-den Of sin-ful deed and thought,
4. O Lord, for-give and strength-en: May we for ev-er-more

As some sweet sum-mer morn-ing In sun-shine af-ter rain;
Our week of ear-nest la-bor, Of use-ful dai-ly toil;
Our hearts' most bit-ter sor-row For all thy work un-wrought;
Up-on thy peace-ful Sab-bath Thy bless-ed name a-dore;

It comes as cool-ing show-ers To dry and thirst-y land,
Fair fruits of self-de-ni-al, Of strong, deep love to thee,
In thy dear pres-ence seek-ing The par-don thou wilt give,
Un-til in joy and glad-ness We reach that home at last,

As shade of clus-tered palm-trees 'Mid wea-ry wastes of sand.
Fos-tered by thine own Spir-it In our hu-mil-i-ty.
And so the peace a-bid-ing In which thy chil-dren live.
Where life's short week of sor-row And sin and strife are past. A-men.

55

HINCHMAN. 7. 8. 7. 8. 7. 7.

BENJAMIN SCHMOLCK, 1714
Translated by CATHERINE WINKWORTH, 1858

UZZIAH C. BURNAP, 1869

1. Light of Light, en - light - en me, Now a - new the day is
2. Fount of all our joy and peace, To thy liv - ing wa - ters
3. Kin - dle thou the sac - ri - fice That up - on my lips is
4. Let me, with my heart to - day, Ho - ly, ho - ly, ho - ly,

dawn - ing; Sun of grace, the shad - ows flee; Bright - en
lead me; Thou from earth my soul re - lease, And with
ly - ing; Clear the shad - ows from my eyes, That, from
sing - ing, Rapt a - while from earth a - way, All my

thou my Sab - bath morn - ing; With thy joy - ous sun - shine
grace and mer - cy feed me; Bless thy word, that it may
ev - ery er - ror fly - ing, No strange fire may in me
soul to thee up - spring - ing, Have a fore - taste in - ly

blest, Hap - py is my day of rest.
prove Rich in fruits that thou dost love.
glow That thine al - tar doth not know.
given How they wor - ship thee in heav'n. A - men.

56

SWABIA. S. M.

John Ellerton, 1867

Johann M. Spiess, 1745

1. This is the day of light: Let there be light to-day;
2. This is the day of rest: Our fail-ing strength re-new;
3. This is the day of peace; Thy peace our spir-its fill;
4. This is the day of prayer: Let earth to heaven draw near:
5. This is the first of days: Send forth thy quicken-ing breath,

O Day-spring, rise up-on our night, And chase its gloom a-way.
On wea-ry brain and troub-led breast Shed thou thy freshening dew.
Bid thou the blasts of dis-cord cease, The waves of strife be still.
Lift up our hearts to seek thee there; Come down to meet us here.
And wake dead souls to love and praise, O Van-quish-er of death! A-men.

57

DOMENICA. S. M.

Stephen T. Bulfinch, 1832

Herbert S. Oakeley, 1874

1. Hail to this ho-ly day! The day di-vine-ly given,
2. Lord, in this sa-cred hour, With-in thy courts we bend,
3. But thou art not a-lone In courts by mor-tals trod;
4. Thy tem-ple is the arch Of yon un-meas-ured sky;

When men to God their hom-age pay, And earth draws near to heaven.
And bless thy love, and own thy power, Our Fa-ther and our Friend.
Nor on-ly is the day thine own When man draws near to God;
Thy Sab-bath, the stu-pen-dous march Of vast e-ter-ni-ty. A-men.

58

AUTUMN. 8. 7. 8. 7. D.

ROBERT ROBINSON, 1774

FRANCOIS H. BARTHELEMON, 1785

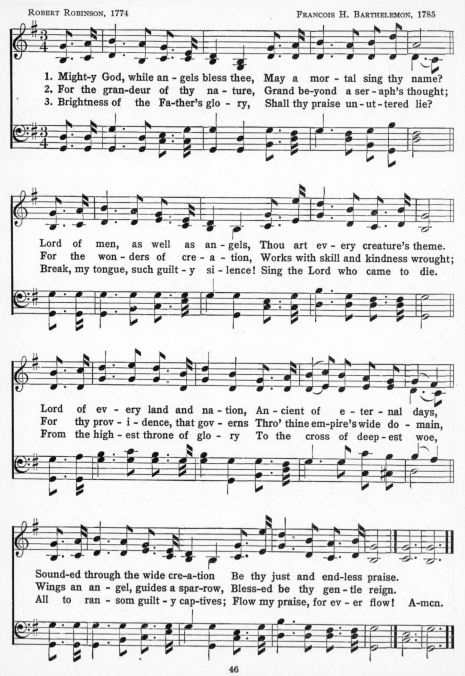

1. Might-y God, while an-gels bless thee, May a mor-tal sing thy name?
2. For the gran-deur of thy na-ture, Grand be-yond a ser-aph's thought;
3. Brightness of the Fa-ther's glo-ry, Shall thy praise un-ut-tered lie?

Lord of men, as well as an-gels, Thou art ev-ery creature's theme.
For the won-ders of cre-a-tion, Works with skill and kindness wrought;
Break, my tongue, such guilt-y si-lence! Sing the Lord who came to die.

Lord of ev-ery land and na-tion, An-cient of e-ter-nal days,
For thy prov-i-dence, that gov-erns Thro' thine em-pire's wide do-main,
From the high-est throne of glo-ry To the cross of deep-est woe,

Sound-ed through the wide cre-a-tion Be thy just and end-less praise.
Wings an an-gel, guides a spar-row, Bless-ed be thy gen-tle reign.
All to ran-som guilt-y cap-tives; Flow my praise, for ev-er flow! A-men.

The Majesty of God

59

MIRIAM. 7. 6. 7. 6. D.

EDWARD H. BICKERSTETH, 1860

JOSEPH P. HOLBROOK, 1865

1. O God, the Rock of A - ges, Who ev - er - more hast been,
2. Our years are like the shad - ows On sun - ny hills that lie,
3. O thou, who canst not slum - ber, Whose light grows nev - er pale,

What time the tem - pest ra - ges, Our dwell - ing - place se - rene:
Or grass - es in the mead - ows That blos - som but to die:
Teach us a - right to num - ber Our years be - fore they fail.

Be - fore thy first cre - a - tions, O Lord, the same as now,
A sleep, a dream, a sto - ry, By stran - gers quick - ly told,
On us thy mer - cy light - en, On us thy good - ness rest,

To end - less gen - er - a - tions, The ev - er - last - ing thou!
An un - re - main - ing glo - ry Of things that soon are old.
And let thy Spir - it bright - en The hearts thy-self hast blessed. A - men.

60

LOUVAN. L. M.

OLIVER WENDELL HOLMES, 1848

VIRGIL C. TAYLOR, 1847

1. Lord of all be - ing, throned a - far, Thy glo - ry
2. Sun of our life, thy quicken - ing ray Sheds on our
3. Our mid - night is thy smile with-drawn; Our noon - tide
4. Lord of all life, be - low, a - bove, Whose light is
5. Grant us thy truth to make us free, And kind - ling

flames from sun and star; Cen - ter and soul of
path the glow of day; Star of our hope, thy
is thy gra - cious dawn; Our rain - bow arch, thy
truth, whose warmth is love, Be - fore thy ev - er -
hearts that burn for thee, Till all thy liv - ing

ev - ery sphere, Yet to each lov - ing heart how near!
soft - ened light Cheers the long watch - es of the night.
mer - cy's sign; All, save the clouds of sin, are thine.
blaz - ing throne We ask no lus - ter of our own.
al - tars claim One ho - ly light, one heaven - ly flame. A-men.

61

ST. ANNE. C. M.

ISAAC WATTS, 1719

WILLIAM CROFT, 1708

1. Our God, our help in a - ges past, Our hope for years to come,
2. Be - fore the hills in or - der stood, Or earth re - ceived her frame,
3. A thou - sand a - ges in thy sight Are like an eve - ning gone;
4. Time, like an ev - er - roll - ing stream, Bears all its sons a - way:
5. Our God, our help in a - ges past, Our hope for years to come,

The Majesty of God

Our shel - ter from the storm - y blast, And our e - ter - nal home!
From ev - er - last - ing thou art God, To end - less years the same.
Short as the watch that ends the night Be - fore the ris - ing sun.
They fly for - got - ten, as a dream Dies at the open - ing day.
Be thou our guard while life shall last, And our e - ter - nal home. A-men.

62

BROMLEY. L. M.

Henry Van Dyke, 1921

Jeremiah Clark, 1700

1. Thy wis - dom and thy might ap - pear, E - ter - nal
2. We wor - ship thee whose will hath laid Thy sov - ereign
3. Yet thou canst make a mar - vel shine A - mid these
4. We turn a - side and tread the ways That lead through
5. If thou hast formed us out of dust Through a - ges

God, through ev - ery year; From day to day, from hour to
rule on all things made; The faith - ful stars, the fruit - ful
might - y laws of thine, As when thy ser - vant Mos - es
won - der up to praise; Wher - ev - er thou by man art
long,— in thee we trust; O grant us in our souls to

hour, Thy works re - veal self - or - dered power.
earth, O - bey thy laws that gave them birth.
came And saw the bush with thee a - flame.
found The home - ly earth is ho - ly ground.
see The liv - ing flame that comes from thee. A - men.

63

ANCIENT OF DAYS. 11. 10. 11. 10.

William C. Doane, 1886

J. Albert Jeffery, 1886

1. An - cient of Days, who sit - test throned in glo - ry,
2. O Ho - ly Fa - ther, who hast led thy chil - dren
3. O Ho - ly Je - sus, Prince of Peace and Sav - iour,
4. O Ho - ly Ghost, the Lord and the Life - giv - er,
5. O Tri - une God, with heart and voice a - dor - ing,

To thee all knees are bent, all voic - es pray;
In all the a - ges, with the fire and cloud,
To thee we owe the peace that still pre - vails,
Thine is the quick - 'ning power that gives in - crease;
Praise we the good - ness that doth crown our days;

Thy love has blessed the wide world's won - drous sto - ry
Through seas dry - shod, through wea - ry wastes be - wil - dering;
Still - ing the rude wills of men's wild be - hav - ior,
From thee have flowed, as from a pleas - ant riv - er,
Pray we that thou wilt hear us, still im - plor - ing

With light and life since E - den's dawn - ing day.
To thee, in rev - erent love, our hearts are bowed.
And calm - ing pas - sion's fierce and storm - y gales.
Our plen - ty, wealth, pros - per - i - ty and peace.
Thy love and fa - vor kept to us al - ways. A - men.

The Majesty of God

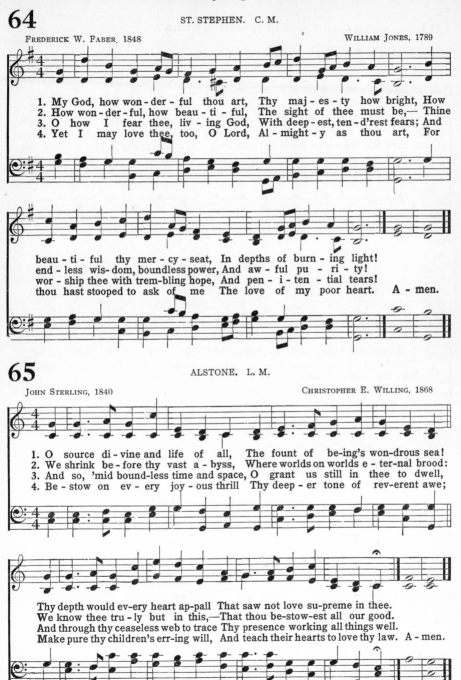

64 ST. STEPHEN. C. M.

FREDERICK W. FABER, 1848

WILLIAM JONES, 1789

1. My God, how won-der-ful thou art, Thy maj-es-ty how bright, How
2. How won-der-ful, how beau-ti-ful, The sight of thee must be,— Thine
3. O how I fear thee, liv-ing God, With deep-est, ten-d'rest fears; And
4. Yet I may love thee, too, O Lord, Al-might-y as thou art, For

beau-ti-ful thy mer-cy-seat, In depths of burn-ing light!
end-less wis-dom, boundless power, And aw-ful pu-ri-ty!
wor-ship thee with trem-bling hope, And pen-i-ten-tial tears!
thou hast stooped to ask of me The love of my poor heart. A-men.

65 ALSTONE. L. M.

JOHN STERLING, 1840

CHRISTOPHER E. WILLING, 1868

1. O source di-vine and life of all, The fount of be-ing's won-drous sea!
2. We shrink be-fore thy vast a-byss, Where worlds on worlds e-ter-nal brood:
3. And so, 'mid bound-less time and space, O grant us still in thee to dwell,
4. Be-stow on ev-ery joy-ous thrill Thy deep-er tone of rev-erent awe;

Thy depth would ev-ery heart ap-pall That saw not love su-preme in thee.
We know thee tru-ly but in this,—That thou be-stow-est all our good.
And through thy ceaseless web to trace Thy presence working all things well.
Make pure thy children's err-ing will, And teach their hearts to love thy law. A-men.

God the Father

66

REGENT SQUARE. 8. 7. 8. 7. 8. 7.

JOHN KEBLE, 1839

HENRY SMART, 1867

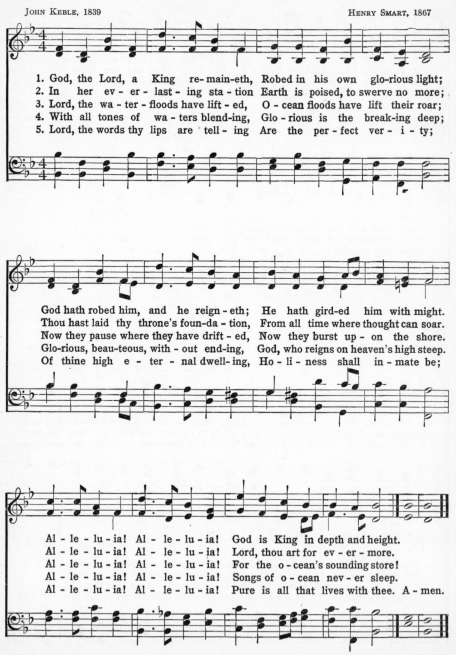

1. God, the Lord, a King re-main-eth, Robed in his own glo-rious light;
2. In her ev-er-last-ing sta-tion Earth is poised, to swerve no more;
3. Lord, the wa-ter-floods have lift-ed, O-cean floods have lift their roar;
4. With all tones of wa-ters blend-ing, Glo-rious is the break-ing deep;
5. Lord, the words thy lips are tell-ing Are the per-fect ver-i-ty;

God hath robed him, and he reign-eth; He hath gird-ed him with might.
Thou hast laid thy throne's foun-da-tion, From all time where thought can soar.
Now they pause where they have drift-ed, Now they burst up-on the shore.
Glo-rious, beau-teous, with-out end-ing, God, who reigns on heaven's high steep.
Of thine high e-ter-nal dwell-ing, Ho-li-ness shall in-mate be;

Al-le-lu-ia! Al-le-lu-ia! God is King in depth and height.
Al-le-lu-ia! Al-le-lu-ia! Lord, thou art for ev-er-more.
Al-le-lu-ia! Al-le-lu-ia! For the o-cean's sounding store!
Al-le-lu-ia! Al-le-lu-ia! Songs of o-cean nev-er sleep.
Al-le-lu-ia! Al-le-lu-ia! Pure is all that lives with thee. A-men.

The Love of God

HEBER. 8. 7. 8. 7. 4. 7.

JOHN S. B. MONSELL, 1856

EDWARD J. HOPKINS, 1868

67

1. God is love, by him up-hold-en Hang the glo-rious
2. And the teem-ing earth re-joic-es In the mes-sage
3. With these an-thems of cre-a-tion Ming-ling in har-
4. Up to him let each af-fec-tion Dai-ly rise, and

orbs of light, In their lan-guage, glad and gold-en,
from a-bove, With ten thou-sand thou-sand voi-ces
mon-ious strife, Chris-tian songs of Christ's sal-va-tion,
round him move; Our whole lives, one res-ur-rec-tion

Speak-ing to us day and night Their great sto-ry,
Tell-ing back, from hill and grove, Her glad sto-ry,
To the world with bless-ings rife, Tell their sto-ry,
To the life of life a-bove; Hal-le-lu-jah!

God is love, and God is might.
God is might, and God is love.
God is love, and God is life.
God is life, and God is love. A-men.

68

CARTER. 8. 7. 8. 7.

JOHN BOWRING, 1825

EDMUND S. CARTER, 1874

1. God is love; his mer - cy bright-ens All the path in which we rove;
2. Chance and change are bus-y ev - er; Man de - cays, and a - ges move;
3. E'en the hour that dark - est seem-eth Will his change-less goodness prove;
4. He with earth - ly care en - twin-eth Hope and com-fort from a - bove;

Bliss he wakes, and woe he light-ens: God is wis-dom, God is love.
But his mer - cy wan - eth nev-er: God is wis-dom, God is love.
From the gloom his brightness streameth: God is wis-dom, God is love.
Ev - 'ry-where his glo - ry shin-eth: God is wis-dom, God is love. A-men.

69

INNOCENTS. 7. 7. 7. 7.

JOHN MILTON, 1623. Altered

Arr. from Handel, 1728

1. Let us with a glad-some mind Praise the Lord, for he is kind;
2. Let us blaze his name a - broad, For of gods he is the God;
3. He the gold - en - tress - ed sun Caused all day his course to run;
4. All things liv - ing he doth feed, His full hand sup-plies their need;

For his mer-cies aye en - dure, Ev - er faith-ful, ev - er sure.
Who by all-com-mand-ing might, Filled the new-made world with light.
Th'horn-ed moon to shine by night, 'Mid her spangled sis-ters bright.
For his mer-cies aye en - dure, Ev - er faith - ful, ev - er sure. A-men.

The Love of God

70

WELLESLEY. 8. 7. 8. 7.

FREDERICK W. FABER, 1854

LIZZIE S. TOURJEE, 1878

1. There's a wide-ness in God's mer-cy, Like the wide-ness of the sea;
2. There is no place where earth's sorrows Are more felt than up in heaven;
3. For the love of God is broad-er Than the meas-ure of man's mind;
4. If our love were but more sim-ple, We should take him at his word;

There's a kind-ness in his jus-tice, Which is more than lib-er-ty.
There is no place where earth's failings Have such kind-ly judg-ment given.
And the heart of the E-ter-nal Is most won-der-ful-ly kind.
And our lives would be all sun-shine In the sweet-ness of our Lord. A-men.

71

JAM LUCIS. L. M.

JOHN HAMPDEN GURNEY, 1838

JOHN BISHOP, 1665–1737

1. Our God is good: in earth and sky, From o-cean depths and spreading wood,
2. The sun that keeps his track-less way, And down-ward pours his gold-en flood,
3. We hear it in the rush-ing breeze: The hills that have for a-ges stood,
4. For all thy gifts we bless thee, Lord; But chief-ly for our heavenly food,

Ten thou-sand voi-ces seem to cry, 'God made us all, and God is good.'
Night's sparkling hosts all seem to say, In ac-cents clear, that God is good.
The echo-ing sky and roar-ing seas, All swell the cho-rus, 'God is good.'
Thy pard'ning grace, thy quick'ning word: These prompt our song, that God is good. A-men.

55

72

PASTOR BONUS. S. M. D.

OSCAR CLUTE, 1840–1901

ALFRED J. CALDICOTT, 1875

1. O love of God most full, O love of God most free,
2. No foe can cast me down, No fear can make me flee,
3. I tri-umph o-ver sin, I put temp-ta-tion down:

Thou warm'st my heart, thou fill'st my soul, With might thou strength'nest me:
No sor-row fill my life with ill; Thy love sur-round-eth me.
The love of God doth give me strength To win the vic-tor's crown.

Warm as the glow-ing sun, So shines thy love on me,
The wild-est sea is calm, The tem-pest brings no fear,
O love of God most full, O love of God most free,

It wraps me round with kindly care, It draws me un-to thee.
The dark-est night is full of light, Be-cause thy love is near.
Come warm my heart, come fill my soul, Come lead me unto thee! A - men.

The Love of God

57

73

BENEDIC ANIMA. 8. 7. 8. 7. 8. 7.

Henry F. Lyte, 1834

John Goss, 1869

1. Praise, my soul, the King of heav - en, To his feet thy
2. Praise him for his grace and fa - vor To our fa - thers
3. Fa - ther - like, he tends and spares us, Well our fee - ble
4. An - gels, help us to a - dore him; Ye be - hold him

trib - ute bring; Ran - somed, healed, re - stored, for - giv - en,
in dis - tress; Praise him, still the same for ev - er,
frame he knows; In his hands he gent - ly bears us,
face to face; Sun and moon, bow down be - fore him,

Who, like me, his praise should sing? Praise him, praise him,
Slow to chide, and swift to bless; Praise him, praise him,
Res - cues us from all our foes; Praise him, praise him,
Dwell - ers all in time and space, Praise him, praise him,

Praise him, praise him, Praise the ev - er - last - ing King.
Praise him, praise him, Glo - rious in his faith - ful - ness!
Praise him, praise him, Wide - ly as his mer - cy flows!
Praise him, praise him, Praise with us the God of grace! A-men.

God, the Father

74

ALDRICH. L. M.

John Haynes Holmes, 1908

Charles Harford Lloyd

1. O Fa-ther, thou who giv-est all The boun-ty
2. We thank thee for the grace of home, For moth-er's
3. For eyes to see and ears to hear, For hands to
4. For faith to con-quer doubt and fear, For love to

of thy per-fect love, We thank thee that up-
love and fa-ther's care; For friends and teach-ers—
serve and arms to lift, For shoul-ders broad and
an-swer ev-ery call, For strength to do, and

on us fall Such ten-der bless-ings from a-bove.
all who come, Our joys and hopes and fears to share.
strong to bear, For feet to run on er-rands swift.
will to dare, We thank thee, O thou Lord of all. A-men.

75

ALMSGIVING. 8. 8. 8. 4.

Christopher Wordsworth, 1863

John B. Dykes, 1875

1. O Lord of heaven, and earth, and sea, To thee all praise and glo-ry be;
2. The gold-en sun-shine, ver-nal air, Sweet flow'rs and fruit thy love de-clare;
3. For peace-ful homes and health-ful days, For all the bless-ings earth dis-plays,
4. We lose what on our-selves we spend; We have as treas-ure with-out end
5. O thou from whom we all de-rive Our life, our gifts, our power to give,

58

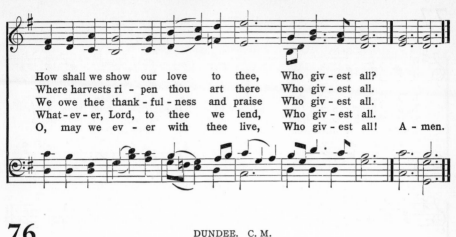

How shall we show our love to thee, Who giv - est all?
Where harvests ri - pen thou art there Who giv - est all.
We owe thee thank - ful - ness and praise Who giv - est all.
What - ev - er, Lord, to thee we lend, Who giv - est all.
O, may we ev - er with thee live, Who giv - est all! A - men.

76

DUNDEE. C. M.

WILLIAM COWPER, 1772

Scottish Psalter, 1615

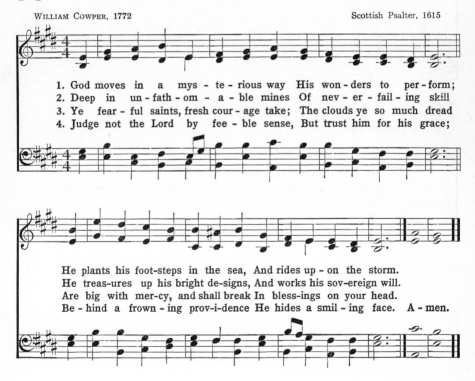

1. God moves in a mys - te - rious way His won - ders to per - form;
2. Deep in un - fath - om - a - ble mines Of nev - er - fail - ing skill
3. Ye fear - ful saints, fresh cour - age take; The clouds ye so much dread
4. Judge not the Lord by fee - ble sense, But trust him for his grace;

He plants his foot-steps in the sea, And rides up - on the storm.
He treas-ures up his bright de-signs, And works his sov-ereign will.
Are big with mer-cy, and shall break In bless-ings on your head.
Be - hind a frown - ing prov-i-dence He hides a smil - ing face. A - men.

5 His purposes will ripen fast,
    Unfolding every hour;
The bud may have a bitter taste,
    But sweet will be the flower.

6 Blind unbelief is sure to err,
    And scan his work in vain:
God is his own Interpreter,
    And he will make it plain.

77   LAMBETH. C. M.

FREDERICK L. HOSMER, 1876   WILHELM A. F. SCHULTHES, 1871

1. O thou, in all thy might so far, In all thy love so near,
2. What heart can com-pre-hend thy name, Or, search-ing, find thee out,
3. Yet, though I know thee but in part, I ask not, Lord, for more:
4. And dear-er than all things I know Is child-like faith to me,

Beyond the range of sun or star, And yet be-side us here,—
Who art with-in, a quick'ning flame, A pres-ence round a-bout?
E-nough for me to know thou art, To love thee and a-dore.
That makes the darkest way I go An o-pen path to thee.   A-men.

78   POSEN. 7. 7. 7. 7.

SAMUEL JOHNSON, 1864   GEORG C. STRATTNER, 1691

1. Life of a-ges, rich-ly poured, Love of God, un-spent and free,
2. Nev-er was to chos-en race That un-stint-ed tide con-fined;
3. Breath-ing in the think-er's creed, Puls-ing in the he-ro's blood,
4. Con-se-crat-ing art and song, Ho-ly book and pil-grim track,
5. Life of a-ges, rich-ly poured, Love of God, un-spent and free,

Flow-ing in the proph-et's word And the peo-ple's lib-er-ty,—
Thine is ev-ery time and place, Foun-tain sweet of heart and mind.
Nerv-ing simplest thought and deed, Freshening time with truth and good.
Hurl-ing floods of ty-rant wrong From the sa-cred lim-its back,—
Flow still in the proph-et's word And the peo-ple's lib-er-ty!   A-men.

The Love of God

79

FAITH. C. M.

JAMES DRUMMOND BURNS, 1858

JOHN B. DYKES, 1867

1. Thou, Lord, art love, and ev-ery-where Thy name is bright-ly shown,
2. Thy word is love; in lines of gold There mer-cy prints its trace;
3. Thy ways are love; though they trans-cend Our fee-ble range of sight,
4. Thy thoughts are love; and Je-sus is The liv-ing voice they find;

Be-neath, on earth, thy foot-stool fair, A-bove, in heaven, thy throne.
In na-ture we thy steps be-hold, The gos-pel shows thy face.
They wind, through darkness, to their end In ev-er-last-ing light.
His love lights up the vast a-byss Of the e-ter-nal mind. A-men.

5 Thy chastisements are love; more deep
  They stamp the seal divine,
And by a sweet compulsion keep
  Our spirits nearer thine.

6 Thy heaven is the abode of love;
  O blessed Lord, that we
May there, when time's deep shades remove,
  Be gathered home to thee.

80

MANOAH. C. M.

ELIZA SCUDDER, 1852

HENRY W. GREATOREX'S "Collection," Boston, 1851
Arranged in

1. Thou Grace di-vine, en-cir-cling all, A sound-less, shore-less sea,
2. When o-ver diz-zy heights we go, One soft hand blinds our eyes,
3. And though we turn us from thy face, And wan-der wide and long,
4. The sad-dened heart, the rest-less soul, The toil-worn frame and mind,

Where-in at last our souls must fall,—O Love of God most free!
The oth-er leads us safe and slow,—O Love of God most wise!
Thou hold'st us still in thine embrace, O Love of God most strong!
A-like con-fess thy sweet con-trol, O Love of God most kind! A-men.

5 But not alone thy care we claim,
  Our wayward steps to win;
We know thee by a dearer name,
  O Love of God within!

6 And, filled and quickened by thy breath,
  Our souls are strong and free
To rise o'er sin and fear and death,
  O Love of God, to thee.

God the Father

81
DOMENICA. S. M.

HORATIUS BONAR, 1861

HERBERT S. OAKELEY, 1874

1. O Ev - er - last - ing Light, Giv - er of dawn and day,
2. O Ev - er - last - ing Health, From which all heal - ing springs,—
3. O Ev - er - last - ing Truth, Tru - est of all that's true,
4. O Ev - er - last - ing Strength, Up - hold me in the way;
5. O Ev - er - last - ing Love, Well-spring of grace and peace:

Dis - pel - ler of the an - cient night In which cre - a - tion lay!
My bliss, my treas - ure, and my wealth, To thee my spir - it clings.
Sure guide for err - ing age and youth, Lead me and teach me, too.
Bring me, in spite of foes, at length To joy, and light, and day.
Pour down thy ful - ness from a - bove, Bid doubt and trou - ble cease. A - men.

82
BLAYDON. S. M.

THOMAS TOKE LYNCH, 1855

HENRY W. LITTLE (1853——)

1. Where is thy God, my soul? Is he with - in thy heart, Or
2. Where is thy God, my soul? On - ly in stars and sun? Or
3. Where is thy God, my soul? Con - fined to Scrip - ture's page? Or
4. O Rul - er of the sky, Rule thou with - in my heart: O

rul - er of a dis - tant realm In which thou hast no part?
have the ho - ly words of truth His light in ev - ery one?
does his Spir - it check and guide The spir - it of each age?
great A - dorn - er of the world, Thy light of life im - part. A - men.

5 Giver of holy words,
Bestow thy holy power,
And aid me, whether work or thought
Engage the varying hour.

6 In thee have I my help,
As all my fathers had;
I'll trust thee when I'm sorrowful,
And serve thee when I'm glad.

The Love of God

83

DENVER. 8. 6. 8. 6. D.

John Haynes Holmes (1879———)

Henry Houseley, 1896

1. O God, whose love is o - ver all The chil - dren of thy grace,
2. To see thee in the sun by day, And in the stars by night,
3. To see thee in each qui - et home, Where faith and love a - bide,

Whose rich and ten - der bless - ings fall On ev - ery age and place;
In wav - ing grass and o - cean spray, And leaves and flow -ers bright;
In school and church, where all may come, To seek thee side by side;

Hear thou the songs and prayers we raise In ea - ger joy to thee,
To hear thy voice, like spok - en word, In ev - ery breeze that blows,
To see thee in each hu - man life, Each strug-gling hu - man heart,

And teach us, as we sound thy praise, In all things thee to see.
In ev - ery song of ev - ery bird, And ev - ery brook that flows.
Each path by which, in ea - ger strife, Men seek the bet - ter part. A-men.

TERRA BEATA. S. M. D.

MALTBIE D. BABCOCK, 1901

Traditional English Melody
Arranged by S. F. L., 1915

1. This is my Fa-ther's world, And to my list-ening ears, All na-ture sings, and round me rings The mu-sic of the spheres. This is my Fa-ther's world, I rest me in the thought Of rocks and trees, of skies and seas—His hand the won-ders wrought.

2. This is my Fa-ther's world, The birds their car-ols raise, The morn-ing light, the lil-y white, De-clare their Ma-ker's praise. This is my Fa-ther's world, He shines in all that's fair; In the rust-ling grass I hear him pass, He speaks to me ev-ery-where.

3. This is my Fa-ther's world, O let me ne'er for-get That though the wrong seems oft so strong, God is the Ru-ler yet. This is my Fa-ther's world, The bat-tle is not done, Je-sus who died shall be sat-is-fied, And earth and heaven be one. A-men.

The Works of God

ROLAND. 7. 7. 7. 7. D.

Stopford A. Brooke, 1881

Caleb Simper, (1856——)

1. Let the whole cre-a-tion cry, Glo-ry to the Lord on high!
2. Chant his hon-or, o-cean fair! Earth, soft rush-ing thro' the air;
3. War-riors fight-ing for the Lord, Proph-ets burn-ing with his word,

Heaven and earth, a-wake and sing, 'God is good, and there-fore King.'
Sun-shine, dark-ness, cloud and storm, Rain and snow, his praise per-form.
Men and wom-en, young and old, Raise the an-them man-i-fold.

Praise him, all ye hosts a-bove, Ev-er bright and fair in love!
Let the blos-soms of the earth Join the u-ni-ver-sal mirth;
And let chil-dren's hap-py hearts In this wor-ship bear their parts:

Sun and moon, up-lift your voice; Night and stars in God re-joice.
Birds, with morn and dew e-late, Sing with joy at heav-en's gate.
Ho-ly, Ho-ly, Ho-ly cry! Glo-ry be to God on high! A-men.

God the Father

86

CREATION. L. M. D.

JOSEPH ADDISON, 1712

Arranged from
FRANZ JOSEPH HAYDN, 1798

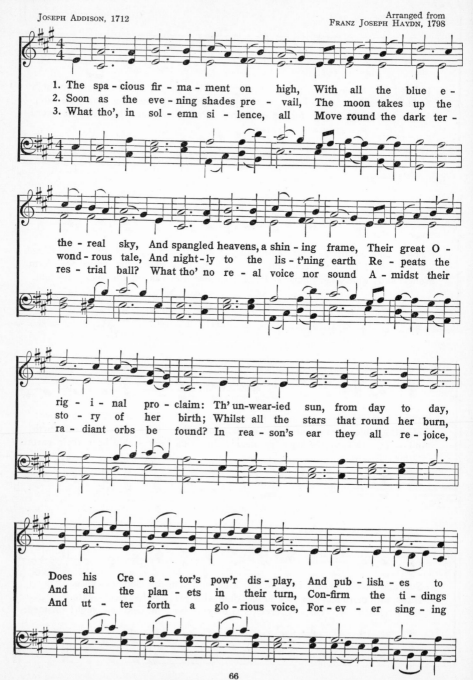

1. The spa-cious fir-ma-ment on high, With all the blue e-the-real sky, And spangled heavens, a shin-ing frame, Their great O-rig-i-nal pro-claim: Th' un-wear-ied sun, from day to day, Does his Cre-a-tor's pow'r dis-play, And pub-lish-es to

2. Soon as the eve-ning shades pre-vail, The moon takes up the wond-rous tale, And night-ly to the lis-t'ning earth Re-peats the sto-ry of her birth; Whilst all the stars that round her burn, And all the plan-ets in their turn, Con-firm the ti-dings

3. What tho', in sol-emn si-lence, all Move round the dark ter-res-trial ball? What tho' no re-al voice nor sound A-midst their ra-diant orbs be found? In rea-son's ear they all re-joice, And ut-ter forth a glo-rious voice, For-ev-er sing-ing

The Works of God

ev - ery land The work of an al - might - y hand.
as they roll, And spread the truth from pole to pole.
as they shine, 'The hand that made us is di - vine.' A-men.

87

DIX. 7. 7. 7. 7. 7. 7.

FOLLIOTT S. PIERPOINT, 1864

Arranged from
CONRAD KOCHER, 1838

1. For the beau - ty of the earth, For the beau - ty of the skies,
2. For the beau - ty of each hour Of the day and of the night,
3. For the joy of ear and eye, For the heart and mind's de - light,
4. For the joy of hu - man love, Broth - er, sis - ter, par - ent, child,
5. For thy church that ev - er - more Lift - eth ho - ly hands a - bove,

For the love which from our birth O - ver and a - round us lies,
Hill and vale, and tree and flower, Sun and moon, and stars of light,
For the mys - tic har - mo - ny Link - ing sense to sound and sight,
Friends on earth, and friends a - bove, For all gen - tle thoughts and mild,
Offer - ing up on ev - ery shore Her pure sac - ri - fice of love,

Refrain

Lord of all, to thee we raise This our hymn of grate-ful praise. A-men.

67

God the Father

ST. CATHERINE. *L. M.* With Refrain

SAMUEL LONGFELLOW, 1864

HENRY F. HEMY and J. G. WALTON, 1874

1. God of the earth, the sky, the sea! Mak-er of all a-
2. Thy love is in the sun-shine's glow, Thy life is in the
3. We feel thy calm at eve-ning's hour, Thy gran-deur in the

bove, be-low! Cre-a-tion lives and moves in thee,
quick-ening air; When light-nings flash and storm-winds blow,
march of night; And, when thy morn-ing breaks in power,

Refrain

Thy pres-ent life through all doth flow.)
There is thy power; thy law is there. } We give thee thanks, thy
We hear thy word, 'Let there be light.')

name we sing, Al-might-y Fa-ther, heaven-ly King. A-men.

The Works of God

89

PATER OMNIUM. 8. 8. 8. 8. 8. 8.

THOMAS MOORE, 1816

HENRY J. E. HOLMES, 1875

1. Thou art, O God, the life and light Of all this won-drous
2. When day, with fare-well beam, de-lays A-mong the open-ing
3. When night with wings of star-ry gloom O'er-shad-ows all the
4. When youth-ful spring a-round us breathes, Thy Spir-it warms her

world we see; Its glow by day, its smile by night,
clouds of even, And we can al-most think we gaze
earth and skies, Like some dark beau-teous bird whose plume
fra-grant sigh; And ev-ery flower the sum-mer wreathes

Are but re-flec-tions caught from thee: Wher-e'er we turn thy
Thro' gold-en vis-tas in-to heaven, Those hues that make the
Is spark-ling with un-num-bered eyes,— That sac-red gloom, those
Is born be-neath that kind-ling eye: Wher-e'er we turn, thy

glo-ries shine, And all things fair and bright are thine.
sun's de-cline So soft, so ra-diant, Lord, are thine.
fires di-vine, So grand, so count-less, Lord, are thine.
glo-ries shine, And all things fair and bright are thine. A-men.

God the Father

BERTHOLD. 7. 6. 7. 6. D.

WILLIAM G. TARRANT, 1888

BERTHOLD TOURS, 1872

1. With hap-py voic-es sing-ing, Thy chil-dren, Lord, ap-pear;
2. For though no eye be-holds thee, No hand thy touch may feel,
3. And shall we not a-dore thee, With more than joy-ous song,

Their joy-ous prais-es bring-ing In an-thems full and clear.
Thy u-ni-verse un-folds thee, Thy star-ry heavens re-veal.
And live in truth be-fore thee, All beau-ti-ful and strong?

For skies of gold-en splen-dor, For az-ure roll-ing sea,
The earth and all its glo-ry, Our homes and all we love,
Lord, bless our souls' en-deav-or Thy ser-vants true to be,

For blos-soms sweet and ten-der, O Lord, we wor-ship thee.
Tell forth the won-drous sto-ry Of One who reigns a-bove.
And through all life, for-ev-er, To live our praise to thee. A-men.

91

WENTWORTH. 8. 4. 8. 4. 8. 4.

Adelaide A. Procter, 1858

Frederick C. Maker, 1876

1. My God, I thank thee, who hast made The earth so bright,
2. I thank thee, too, that thou hast made Joy to a - bound;
3. I thank thee more that all, our joy Is touched with pain;
4. I thank thee, Lord, that thou hast kept The best in store;
5. I thank thee, Lord, that here our souls, Though am - ply blest,

So full of splen - dor and of joy, Beau - ty and light;
So man - y gen - tle thoughts and deeds Cir - cling us round;
That shad - ows fall on bright - est hours; That thorns re - main;
We have e - nough, yet not too much To long for more:
Can nev - er find, al - though they seek, A per - fect rest;

So man - y glo - rious things are here, No - ble and right.
That in the dark - est spot of earth Some love is found.
So that earth's bliss may be our guide, And not our chain.
A yearn - ing for a deep - er peace, Not known be - fore.
Nor ev - er shall, un - til they lean On Je - sus' breast. A-men.

God the Father

92

ELLACOMBE. C. M. D.

Isaac Watts, 1719

Gesang Buch der Herzogl, 1784

1. With songs and hon - ors sound - ing loud, Ad - dress the Lord on high;
2. His stead - y coun - sels change the face Of the de - clin - ing year;
3. He sends his word, and melts the snow, The fields no long - er mourn;

O - ver the heavens he spreads his cloud, And wa - ters veil the sky;
He bids the sun cut short his race, And win - try days ap - pear;
He calls the warm - er gales to blow, And bids the spring re - turn.

He sends his showers of bless - ing down To cheer the plains be - low;
His hoar - y frost, his fleec - y snow, De - scend and clothe the ground;
The chang - ing wind, the fly - ing cloud, O - bey his might - y word:

He makes the grass the mountains crown, And corn in val - leys grow.
The liq - uid streams re - fuse to flow, In i - cy fet - ters bound.
With songs and hon - ors sound - ing loud, Praise ye the sov -'reign Lord. A - men.

The Seasons, Spring

NOEL. C. M. D.

English Folk Song
Arranged by ARTHUR S. SULLIVAN, 1874

THOMAS H. GILL, 1867

1. The glo - ry of the spring how sweet, The new - born life how glad;
2. But O these won - ders of thy grace, These no - bler works of thine,
3. Cre - a - tor Spir - it, work in me These won-ders sweet of thine,

What joy the hap - py earth to greet In new, bright rai - ment clad.
These mar - vels sweet-er far to trace, These new-births more di - vine,
Di - vine Re - new - er, gra - cious - ly Re - new this heart of mine.

Di - vine Re - new - er, thee I bless; I greet thy go - ing forth:
This new-born glow of faith so strong, This bloom of love so fair,
Still let new life and strength up-spring, Still let new joy be given;

I love thee in the love - li - ness Of thy re - new - ed earth.
This new-born ec - sta - sy of song And fra - gran - cy of prayer!
And grant the glad new song to ring Thro' the new earth and heaven. A-men.

94

DRESDEN. 7. 6. 7. 6. D. With Refrain

Matthias Claudius, 1782
Translated by Jane M. Campbell, 1861

Iohann A. P. Schultz, 1800

1. We plough the fields, and scat - ter The good seed on the land,
2. He on - ly is the Mak - er Of all things near and far;
3. We thank thee, then, O Fa - ther, For all things bright and good,

But it is fed and wa - tered By God's al - might - y hand;
He paints the way - side flow - er, He lights the eve - ning star;
The seed - time and the har - vest, Our life, our health, our food:

He sends the snow in win - ter, The warmth to swell the grain,
The winds and waves o - bey him, By him the birds are fed;
No gifts have we to of - fer, For all thy love im - parts,

The breez - es and the sun - shine, And soft re - fresh - ing rain.
Much more to us, his chil - dren, He gives our dai - ly bread.
But that which thou de - sir - est, Our hum - ble, thank - ful hearts.

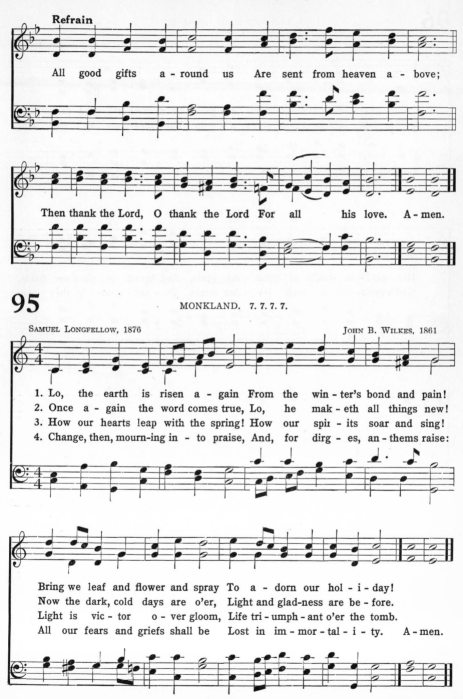

Refrain

All good gifts a-round us Are sent from heaven a-bove;

Then thank the Lord, O thank the Lord For all his love. A-men.

95

MONKLAND. 7. 7. 7. 7.

SAMUEL LONGFELLOW, 1876

JOHN B. WILKES, 1861

1. Lo, the earth is risen a-gain From the win-ter's bond and pain!
2. Once a-gain the word comes true, Lo, he mak-eth all things new!
3. How our hearts leap with the spring! How our spir-its soar and sing!
4. Change, then, mourn-ing in-to praise, And, for dirg-es, an-thems raise:

Bring we leaf and flower and spray To a-dorn our hol-i-day!
Now the dark, cold days are o'er, Light and glad-ness are be-fore.
Light is vic-tor o-ver gloom, Life tri-umph-ant o'er the tomb.
All our fears and griefs shall be Lost in im-mor-tal-i-ty. A-men.

God the Father

LAND OF REST. C. M. D.

SAMUEL LONGFELLOW, 1859

RICHARD S. NEWMAN, 1879

1. The sum - mer days are come a - gain; Once more the glad earth yields
2. The sum - mer days are come a - gain; The birds are on the wing;

Her gold - en wealth of ripen - ing grain, And breath of clo - ver fields,
God's prais - es, in their lov - ing strain, Un - con - scious - ly they sing:

And deep - 'ning shade of sum - mer woods, And glow of sum - mer air,
We know who giv - eth all the good That doth our cup o'er - brim,

And wing - ing tho'ts, and hap - py moods Of love and joy and prayer.
For sum - mer joy in field and wood We lift our song to him. A - men.

The Seasons, Summer

97

RUTH. 6. 5. 6. 5. D.

WILLIAM WALSHAM HOW, 1871

SAMUEL SMITH, 1870

1. Sum - mer suns are glow - ing O - ver land and sea;
2. God's free mer - cy stream - eth O - ver all the world,
3. Lord, up - on our blind - ness Thy pure ra - diance pour;
4. We will nev - er doubt thee, Tho' thou veil thy light;

Hap - py light is flow - ing, Boun - ti - ful and free;
And his ban - ner gleam - eth Ev - ery - where un - furled;
For thy lov - ing kind - ness Make us love thee more.
Life is dark with - out thee, Death with thee is bright.

Ev - ery - thing re - joic - es In the mel - low rays,
Broad and deep and glo - rious As the heaven a - bove,
And when clouds are drift - ing Dark a - cross the sky,
Light of light, shine o'er us On our pil - grim way,

All earth's thou-sand voi - ces Swell the psalm of praise.
Shines in might vic - to - rious His e - ter - nal love.
Then, the mist up - lift - ing, Fa - ther, be thou nigh.
Go thou still be - fore us To the end - less day. A-men.

God the Father

98

ST. GEORGE'S, WINDSOR. 7. 7. 7. 7. D.

HENRY ALFORD, 1844. ANNA L. BARBAULD, 1772
Altered by HUGH HARTSHORNE, 1915

GEORGE J. ELVEY, 1858

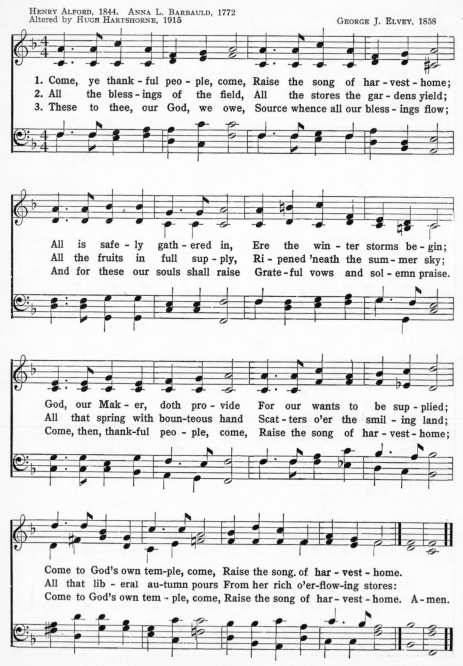

1. Come, ye thank - ful peo - ple, come, Raise the song of har - vest-home;
2. All the bless - ings of the field, All the stores the gar - dens yield;
3. These to thee, our God, we owe, Source whence all our bless - ings flow;

All is safe - ly gath - ered in, Ere the win - ter storms be - gin;
All the fruits in full sup - ply, Ri - pened 'neath the sum - mer sky;
And for these our souls shall raise Grate - ful vows and sol - emn praise.

God, our Mak - er, doth pro - vide For our wants to be sup - plied;
All that spring with boun - teous hand Scat - ters o'er the smil - ing land;
Come, then, thank - ful peo - ple, come, Raise the song of har - vest-home;

Come to God's own tem-ple, come, Raise the song. of har - vest - home.
All that lib - eral au-tumn pours From her rich o'er-flow-ing stores:
Come to God's own tem - ple, come, Raise the song of har - vest - home. A - men.

99

GOSS. 7. 7. 7. 7. D.

WILLIAM C. GANNETT, 1882

JOHN GOSS, 1800–1880

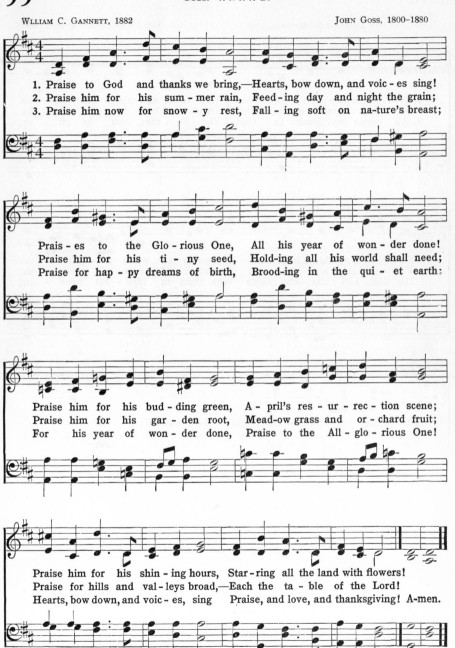

1. Praise to God and thanks we bring,—Hearts, bow down, and voic-es sing!
2. Praise him for his sum-mer rain, Feed-ing day and night the grain;
3. Praise him now for snow-y rest, Fall-ing soft on na-ture's breast;

Prais-es to the Glo-rious One, All his year of won-der done!
Praise him for his ti-ny seed, Hold-ing all his world shall need;
Praise for hap-py dreams of birth, Brood-ing in the qui-et earth:

Praise him for his bud-ding green, A-pril's res-ur-rec-tion scene;
Praise him for his gar-den root, Mead-ow grass and or-chard fruit;
For his year of won-der done, Praise to the All-glo-rious One!

Praise him for his shin-ing hours, Star-ring all the land with flowers!
Praise for hills and val-leys broad,—Each the ta-ble of the Lord!
Hearts, bow down, and voic-es, sing Praise, and love, and thanksgiving! A-men.

By permission of Novello and Company, Limited

100

NUN DANKET. P. M.

MARTIN RINKART, 1636
Translated by CATHERINE WINKWORTH, 1858

CRÜGER's Praxis Pietatis Melica, 1648

UNISON

1. Now thank we all our God With heart and hands and voic - es,
2. O may this boun-teous God Thro' all our life be near us,
3. All praise and thanks to God, The Fa - ther, now be giv - en,

Who won - drous things hath done, In whom his world re - joic - es;
With ev - er joy - ful hearts And bless - ed peace to cheer us;
The Son, and him who reigns With them in high - est heav - en;

Who, from our moth - ers' arms Hath blessed us on our way
And keep us in his grace, And guide us when per - plexed,
The one e - ter - nal God, Whom earth and heaven a - dore;

With count - less gifts of love, And still is ours to - day.
And free us from all ills In this world and the next.
For thus it was, is now, And shall be ev - er - more. A - men.

The Seasons, Autumn

101

CALVERT. 9. 8. 9. 8.

John W. Chadwick, 1871

R. J. C., 1910

1. Now sing we a song for the har - vest; Thanks - giv - ing and
2. For grass - es of up - land and low - land, For fruits of the
3. And thanks for the har - vest of beau - ty, For that which the
4. We reap it on moun - tain and moor - land, We glean it from

hon - or and praise, For all that the boun - ti - ful
gar - den and field, For gold which the mine and the
hands can - not hold; The har - vest, eyes on - ly can
mead - ow and lea, We gar - ner it in from the

Giv - er Hath giv - en to glad - den our days;
fur - row To del - ver and hus - band - man yield.
gath - er, And on - ly our hearts can en - fold.
cloud - land, We bind it in sheaves from the sea. A - men.

5 But now we sing deeper and higher,
  Of harvests that eye cannot see;
They ripen on mountains of duty,
  Are reaped by the brave and the free.

6 O thou who art Lord of the harvest,
  The Giver who gladdens our days,
Our hearts are forever repeating,
  Thanksgiving, and honor, and praise!

God the Father

102

SHACKELFORD. C. M. D.

Frances Whitmarsh Wile, (1878——)

Frederick H. Cheeswright, 1889

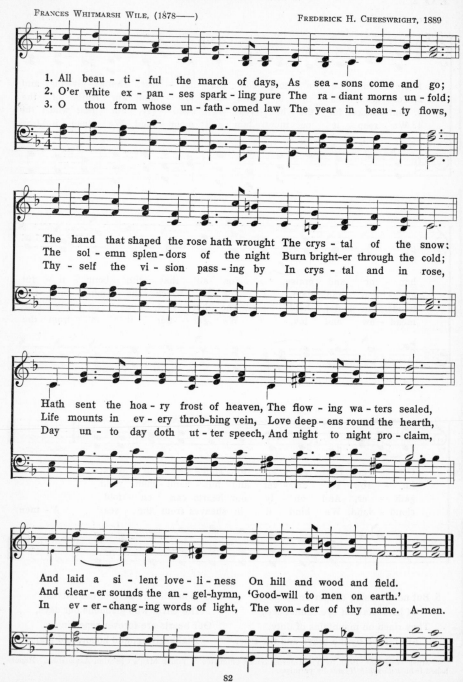

1. All beau - ti - ful the march of days, As sea - sons come and go;
2. O'er white ex - pan - ses spark - ling pure The ra - diant morns un - fold;
3. O thou from whose un - fath - omed law The year in beau - ty flows,

The hand that shaped the rose hath wrought The crys - tal of the snow:
The sol - emn splen - dors of the night Burn bright - er through the cold;
Thy - self the vi - sion pass - ing by In crys - tal and in rose,

Hath sent the hoa - ry frost of heaven, The flow - ing wa - ters sealed,
Life mounts in ev - ery throb-bing vein, Love deep - ens round the hearth,
Day un - to day doth ut - ter speech, And night to night pro - claim,

And laid a si - lent love - li - ness On hill and wood and field.
And clear - er sounds the an - gel-hymn, 'Good-will to men on earth.'
In ev - er-chang - ing words of light, The won - der of thy name. A-men.

103

THE GOLDEN CHAIN. 8. 7. 8. 7. 8. 8. 7.

JAMES HAMILTON, 1882   JOSEPH BARNBY, 1887

1. A - cross the sky the shades of night This win - ter's eve are fleet - ing;
2. And, while we kneel, we lift our eyes To dear ones gone be - fore us;
3. We gath - er up in this brief hour The mem - ory of thy mer - cies;
4. Then, O great God, in years to come, What - ev - er fate be - tide us,

We seek thee, ev - er - last - ing Light, In sol - emn wor - ship meet - ing:
Safe housed with thee in par - a - dise, Their spir - its hover - ing o'er us:
Thy won-drous good-ness, love and power Our grate-ful song re - hears - es:
Right on-ward through our jour-ney home Be thou at hand to guide us:

And as the year's last hours go by, We lift to thee our
And beg of thee, when life is past, To re - u - nite us
For thou hast been our strength and stay, In man - y a dark and
Nor leave us till, at close of life, Safe from all per - ils,

ear - nest cry, Once more thy love en - treat - ing.
all at last, And to our lost re - store us.
drear - y day Of sor - row and re - vers - es.
toil, and strife, Heaven shall en - fold and hide us. A - men.

God the Father

104

BENEVENTO. 7. 7. 7. 7. D.

John Newton, 1774

Arranged from
Samuel Webbe, 1792

1. While with cease-less course the sun Hast-ed through the for-mer year,
2. As the wing-ed ar-row flies Speed-i-ly the mark to find,
3. Thanks for mer-cies past re-ceived; Par-don of our sins re-new;

Man-y souls their race have run, Nev-er-more to meet us here:
As the light-ning from the skies Darts, and leaves no trace be-hind,—
Teach us hence-forth how to live With e-ter-ni-ty in view;

Fixed in an e-ter-nal state, They have done with all be-low;
Swift-ly thus our fleet-ing days Bear us down life's rap-id stream;
Bless thy word to young and old; Fill us with a Sav-iour's love;

We a lit-tle lon-ger wait, But how lit-tle none can know.
Up-ward, Lord, our spir-its raise, All be-low is but a dream.
And when life's short tale is told, May we dwell with thee a-bove. A-men.

105

DEDICATION. 7. 5. 7. 5. D.

LAWRENCE TUTTIETT, 1864

MYLES B. FOSTER, 1890

1. Fa - ther, let me ded - i - cate All this year to thee,
2. Can a child pre - sume to choose Where or how to live?
3. If in mer - cy thou wilt spare Joys that yet are mine;
4. If thou call - est to the cross, And its shad - ow come,

In what - ev - er world - ly state Thou wilt have me be:
Can a Fa - ther's love re - fuse All the best to give?
If on life, se - rene and fair, Bright - er rays may shine;
Turn - ing all my gain to loss, Shroud - ing heart and home;

Not from sor - row, pain, or care Free - dom dare I claim;
More thou giv - est ev - ery day Than the best can claim,
Let my glad heart, while it sings, Thee in all pro - claim,
Let me think how thy dear Son To his glo - ry came,

This a - lone shall be my prayer, Glo - ri - fy thy Name.
Nor with - hold - est aught that may Glo - ri - fy thy Name.
And, what - e'er the fu - ture brings, Glo - ri - fy thy Name.
And in deep - est woe pray on, Glo - ri - fy thy Name. A - men.

106

EDENGROVE. 7. 6. 7. 6. D.

Frances R. Havergal, 1874

Samuel Smith, 1874

1. An - oth - er year is dawn - ing! Dear Fa - ther, let it be
2. An - oth - er year of mer - cies, Of faith - ful - ness and grace;
3. An - oth - er year of ser - vice, Of wit - ness for thy love;

In work - ing or in wait - ing An - oth - er year with thee!
An - oth - er year of glad - ness In the shin - ing of thy face.
An - oth - er year of train - ing For holi - er work a - bove.

An - oth - er year of lean - ing Up - on thy lov - ing breast,
An - oth - er year of pro - gress, An - oth - er year of praise,
An - oth - er year is dawn - ing! Dear Fa - ther, let it be

An - oth - er year of trust - ing, Of qui - et, hap - py rest.
An - oth - er year of prov - ing Thy pres-ence 'all the days.'
On earth, or else in heav - en, An - oth - er year for thee. A - men.

107

WILD BELLS. L. M.

ALFRED TENNYSON, 1850

HENRY LAHEE, 1826–1912

1. Ring out, wild bells, to the wild, wild sky, The
2. Ring out the old, ring in the new, Ring,
3. Ring out a slow - ly dy - ing cause, And
4. Ring out old shapes of foul dis - ease; Ring
5. Ring in the val - iant man and free, The

fly - ing cloud, the frost - y light; The year is dy - ing
hap - py bells, a - cross the snow; The year is go - ing,
an - cient forms of par - ty strife, Ring in the no - bler
out the nar - rowing lust of gold; Ring out the thou - sand
larg - er heart, the kind - lier hand; Ring out the dark - ness

in the night; Ring out, wild bells, and let him die.
let him go; Ring out the false, ring in the true.
modes of life, With sweet - er man - ners, pur - er laws.
wars of old, Ring in the thou - sand years of peace.
of the land, Ring in the Christ that is to be. A - men.

The Son of God

108

WALTHAM. L. M.

Henry W. Longfellow, 1863

J. Baptiste Calkin, 1872

1. I heard the bells on Christ-mas day Their old fa - mil - iar car - ols play,
2. I thought how, as the day had come, The bel - fries of all Chris-ten-dom
3. And in de - spair I bowed my head: 'There is no peace on earth,' I said,
4. Then pealed the bells more loud and deep: 'God is not dead, nor doth he sleep;
5. Till, ring - ing, sing - ing on its way, The world re-volved from night to day,

And wild and sweet the words re-peat Of peace on earth, good-will to men.
Had rolled along the un-bro-ken song Of peace on earth, good-will to men,
'For hate is strong, and mocks the song Of peace on earth, good-will to men.'
The wrong shall fail, the right pre-vail, With peace on earth, good-will to men':
A voice, a chime, a chant sub-lime, Of peace on earth, good-will to men! A-men.

109

SARDIS. 8. 7. 8. 7.

James A. Blaisdell, 1900

Arranged from
Ludwig von Beethoven, 1770-1827

1. Chris-tians, lo, the star ap - pear - eth; Lo, 'tis yet Mes - si - ah's day;
2. Where a life is spent in ser - vice Walk-ing where the Mas-ter trod,
3. Who - so bears his broth - er's bur - den, Who - so shares an-oth-er's woe,
4. When we soothe earth's wear - y chil - dren Tend-ing best the least of them,
5. Chris-tians, lo, the star ap - pear - eth Lead-ing still the an - cient way;

Still with trib-ute treas-ure la - den Come the wise men on their way.
There is scattered myrrh most fragrant For the bless-ed Christ of God.
Brings his frank-in-cense to Je - sus With the men of long a - go.
'Tis the Lord him-self we wor - ship, Bring-ing gold to Beth - le - hem.
Christians, onward with your treasure; It is still Mes - si - ah's day. A-men.

110

BLESSED HOME. 6. 6. 6. 6. D.

Thomas T. Lynch, 1856

John Stainer, 1875

1. Lift up your heads, re - joice, Re - demp - tion draw - eth nigh:
2. Lift up your heads, re - joice, Re - demp - tion draw - eth nigh:
3. Lift up your heads, re - joice, Re - demp - tion draw - eth nigh:
4. He comes, the wide world's King; He comes, the true heart's Friend,

Now breathes a soft - er air, Now shines a mild - er sky;
Now mount the lad - en clouds, Now flames the darken - ing sky;
O note the vary - ing signs Of earth, and air, and sky!
New glad - ness to be - gin, And an - cient wrong to end;

The ear - ly trees put forth Their new and ten - der leaf; Hushed
The ear - ly scat-tered drops Des - cend with heav - y fall, And
The God of glo - ry comes In gen - tle - ness and might, To
He comes, to fill with light The wear - y, wait - ing eye: Lift

is the moan - ing wind That told of win - ter's grief.
to the wait - ing earth The hid - den thun - ders call.
com - fort and a - larm, To suc - cor and to smite.
up your heads, re - joice, Re - demp - tion draw - eth nigh. A - men.

The Son of God

111

VENI EMMANUEL. 8. 8. 8. 8. With Refrain

Based on Ancient-Latin Antiphons:
Translated by JOHN M. NEALE, 1851
HENRY S. COFFIN, 1916

Ancient Plain Song, 13th Century

UNISON

1. O come, O come, Em - man - u - el, And ran - som cap - tive
2. O come, thou Wis - dom from on high, And or - der all things,
3. O come, De - sire of na - tions, bind All peo - ples in one

Is - ra - el; That mourns in lone - ly ex - ile here,
far and nigh; To us the path of knowl - edge show,
heart and mind; Bid en - vy, strife and quar - rels cease;

Refrain HARMONY

Un - til the Son of God ap - pear.
And cause us in her ways to go. } Re - joice! Re - joice!
Fill the whole world with heav - en's peace.

Em - man - u - el Shall come to thee, O Is - ra - el! A - men.

112

ANTIOCH. C. M.

Arranged from HANDEL'S Messiah, 1742
by LOWELL MASON, 1830

ISAAC WATTS, 1719

1. Joy to the world! the Lord is come; Let earth re-ceive her King;
2. Joy to the world! the Sav-iour reigns; Let men their songs em-ploy;
3. He rules the world with truth and grace, And makes the na-tions prove

Let ev-ery heart...... pre-pare him room,.....
While fields and floods,..... rocks, hills and plains.....
The glo-ries of........ his right-eous-ness, ...

And heaven and na-ture sing, And heaven and na-ture
Re-peat the sound-ing joy, Re-peat the sound-ing
And won-ders of his love, And won-ders of his

And heaven and na-ture sing, And

sing, And heaven, and heaven.... and na-ture sing.
joy, Re-peat, re-peat...... the sound-ing joy.
love, And won-ders, and won-ders of his love. A-men.

heaven and na-ture sing,

The Son of God

WATCHMAN. 7. 7. 7. 7. D.

JOHN BOWRING, 1825

LOWELL MASON, 1830

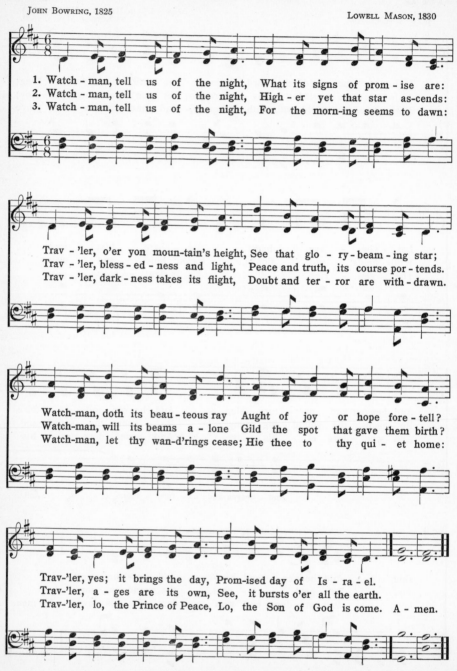

1. Watch - man, tell us of the night, What its signs of prom - ise are:
2. Watch - man, tell us of the night, High - er yet that star as - cends:
3. Watch - man, tell us of the night, For the morn - ing seems to dawn:

Trav - 'ler, o'er yon moun - tain's height, See that glo - ry - beam - ing star;
Trav - 'ler, bless - ed - ness and light, Peace and truth, its course por - tends.
Trav - 'ler, dark - ness takes its flight, Doubt and ter - ror are with - drawn.

Watch-man, doth its beau - teous ray Aught of joy or hope fore - tell?
Watch-man, will its beams a - lone Gild the spot that gave them birth?
Watch-man, let thy wan-d'rings cease; Hie thee to thy qui - et home:

Trav-'ler, yes; it brings the day, Prom-ised day of Is - ra - el.
Trav-'ler, a - ges are its own, See, it bursts o'er all the earth.
Trav-'ler, lo, the Prince of Peace, Lo, the Son of God is come. A - men.

114

MENDELSSOHN. 7. 7. 7. 7. D.

CHARLES WESLEY, 1739

Arranged from
MENDELSSOHN, 1840

1. Hark! the her-ald an-gels sing, 'Glo-ry to the new-born King;
2. Christ, by high-est heaven a-dored, Christ, the ev-er-last-ing Lord!
3. Hail, the heaven-born Prince of Peace! Hail, the Sun of Right-eous-ness!

Peace on earth, and mer-cy mild, God and sin-ners rec-on-ciled!'
Come, De-sire of Na-tions, come, Fix in us thy hum-ble home.
Light and life to all he brings, Risen with heal-ing in his wings;

Joy-ful, all ye na-tions, rise, Join the tri-umph of the skies;
Veiled in flesh the God-head see; Hail th' In-car-nate De-i-ty,
Mild he lays his glo-ry by, Born that man no more may die,

With th' an-gel-ic host pro-claim, 'Christ is born in Beth-le-hem!'
Pleased as man with men to dwell; Je-sus, our Em-man-u-el!
Born to raise the sons of earth, Born to give them sec-ond birth;

Hark! the her-ald an-gels sing, 'Glo-ry to the new-born King!' A-men.

The Son of God

115

CAROL. C. M. D.

EDMUND H. SEARS, 1849

RICHARD S. WILLIS, 1850

1. It came up-on the mid-night clear, That glo-rious song of old,
2. Still through the clo-ven skies they come, With peace-ful wings un-furled;
3. And ye, be-neath life's crush-ing load, Whose forms are bend-ing low,
4. For lo! the days are has-tening on, By proph-et-bards fore-told,

From an-gels bend-ing near the earth, To touch their harps of gold:
And still their heaven-ly mu-sic floats O'er all the wea-ry world:
Who toil a-long the climb-ing way, With pain-ful steps and slow,—
When, with the ev-er-cir-cling years Comes round the age of gold;

'Peace on the earth, good-will to men, From heaven's all-gra-cious King;'
A-bove its sad and low-ly plains They bend on heaven-ly wing,
Look now, for glad and gold-en hours Come swift-ly on the wing;
When peace shall o-ver all the earth Its an-cient splen-dors fling,

The world in sol-emn still-ness lay To hear the an-gels sing.
And ev-er o'er its Ba-bel sounds The bless-ed an-gels sing.
O rest be-side the wea-ry road, And hear the an-gels sing!
And the whole world give back the song Which now the an-gels sing. A-men.

116

TEIGNMOUTH. C. M. D.

NAHUM TATE, 1703

Anonymous

1. While shepherds watched their flocks by night, All seat-ed on the ground,
2. 'To you, in Dav-id's town, this day, Is born of Dav-id's line,
3. Thus spake the ser-aph, and forth-with Ap-peared a shin-ing throng

The an-gel of the Lord came down, And glo-ry shone a-round.
The Sav-iour, who is Christ, the Lord; And this shall be the sign:
Of an-gels, prais-ing God, and thus Ad-dressed their joy-ful song:

'Fear not,' said he, for might-y dread Had seized their troub-led mind;
The heaven-ly Babe you there shall find To hu-man view dis-played,
'All glo-ry be to God on high, And to the earth be peace;

'Glad tid-ings of great joy I bring To you, and all man-kind.'
All mean-ly wrapped in swath-ing bands, And in a man-ger laid.'
Good-will hence-forth from heaven to men Be-gin, and nev-er cease.' A-men.

The Son of God

117

REGENT SQUARE. 8. 7. 8. 7. With Refrain

James Montgomery, 1816

Henry Smart, 1867

1. An - gels, from the realms of glo - ry, Wing your flight o'er
2. Shep - herds, in the fields a - bid - ing, Watch - ing o'er your
3. Sa - ges, leave your con - tem - pla - tions, Bright - er vi - sions
4. Saints be - fore the al - tar bend - ing, Watch - ing long in

all the earth; Ye who sang cre - a - tion's sto - ry,
flocks by night, God with man is now re - sid - ing,
beam a - far; Seek the great De - sire of na - tions,
hope and fear, Sud - den - ly the Lord, de - scend - ing,

Refrain

Now pro - claim Mes - si - ah's birth:
Yon - der shines the in - fant light;
Ye have seen his na - tal star:
In his tem - ple shall ap - pear;

Come and wor - ship,

Come and wor - ship, Wor - ship Christ, the new - born King. A - men.

118   ADESTE FIDELES. (PORTUGUESE HYMN.)   Irregular.   With Refrain

Latin Hymn, 17th Century
Translated by FREDERICK OAKELEY, 1841

WADE'S Cantus Diversi, 1751

1. O come, all ye faith - ful, joy - ful and tri - umph - ant, O
2. Sing, choirs of an - gels, sing in ex - ul - ta - tion, O
3. Yea, Lord, we greet thee, born this hap - py morn - ing,

come ye, O come ye to Beth - le - hem;
sing, all ye bright hosts of heaven a - bove;
Je - sus, to thee be all glo - ry given;

Come and be - hold him born the King of an - gels;
Glo - ry to God, all glo - ry in the high - est;
Word of the Fa - ther, now in flesh ap - pear - ing;

Refrain

O come, let us a - dore him, O come, let us a - dore him,

O come, let us a - dore him, Christ, the Lord. A - men.

The Son of God

119

ST. LOUIS.   8. 6. 8. 6. 7. 6. 8. 6.

PHILLIPS BROOKS, 1868

LEWIS H. REDNER, 1868

1. O lit-tle town of Beth-le-hem, How still we see thee lie!
2. For Christ is born of Ma-ry, And gath-ered all a-bove,
3. How si-lent-ly, how si-lent-ly The won-drous gift is given!
4. O ho-ly Child of Beth-le-hem, De-scend to us, we pray;

A-bove thy deep and dream-less sleep The si-lent stars go by;
While mor-tals sleep, the an-gels keep Their watch of won-dering love.
So God im-parts to hu-man hearts The bless-ings of his heaven.
Cast out our sin, and en-ter in; Be born in us to-day.

Yet in thy dark streets shin-eth The ev-er-last-ing Light;
O morn-ing stars, to-geth-er Pro-claim the ho-ly birth,
No ear may hear his com-ing, But in this world of sin,
We hear the Christ-mas an-gels The great glad ti-dings tell;

The hopes and fears of all the years Are met in thee to-night.
And prais-es sing to God the King, And peace to men on earth!
Where meek souls will re-ceive him, still The dear Christ en-ters in.
O come to us, a-bide with us, Our Lord Em-man-u-el! A-men.

120

JOY. 8. 6. 8. 6. 8. 6. 8. 8.

William C. Dix, about 1865

Henry Gadsby, 1842–1907

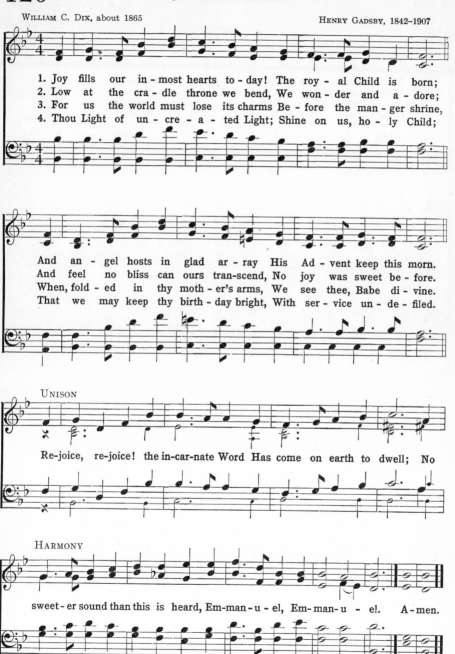

1. Joy fills our in - most hearts to - day! The roy - al Child is born;
2. Low at the cra - dle throne we bend, We won - der and a - dore;
3. For us the world must lose its charms Be - fore the man - ger shrine,
4. Thou Light of un - cre - a - ted Light; Shine on us, ho - ly Child;

And an - gel hosts in glad ar - ray His Ad - vent keep this morn.
And feel no bliss can ours tran-scend, No joy was sweet be - fore.
When, fold - ed in thy moth - er's arms, We see thee, Babe di - vine.
That we may keep thy birth - day bright, With ser - vice un - de - filed.

Unison

Re-joice, re-joice! the in-car-nate Word Has come on earth to dwell; No

Harmony

sweet - er sound than this is heard, Em-man-u - el, Em-man-u - el. A-men.

The Son of God

THE FIRST NOEL. Irregular. With Refrain

Traditional

Traditional

1. The first No - el the an - gel did say Was to
2. They look - ed up and saw a star Shin - ing
3. And by the light of that same star, Three
4. This star drew nigh to the north - west, O'er
5. Then en - tered in those wise - men three, Full

cer - tain poor shep - herds in fields as they lay; In
in the east, be - yond them far, And
wise - men came from coun - try far; To
Beth - le - hem it took its rest, And
rev - er - ent - ly up - on the knee, And

fields where they lay keep - ing their sheep, On a cold win - ter's
to the earth it gave great light, And so it con -
seek for a king was their in - tent, And to fol - low the
there it did both stop and stay, Right o - ver the
of - fered there, in his pres - ence, Their gold, and

Refrain

night that was so deep.
tin - ued both day and night.
star wher - ev - er it went. } No - el, No - el, No -
place where Je - sus lay.
myrrh, and frank - in - cense.

100

Nativity

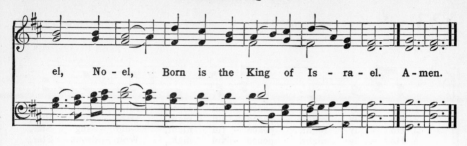

el, No - el, Born is the King of Is - ra - el. A - men.

122

BONN. 8. 3. 3. 6. D.

PAUL GERHARDT, 1656
Translated by CATHERINE WINKWORTH, 1858

JOHANN G. EBELING, 1666

1. All my heart this night re - joic - es, As I hear, Far and near,
2. Hark! a voice from yon - der man - ger, Soft and sweet, Doth en - treat,
3. Come, then, let us hast - en yon - der! Here let all, Great and small,
4. Thee, dear Lord, with heed I'll cher - ish, Live to thee, And with thee,

Sweet-est an - gel voic - es; 'Christ is born,' their choirs are sing - ing,
'Flee from woe and dan - ger! Breth-ren, come! from all doth grieve you,
Kneel in awe and won - der! Love him who with love is yearn - ing!
Dy - ing, shall not per - ish; But shall dwell with thee for - ev - er,

Till the air Ev - ery - where Now with joy is ring - ing.
You are freed; All you need I will sure - ly give you.'
Hail the star That from far Bright with hope is burn - ing!
Far on high, In the joy That can al - ter nev - er. A - men.

The Son of God

123

STILLE NACHT. Irregular

Translated from
JOSEPH MOHR, 1818

FRANZ GRÜBER, 1818

1. Ho - ly night, peace - ful night, All is dark, save the light Yon - der where they sweet vig - il keep O'er the Babe, who in si - lent sleep, Rests in heav - en - ly peace, Rests in heav - en - ly peace.

2. Ho - ly night, peace - ful night, Dark - ness flies, all is light, Shep - herds hear the an - gels sing: 'Al - le - lu - ia! hail the King, Je - sus the Sav - iour is here, Je - sus the Sav - iour is here.'

3. Ho - ly night, peace - ful night, Guid - ing Star, lend thy light! See the east - ern wise men bring Gifts and hom - age to our King, Je - sus the Sav - iour is here, Je - sus the Sav - iour is here.

4. Ho - ly night, peace - ful night, Won - drous Star, lend thy light! With the an - gels let us sing Al - le - lu - ia to our King. Je - sus the Sav - iour is here, Je - sus the Sav - iour is here. A - men.

124

MORNING STAR. 11. 10. 11. 10.

REGINALD HEBER, 1811

JOHN P. HARDING, 1861–

1. Bright - est and best of the sons of the morn - ing,
2. Say, shall we yield him, in cost - ly de - vo - tion,
3. Vain - ly we of - fer each am - ple ob - la - tion,
4. Cold on his cra - dle the dew - drops are shin - ing,

Dawn on our dark - ness and lend us thine aid,
O - dors of E - dom and of - ferings di - vine,
Vain - ly with gifts would his fa - vor se - cure;
Low lies his head with the beasts of the stall;

Star of the east, the ho - ri - zon a - dorn - ing,
Gems of the moun - tain and pearls of the o - cean,
Rich - er by far is the heart's ad - o - ra - tion,
An - gels a - dore him in slum - ber re - clin - ing,

Guide where our in - fant Re - deem - er is laid.
Myrrh from the for - est, or gold from the mine?
Dear - er to God are the prayers of the poor.
Mak - er and Mon - arch and Sav - iour of all. A - men.

The Son of God

125

ROSMORE. 6. 5. 6. 5. D. With Refrain

GODFREY THRING, 1873

HENRY G. TREMBATH, 1893

1. From the east-ern moun - tains, Press-ing on, they come, Wise men in their
2. Thou who in a man - ger Once hast low - ly lain, Who dost now in
3. Gath - er in the out - casts, All who've gone a-stray; Throw thy ra - diance
4. Un - til ev - ery na - tion Wheth-er bond or free, 'Neath thy star - lit

wis - dom, To his hum - ble home; Stirred by deep de - vo - tion,
glo - ry O'er all king-doms reign, Gath - er in the peo - ple,
o'er them, Guide them on their way; Those who nev - er knew thee,
ban - ner, Je - sus, fol - lows thee O'er the dis - tant moun - tains

Hast-ing from a - far, Ev - er journeying on - ward, Guid-ed by a star.
Who in lands a - far Ne'er have seen the brightness Of thy guid-ing star.
Those who've wandered far, Guide them by the brightness Of thy guid-ing star.
To that heavenly home, Where no sin nor sor - row Ev-er-more shall come.

Refrain

Light of life that shin - eth, Ere the worlds be - gan,

Draw thou near and light - en Ev - ery heart of man. A - men.

126

DIX. 7. 7. 7. 7. 7. 7.

William C. Dix, 1860

Arranged from
Conrad Kocher, 1838

1. As with glad - ness men of old   Did the guid - ing star be - hold;
2. As with joy - ful steps they sped   To that low - ly man - ger - bed,
3. As they of - fered gifts most rare,   At that man - ger rude and bare,
4. Ho - ly Je - sus, ev - ery day   Keep us in the nar - row way;

As with joy they hailed its light,   Lead - ing on - ward, beam - ing bright;
There to bend the knee be - fore   Him whom heaven and earth a - dore;
So may we with ho - ly joy,   Pure and free from sin's al - loy,
And, when earth - ly things are past,   Bring our ran - somed souls at last

So, most gra - cious Lord, may we   Ev - er - more be led to thee.
So may we with will - ing feet   Ev - er seek thy mer - cy - seat.
All our cost - liest treas - ures bring,   Christ, to thee, our heavenly King.
Where they need no star to guide,   Where no clouds thy glo - ry hide. A - men.

The Son of God

127

MARGARET. Irregular

EMILY E. S. ELLIOTT, 1864

TIMOTHY R. MATTHEWS, 1876

1. Thou didst leave thy throne And thy king-ly crown When thou
2. Heav-en's arch-es rang When the an-gels sang Pro-
3. The fox-es found rest, And the birds their nest In the
4. Thou cam-est, O Lord, With the liv-ing word That should
5. When the heav-ens shall ring, And the an-gels sing, At thy

cam-est to earth for me; But in Beth-le-hem's home
claim-ing thy roy-al de-gree; But of low-ly birth
shade of the for-est tree; But thy couch was the sod,
set thy peo-ple free; But with mock-ing scorn,
com-ing to vic-to-ry, Let thy voice call me home,

Was there found no room For thy ho-ly na-tiv-i-ty:
Didst thou come to earth, And in great-est hu-mil-i-ty:
O thou Son of God, In the des-erts of Gal-i-lee:
And with crown of thorn, They bore thee to Cal-va-ry:
Say-ing, 'Yet there is room, There is room at my side for thee;'

Refrain

1-4. O come to my heart, Lord Je-sus, There is room in my heart for thee.
5. My heart shall rejoice, Lord Je-sus, When thou comest and call-est for me. A-men.

Life and Ministry

128

AMESBURY. C. M. D.

Jay T. Stocking, 1912

Uzziah C. Burnap, 1895

1. O Mas - ter work - man of the race, Thou man of Gal - i - lee,
2. O Car - pen - ter of Naz - a - reth, Build - er of life di - vine,
3. O thou who dost the vis - ion send And gives to each his task,

Who with the eyes of ear - ly youth E - ter - nal things did see,
Who shap - est man to God's own law, Thy - self the fair de - sign,
And with the task suf - fi - cient strength, Show us thy will, we ask;

We thank thee for thy boy - hood faith That shone thy whole life through;
Build us a tower of Christ - like height, That we the land may view,
Give us a con - science bold and good, Give us a pur - pose true,

'Did ye not know it is my work My Fa - ther's work to do?'
And see like thee our no - blest work Our Fa - ther's work to do.
That it may be our high - est joy, Our Fa - ther's work to do. A - men.

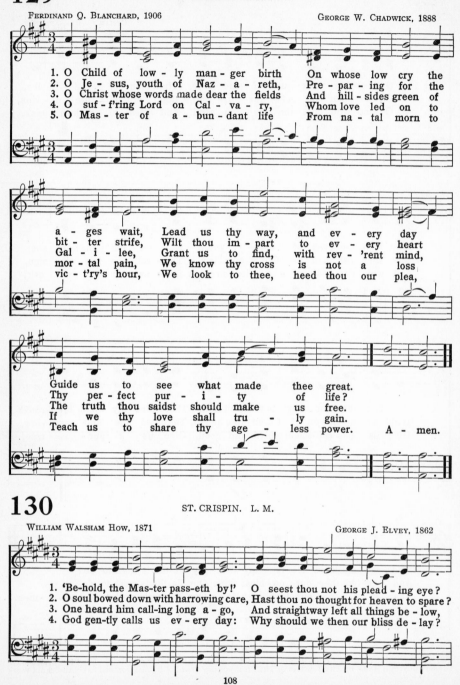

The Son of God

129

EATON. L. M.

FERDINAND Q. BLANCHARD, 1906

GEORGE W. CHADWICK, 1888

1. O Child of low-ly man-ger birth On whose low cry the
2. O Je-sus, youth of Naz-a-reth, Pre-par-ing for the
3. O Christ whose words made dear the fields And hill-sides green of
4. O suf-f'ring Lord on Cal-va-ry, Whom love led on to
5. O Mas-ter of a-bun-dant life From na-tal morn to

a-ges wait, Lead us thy way, and ev-ery day
bit-ter strife, Wilt thou im-part to ev-ery heart
Gal-i-lee, Grant us to find, with rev-'rent mind,
mor-tal pain, We know thy cross is not a loss
vic-t'ry's hour, We look to thee, heed thou our plea,

Guide us to see what made thee great.
Thy per-fect pur-i-ty of life?
The truth thou saidst should make us free.
If we thy love shall tru-ly gain.
Teach us to share thy age-less power. A-men.

130

ST. CRISPIN. L. M.

WILLIAM WALSHAM HOW, 1871

GEORGE J. ELVEY, 1862

1. 'Be-hold, the Mas-ter pass-eth by!' O seest thou not his plead-ing eye?
2. O soul bowed down with harrowing care, Hast thou no thought for heaven to spare?
3. One heard him call-ing long a-go, And straightway left all things be-low,
4. God gen-tly calls us ev-ery day: Why should we then our bliss de-lay?

With low sad voice he call-eth thee: Leave this vain world and follow me.
From earthly toils lift up thine eye: Be - hold, the Mas-ter passeth by.
Counting his earth - ly gain as loss For Je - sus and his bless-ed cross.
Thou, Lord, e'en now art call-ing me: I will leave all, and fol-low thee. A-men.

131

ROCKINGHAM. L. M.

ISAAC WATTS, 1709

EDWARD MILLER, 1790

1. My dear Re - deem - er and my Lord, I read my du - ty
2. Such was thy truth, and such thy zeal, Such defer-ence to thy
3. Cold moun - tains and the mid - night air Wit-nessed the fer - vor
4. Be thou my pat - tern; make me bear More of thy gra - cious

in thy Word; But in thy life the law ap - pears
Fa - ther's will, Such love and meek - ness so di - vine,—
of thy prayer; The des - ert thy temp - ta - tions knew,
im - age here; Then God, the Judge, shall own my name

Drawn out in liv - ing char - ac - ters.
I would trans - cribe and make them mine.
Thy con - flict and thy vic - tory too.
A - mong the fol - lowers of the Lamb. A - men.

The Son of God

132

CUSHMAN. 11. 10. 11. 10.

J. Edgar Park, 1913

Herbert B. Turner, 1905

1. We would see Jesus, lo! his star is shining
2. We would see Jesus, Mary's son most holy,
3. We would see Jesus, on the mountain teaching,
4. We would see Jesus, in his work of healing,
5. We would see Jesus, in the early morning

A-bove the sta-ble while the an-gels sing;
Light of the vil-lage life from day to day;
With all the lis-tening peo-ple gath-ered round;
At ev-en-tide be-fore the sun was set;
Still as of old he call-eth, 'Fol-low Me';

There in a man-ger on the hay re-clin-ing,
Shin-ing re-vealed through ev-ery task most low-ly,
While birds and flowers and sky a-bove are preach-ing,
Di-vine and hu-man, in his deep re-veal-ing,
Let us a-rise, all mean-er serv-ice scorn-ing,

Haste, let us lay our gifts be-fore the King.
The Christ of God, the Life, the Truth, the Way.
The bless-ed-ness which sim-ple trust has found.
Of God and man in lov-ing serv-ice met.
Lord, we are thine, we give our-selves to thee! A-men.

133

ARMSTRONG. 7. 7. 5. 7. 7. 5.

STOPFORD A. BROOKE, 1881

GEORGE W. CHADWICK, 1887

1. When the Lord of love was here, Hap-py
2. Meek and low-ly were his ways, From his
3. When he walked the fields, he drew From the
4. Fill us with thy deep de-sire All the

hearts to him were dear, Though his heart was sad;
lov-ing grew his praise, From his giv-ing, prayer;
flowers and birds and dew, Par-a-bles of God;
sin-ful to in-spire With the Fa-ther's life;

Worn and lone-ly for our sake, Yet he turned a-
All the out-cast thronged to hear, All the sor-row-
For with-in his heart of love All the soul of
Free us from the cares that press On the heart of

side to make All the wea-ry glad.
ful drew near To en-joy his care.
man did move, God had his a-bode.
world-li-ness, From the fret and strife. A-men.

The Son of God

134

SERENITY. C. M.

JOHN G. WHITTIER, 1866

Arranged from
WILLIAM V. WALLACE, 1855

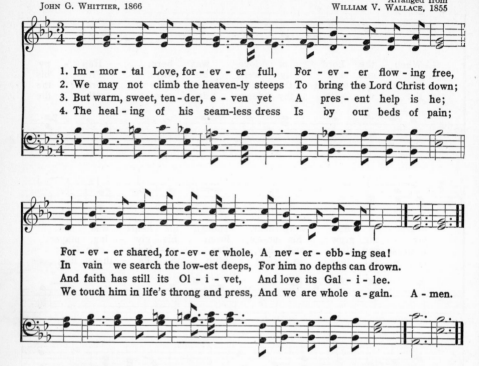

1. Im - mor - tal Love, for - ev - er full, For - ev - er flow - ing free,
2. We may not climb the heaven-ly steeps To bring the Lord Christ down;
3. But warm, sweet, ten - der, e - ven yet A pres - ent help is he;
4. The heal - ing of his seam-less dress Is by our beds of pain;

For - ev - er shared, for - ev - er whole, A nev - er - ebb - ing sea!
In vain we search the low-est deeps, For him no depths can drown.
And faith has still its Ol - i - vet, And love its Gal - i - lee.
We touch him in life's throng and press, And we are whole a - gain. A - men.

5 Through him the first fond prayers are said
  Our lips of childhood frame,
  The last low whispers of our dead
  Are burdened with his name.

6 O Lord and Master of us all,
  Whate'er our name or sign,
  We own thy sway, we hear thy call,
  We test our lives by thine.

135

COLLEGE. 8. 5. 8. 5.

HENRY S. NINDE

F. K. MARCH

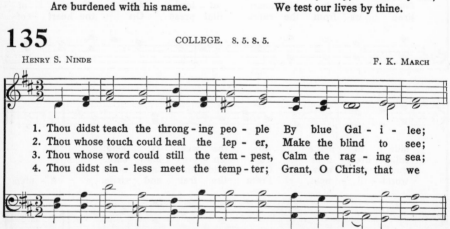

1. Thou didst teach the throng - ing peo - ple By blue Gal - i - lee;
2. Thou whose touch could heal the lep - er, Make the blind to see;
3. Thou whose word could still the tem - pest, Calm the rag - ing sea;
4. Thou didst sin - less meet the temp - ter; Grant, O Christ, that we

Speak to us, thy err - ing chil - dren, Teach us pur - i - ty.
Touch our hearts and turn the sin - ning In - to pur - i - ty.
Hush the storm of hu - man pas - sion, Give us pur - i - ty.
May o'er-come the bent to e - vil By thy pur - i - ty. A - men.

136

BREAD OF LIFE. 6.4.6.4. D.

MARY A. LATHBURY, 1880

WILLIAM F. SHERWIN, 1877

1. Break thou the bread of life, Dear Lord, to me, As thou didst
2. Bless thou the truth, dear Lord, To me, to me, As thou didst

break the loaves Be - side the sea; Be - yond the sa - cred page
bless the bread By Gal - i - lee; Then shall all bond - age cease,

I seek thee, Lord; My spir - it pants for thee, O liv - ing Word!
All fet - ters fall; And I shall find my peace, My All - in - All. A - men.

137

DELIVERANCE. C. M. D.

EDWARD H. PLUMPTRE, 1864

JOSEPH BARNBY, 1867

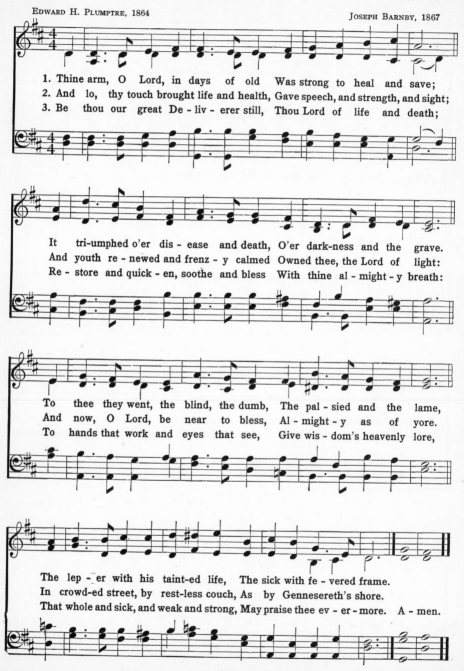

1. Thine arm, O Lord, in days of old Was strong to heal and save;
2. And lo, thy touch brought life and health, Gave speech, and strength, and sight;
3. Be thou our great De - liv - erer still, Thou Lord of life and death;

It tri-umphed o'er dis - ease and death, O'er dark-ness and the grave.
And youth re - newed and frenz - y calmed Owned thee, the Lord of light:
Re - store and quick - en, soothe and bless With thine al - might - y breath:

To thee they went, the blind, the dumb, The pal - sied and the lame,
And now, O Lord, be near to bless, Al - might - y as of yore.
To hands that work and eyes that see, Give wis - dom's heavenly lore,

The lep - er with his taint-ed life, The sick with fe - vered frame.
In crowd-ed street, by rest-less couch, As by Gennesereth's shore.
That whole and sick, and weak and strong, May praise thee ev - er-more. A - men.

138

SWEET STORY. Irregular

Greek Folksong
Arranged by WILLIAM B. BRADBURY, 1859
Harmonized by WINFRED DOUGLAS, 1918

JEMIMA LUKE, 1841

1. I think when I read that sweet sto - ry of old,
2. I wish that his hands had been placed on my head,
3. Yet still to his foot - stool in prayer I may go,
4. But thou - sands and thou - sands who wan - der and fall,
5. I long for the joy of that glo - ri - ous time,

When Je - sus was here a - mong men,
That his arm had been thrown a - round me,
And ask for a share in his love;
Nev - er heard of that heav - en - ly home;
The sweet - est and bright - est and best,

How he called lit - tle chil - dren as lambs to his fold,
And that I might have seen his kind look when he said:
And if I thus ear - nest - ly seek him be - low,
I wish they could know there is room for them all,
When the dear lit - tle chil - dren of ev - er - y clime

I should like to have been with them then.
'Let the lit - tle ones come un - to me.'
I shall see him and hear him a - bove,
And that Je - sus has bid them to come.
Shall crowd to his arms and be blest. A - men.

The Son of God

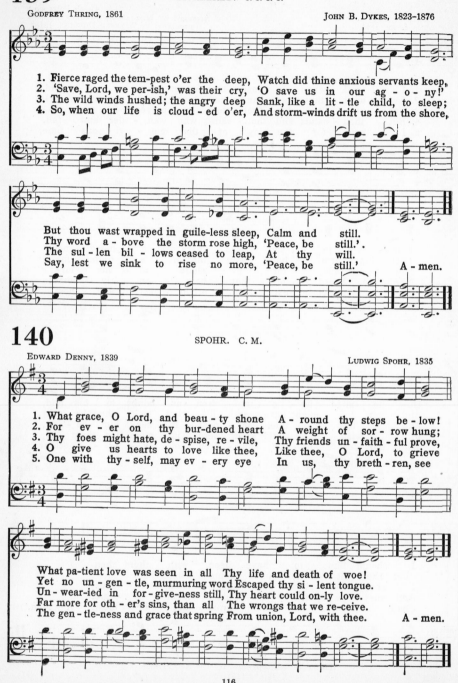

139

ST. AELRED. 8. 8. 8. 3.

GODFREY THRING, 1861

JOHN B. DYKES, 1823–1876

1. Fierce raged the tem-pest o'er the deep, Watch did thine anxious servants keep,
2. 'Save, Lord, we per-ish,' was their cry, 'O save us in our ag-o-ny!'
3. The wild winds hushed; the angry deep Sank, like a lit-tle child, to sleep;
4. So, when our life is cloud-ed o'er, And storm-winds drift us from the shore,

But thou wast wrapped in guile-less sleep, Calm and still.
Thy word a-bove the storm rose high, 'Peace, be still.'.
The sul-len bil-lows ceased to leap, At thy will.
Say, lest we sink to rise no more, 'Peace, be still.' A-men.

140

SPOHR. C. M.

EDWARD DENNY, 1839

LUDWIG SPOHR, 1835

1. What grace, O Lord, and beau-ty shone A-round thy steps be-low!
2. For ev-er on thy bur-dened heart A weight of sor-row hung;
3. Thy foes might hate, de-spise, re-vile, Thy friends un-faith-ful prove,
4. O give us hearts to love like thee, Like thee, O Lord, to grieve
5. One with thy-self, may ev-ery eye In us, thy breth-ren, see

What pa-tient love was seen in all Thy life and death of woe!
Yet no un-gen-tle, murmuring word Escaped thy si-lent tongue.
Un-wear-ied in for-give-ness still, Thy heart could on-ly love.
Far more for oth-er's sins, than all The wrongs that we re-ceive.
The gen-tle-ness and grace that spring From union, Lord, with thee. A-men.

141

AGNES. 7. 7. 7 6.

W. RUSSELL BOWIE, 1909

EDWARD BUNNETT, 1897

1. Love - ly to the out - ward eye Seemed Je - ru - sa - lem to lie—
2. Far-brought stones and mar - ble rare Made its towers and cir - cuits fair,
3. And would all the crowd-ed mart, Wealth and splen - did ease and art
4. Wouldst thou call our boast-ing good, If thou sawest our tri-umphs stood
5. Je - sus, par - don where we fall; Je - sus, our whole life en - thrall;

Yet 'twas there thou cam'st to die, Je - sus, Son of Ma - ry.
Yet thy cross was wait-ing there, Wear-ied Son of Ma - ry.
Of our own world please thy heart, O thou Son of Ma - ry?
On the wreck of broth-er-hood, Lov-ing Son of Ma - ry?
Let thy Spir - it rule it all, Bless-ed Son of Ma - ry. A - men.

142

ST. DROSTANE. L. M.

HENRY H. MILMAN, 1827

JOHN B. DYKES, 1862

1. Ride on, ride on in maj - es - ty! Hark! all the tribes Ho - san - na cry;
2. Ride on, ride on in maj - es - ty! In low - ly pomp ride on to die;
3. Ride on, ride on in maj - es - ty! The wing-ed squad-rons of the sky
4. Ride on, ride on in maj - es - ty! The last and fierc-est strife is nigh;

O Sav-iour meek, pur-sue thy road, With palms and scattered garments strowed.
O Christ, thy tri-umphs now be-gin O'er cap-tive death and conquered sin.
Look down with sad and wondering eyes To see th' ap-proach-ing sac-ri-fice.
Bow thy meek head to mor-tal pain, Then take, O Christ, thy power and reign. A-men.

The Son of God

143

ST. THEODULPH 7. 6. 7. 6. D.

THEODULPH OF ORLEANS, about 820
Translated by JOHN M. NEALE, 1854

MELCHIOR TESCHNER, 1615

1. All glo - ry, laud and hon - or To thee, Re - deem - er, King,
2. Thou art the King of Is - rael, Thou Da - vid's roy - al Son,
3. Thou didst ac - cept their prais - es; Ac - cept the prayers we bring,

To whom the lips of chil - dren Made sweet ho - san - nas ring!
Who in the Lord's name com - est, The King and bless - ed One!
Who in all good de - light - est, Thou good and gra - cious King!

The peo - ple of the He - brews With palms be - fore thee went;
To thee, be - fore thy pas - sion, They sang their hymns of praise;
All glo - ry, laud and hon - or To thee, Re - deem - er, King,

Our praise and prayer and an - thems Be - fore thee we pre - sent.
To thee, now high ex - alt - ed Our mel - o - dy we raise.
To whom the lips of chil - dren Made sweet ho-san - nas ring! A - men.

118

Suffering and Death

144

MARZO. Irregular

Katherine Lee Bates, 1921

Eduardo Marzo, 1922

1. Ho - san - na to the Son of Da - vid. Ho -
2. Ho - san - na to the Son of Da - vid. Ho -
3. Ho - san - na to the Son of Da - vid. Ho -

san - na! Thy palm - trees fed with dew, and sun, Thy
san - na! Let oaks and elms take up thy praise. Let
san - na! Thou art the vine, to thee we bring Our -

ce - dars crown - ing Le - ba - non. Thine o - lives of Geth - sem - a -
ma - ples, birch - es, wil - lows raise A - dor - ing branch - es in thy
selves thy branch - es, glad with spring. By ripen - ing fruit may we be

ne, Lord of Light, all wor - shipped thee.
sight, Lord of Beau - ty, Lord of Light.
known, Lord of Light and Love, thine own. A - men.

Music copyrighted 1923, by The Century Co., Hymn used by permission of A. W. Harris

119

The Son of God

145

GETHSEMANE. 7. 7. 7. 7. 7. 7.

JAMES MONTGOMERY, 1820

RICHARD REDHEAD, 1853

1. Go to dark Geth-sem-a-ne, Ye that feel the
2. See him at the judg-ment hall, Beat-en, bound, re-
3. Cal-vary's mourn-ful moun-tain climb; There a-dor-ing

tempt-er's power; Your Re-deem-er's con-flict see;
viled, ar-raigned; See him meek-ly bear-ing all;
at his feet, Mark that mir-a-cle of time,

Watch with him one bit-ter hour; Turn not from his
Love to man his soul sus-tained; Shun not suf-fering,
God's own sac-ri-fice com-plete: 'It is fin-ished!'

griefs a-way; Learn of Je-sus Christ to pray.
shame or loss; Learn of Christ to bear the cross.
hear him cry; Learn of Je-sus Christ to die. A-men.

Suffering and Death

146

LANIER. P. M.

SIDNEY LANIER, (1842–1881)
PETER C. LUTKIN (1858 ——)

1. In - to the woods my Mas - ter went, Clean for - spent, for - spent;
2. Out of the woods my Mas - ter went, And he was well con - tent;

In - to the woods my Mas - ter came, For-spent with love and shame. But the
Out of the woods my Mas - ter came, Con-tent with death and shame. When

ol - ives they were not blind to him, The lit - tle gray leaves were kind to him, The
death and shame would woo him last, From under the trees they drew him last, 'Twas

thorn-tree had a mind to him, When in - to the woods he came.
on a tree they slew him last, When out of the woods he came. A - men.

147

OLIVE'S BROW. L. M.

WILLIAM B. TAPPAN, 1822

WILLIAM B. BRADBURY, 1853

1. 'Tis mid-night; and on Ol-ive's brow The star is dimmed that late-ly shone:
2. 'Tis mid-night; and from all re-moved, The Sav-iour wres-tles lone with fears;
3. 'Tis mid-night; and for oth-ers' guilt The Man of Sor-rows weeps in blood;
4. 'Tis mid-night; and from heavenly plains Is borne the song that an - gels know;

'Tis mid-night; in the gar - den now The suffering Saviour prays a-lone.
E'en that dis-ci-ple whom he loved Heeds not his Mas-ter's grief and tears.
Yet he that hath in an-guish knelt Is not for-sa-ken by his God.
Un-heard by mor-tals are the strains That sweetly soothe the Saviour's woe. A-men.

148

CRUX CRUDELIS L. M.

JAMES MARTINEAU, 1840

ALBERT L. PEACE, 1885

1. A voice up - on the mid - night air, Where Kedron's moonlit wa - ters stray,
2. Ah! thou who sorrowest un - to death, We con - quer in thy mor - tal fray;
3. O Lord of sor - row, meek-ly die; Thou'lt heal or hal - low all our woe;
4. Great Chief of faithful souls, a - rise; None else can lead the mar-tyr-band
5. O King of earth, the cross as-cend; O'er climes and a - ges 'tis thy throne;

Weeps forth in ag - o - ny of prayer, 'O Fa-ther, take this cup a-way.'
And earth for all her chil-dren saith, 'O God, take not this cup a-way.'
Thy Name re-fresh the mourner's sigh, Thy peace revive the faint and low.
Who teach the brave how per - il flies, When faith, unarmed, uplifts the hand.
Wher - e'er thy fad - ing eye may bend, The desert blooms, and is thine own. Amen.

Suffering and Death

149

STRENGTH AND STAY. 11. 10. 11. 10.

JACQUES BRIDAINE (1701–1767)
Translated by THOMAS B. POLLOCK, 1887

JOHN B. DYKES, 1875

1. My Lord, my Mas-ter, at thy feet a-dor-ing,
2. Thine own dis-ci-ple to the Jews has sold thee;
3. With taunts and scoffs they mock what seems thy weak-ness,
4. My Lord, my Sav-iour, when I see thee wear-ing
5. O vic-tim of thy love! O pangs most heal-ing!

I see thee bowed be-neath thy load of woe;
With friend-ship's kiss and loy-al word he came:
With blows and out-rage add-ing pain to pain:
Up-on thy bleed-ing brow the crown of thorn,
O sav-ing death! O wounds that I a-dore!

For me, a sin-ner, is thy life-blood pour-ing;
How oft of faith-ful love my lips have told thee,
Thou art un-moved and stead-fast in thy meek-ness;
Shall I for pleas-ure live, or shrink from bear-ing
O shame most glo-rious! Christ, be-fore thee kneel-ing,

For thee, my Sav-iour, scarce my tears will flow.
While thou hast seen my false-hood and my shame!
When I am wronged how quick-ly I com-plain!
What-e'er my lot may be of pain or scorn?
I pray thee keep me thine for ev-er-more. A-men.

The Son of God

150

ST. CHRISTOPHER. 7. 6. 8. 6. 8. 6. 8. 6.

ELIZABETH C. CLEPHANE, 1868

FREDERICK C. MAKER, 1881

1. Be - neath the cross of Je - sus I fain would take my stand,
2. Up - on that cross of Je - sus Mine eye at times can see
3. I take, O cross, thy shad - ow For my a - bid - ing place;

The shad - ow of a might - y rock With - in a wea - ry land;
The ver - y dy - ing form of One Who suf - fered there for me;
I ask no oth - er sun - shine than The sun - shine of his face;

A home with - in the wil - der - ness, A rest up - on the way,
And from my smit - ten heart with tears Two won - ders I con - fess,—
Con - tent to let the world go by, To know no gain nor loss,

From the burning of the noon-tide heat, And the bur - den of the day.
The won - ders of his glo-rious love And my un - wor - thi - ness.
My sin - ful self my on - ly shame, My glo - ry all the cross. A - men.

Suffering and Death

151

PASSION CHORALE. 7. 6. 7. 6. D.

BERNARD OF CLAIRVAUX, 1091–1153
Translated by JAMES W. ALEXANDER, 1830

HANS LEO HASSLER, 1601

UNISON

1. O sa-cred Head, now wound-ed, With grief and shame weighed down,
2. What lan-guage shall I bor-row To thank thee, dear-est Friend,
3. Be near me when I'm dy-ing, O show thy cross to me!

Now scorn-ful-ly sur-round-ed With thorns, thy on-ly crown,
For this thy dy-ing sor-row, Thy pit-y with-out end?
And for my suc-cor fly-ing, Come, Lord, and set me free!

How art thou pale with an-guish, With sore a-buse and scorn!
O make me thine for-ev-er! And should I faint-ing be,
These eyes new faith re-ceiv-ing, From Je-sus shall not move;

How does that vis-age lan-guish, Which once was bright as morn!
Lord, let me nev-er, nev-er, Out-live my love to thee!
For he who dies be-liev-ing, Dies safe-ly through thy love. A-men.

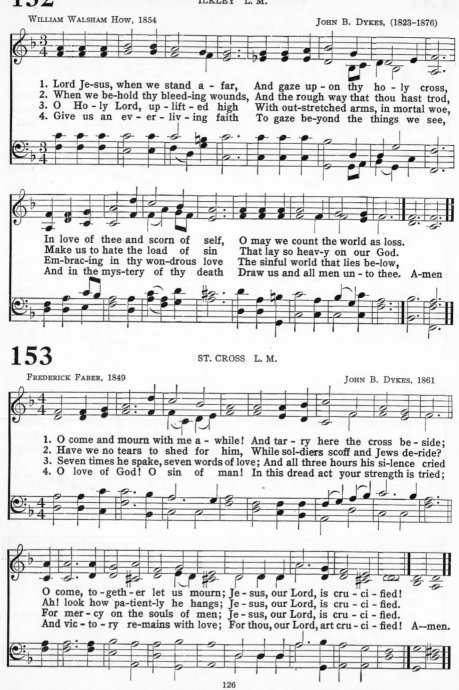

152

ILKLEY L. M.

WILLIAM WALSHAM HOW, 1854

JOHN B. DYKES, (1823–1876)

1. Lord Je-sus, when we stand a - far, And gaze up - on thy ho - ly cross,
2. When we be-hold thy bleed-ing wounds, And the rough way that thou hast trod,
3. O Ho - ly Lord, up - lift - ed high With out-stretched arms, in mortal woe,
4. Give us an ev - er - liv - ing faith To gaze be-yond the things we see,

In love of thee and scorn of self, O may we count the world as loss.
Make us to hate the load of sin That lay so heav-y on our God.
Em-brac-ing in thy won-drous love The sinful world that lies be-low,
And in the mys-tery of thy death Draw us and all men un - to thee. A-men

153

ST. CROSS L. M.

FREDERICK FABER, 1849

JOHN B. DYKES, 1861

1. O come and mourn with me a - while! And tar - ry here the cross be - side;
2. Have we no tears to shed for him, While sol-diers scoff and Jews de-ride?
3. Seven times he spake, seven words of love; And all three hours his si-lence cried
4. O love of God! O sin of man! In this dread act your strength is tried;

O come, to-geth-er let us mourn; Je-sus, our Lord, is cru - ci - fied!
Ah! look how pa-tient-ly he hangs; Je-sus, our Lord, is cru - ci - fied.
For mer - cy on the souls of men; Je-sus, our Lord, is cru - ci - fied.
And vic - to - ry re-mains with love; For thou, our Lord, art cru - ci - fied! A--men.

154 HAMBURG. L. M.

ISAAC WATTS, 1707

Gregorian Chant
Arranged by LOWELL MASON, 1824

1 When I sur-vey the won-drous cross On which the Prince of glo-ry died,
2. For-bid it, Lord, that I should boast, Save in the death of Christ, my God;
3. See, from his head, his hands, his feet, Sor-row and love flow min-gled down!
4. Were the whole realm of na-ture mine, That were a pres-ent far too small;

My rich-est gain I count but loss, And pour con-tempt on all my pride.
All the vain things that charm me most, I sac-ri-fice them to his blood.
Did e'er such love and sor-row meet, Or thorns compose so rich a crown?
Love so a-maz-ing, so di-vine, Demands my soul, my life, my all. A-men.

155 RATHBUN. 8. 7. 8. 7.

JOHN BOWRING, 1325

ITHAMAR CONKEY, 1847

1. In the cross of Christ I glo-ry, Tower-ing o'er the wrecks of time;
2. When the woes of life o'er-take me, Hopes de-ceive, and fears an-noy,
3. When the sun of bliss is beam-ing Light and love up-on my way,
4. Bane and bless-ing, pain and pleas-ure, By the cross are sanc-ti-fied;

All the light of sa-cred sto-ry Gathers round its head sub-lime.
Nev-er shall the cross for-sake me; Lo! it glows with peace and joy.
From the cross the ra-diance stream-ing Adds new lus-tre to the day.
Peace is there that knows no meas-ure, Joys that thro' all time a-bide. A-men.

The Son of God

156

STEBBINS. C. M. With Refrain

CECIL F. ALEXANDER, 1848

GEORGE C. STEBBINS, 1878

1. There is a green hill far a - way, With - out a cit - y wall,
2. We may not know, we can - not tell What pains he had to bear;
3. He died that we might be for-given, He died to make us good,
4. There was no oth - er good e-nough To pay the price of sin;

Where the dear Lord was cru - ci - fied, Who died to save us all.
But we be - lieve it was for us He hung and suf - fered there.
That we might go at last to heaven, Saved by his pre - cious blood.
He on - ly could un - lock the gate Of heaven, and let us in.

Refrain

Oh dear - ly, dear - ly has he loved, And we must love him too,

And trust in his re - deem - ing blood, And try his works to do. A - men.

157

MEDITATION. C. M.

JANE CREWDSON, 1860

JOHN H. GOWER, 1890

1. There's not a grief, how - ev - er light, Too light for sym - pa - thy;
2. Thou who hast trod the thorn - y road Wilt share each small dis - tress;
3. There's not a se - cret sigh we breathe But meets thine ear di - vine,
4. Life's woes with - out, sin's strife with - in, The heart would o - ver - flow,

There's not a care, how - ev - er slight, Too slight to bring to thee.
For he who bore the great - er load Will not re - fuse the less.
And ev - ery cross grows light beneath The shad - ow, Lord, of thine.
But for that love which died for sin, That love which wept with woe. A-men.

Copyright by John H. Gower

158

MOUNT CALVARY. C. M.

JOHN H. GURNEY, 1838

ROBERT P. STEWART, 1825–1894

1. Lord, as to thy dear cross we flee, And pray to be for - given,
2. Help us, through good re - port and ill, Our dai - ly cross to bear;
3. Let grace our self - ish - ness ex - pel, Our earth - li - ness re - fine;
4. If joy shall at thy bid - ding fly, And grief's dark day come on,
5. Kept peace - ful in the midst of strife, For - giv - ing and for - given,

So let thy life our pat - tern be, And form our souls for heaven.
Like thee, to do our Fa - ther's will, Our bro - ther's griefs to share.
And kind - ness in our bo - soms dwell, As free and true as thine.
We, in our turn, would meek - ly cry, 'Fa - ther, thy will be done.'
O may we lead the pil - grim's life, And fol - low thee to heaven. A-men.

129

The Son of God

159   FORTUNATUS. 11. 11. 11. 11. With Refrain

VENANTIUS FORTUNATUS, 590
Translated by JOHN ELLERTON, 1868

ARTHUR S. SULLIVAN, 1872

1. 'Wel-come, hap-py morn-ing!' age to age shall say; Hell to-day is
2. Earth her joy con-fess-es, cloth-ing her for spring, All good gifts re-
3. Months in due suc-ces-sion, days of lengthen-ing light, Hours and pass-ing
4. Come then, True and Faith-ful, now ful-fil thy word, 'Tis thine own third

vanquished, heaven is won to-day! Lo! the Dead is liv-ing,
turned with her re-turn-ing King: Bloom in ev-ery mead-ow,
mo-ments praise thee in their flight; Bright-ness of the morn-ing,
morn-ing; rise, O bur-ied Lord. Show thy face in bright-ness,

God for ev-er-more! Him, their true Cre-a-tor, all his works a-dore!
leaves on ev-ery bough, Speak his sor-rows end-ed, hail his tri-umph now.
sky, and fields and sea, Van-quish-er of dark-ness, bring their praise to thee!
bid the na-tions see; Bring a-gain our day-light; day re-turns with thee.

Refrain

'Wel-come, hap-py morn-ing!' age to age shall say. A-men.

Resurrection

160

LANCASHIRE. 7. 6. 7. 6. D.

JOHN OF DAMASCUS, about 750
Translated by JOHN M. NEALE, 1862

HENRY SMART, 1836

1. The day of res - ur - rec - tion,— Earth, tell it out a - broad,—
2. Our hearts be pure from e - vil, That we may see a - right
3. Now let the heavens be joy - ful, Let earth her song be - gin,

The pass - o - ver of glad - ness, The pass - o - ver of God.
The Lord in rays e - ter - nal Of res - ur - rec - tion light,
Let the round world keep tri - umph And all that is there - in,

From death to life e - ter - nal, From this world to the sky,
And, list - 'ning to his ac - cents, May hear, so calm and plain,
In - vis - i - ble and vis - i - ble, Their notes let all things blend;

Our Christ hath brought us o - ver With hymns of vic - to - ry.
His own 'All hail!' and, hear - ing, May raise the vic - tor - strain.
For Christ the Lord hath ris - en, Our joy that hath no end. A - men.

131

The Son of God

161

EASTER HYMN 7. 7. 7. 7. With Alleluia

CHARLES WESLEY, 1739

'Lyra Davidica,' 1708

1. Christ the Lord is risen to-day, Al - - le - lu - ia!
2. Lives a - gain our glo - rious King: Al - - le - lu - ia!
3. Love's re - deem - ing work is done, Al - - le - lu - ia!
4. Soar we now, where Christ has led, Al - - le - lu - ia!

Sons of men and an - gels say: Al - - le - lu - ia!
Where, O death, is now thy sting? Al - - le - lu - ia!
Fought the fight, the bat - tle won; Al - - le - lu - ia!
Fol - lowing our ex - alt - ed Head; Al - - le - lu - ia!

Raise your joys and tri - umphs high, Al - - le - lu - ia!
Dy - ing once, he all doth save: Al - - le - lu - ia!
Death in vain for - bids him rise; Al - - le - lu - ia!
Made like him, like him we rise, Al - - le - lu - ia!

Sing, ye heav'ns, and earth re - ply. Al - - le - lu - ia!
Where thy vic - to - ry, O grave? Al - - le - lu - ia!
Christ has o - pened Par - a - dise. Al - - le - lu - ia!
Ours the cross, the grave, the skies. Al - - le - lu - ia! A - men.

Resurrection

162

ST. KEVIN. 7. 6. 7. 6. D.

JOHN OF DAMASCUS, about 750
Translated by JOHN M. NEALE, 1859

ARTHUR S. SULLIVAN, 1872

1. Come, ye faith-ful, raise the strain Of tri-umph-ant glad-ness!
2. 'Tis the spring of souls to-day: Christ hath burst his pris-on,
3. Now the queen of sea-sons, bright With the day of splen-dor,
4. 'Al-le-lu-ia!' now we cry To our King Im-mor-tal,

God hath brought his Is-ra-el In-to joy from sad-ness;
And from three days sleep in death As a sun hath ris-en;
With the roy-al feast of feasts, Comes its joy to ren-der;
Who, tri-umph-ant burst the bars Of the tomb's dark por-tal;

Loosed from Pha-raoh's bit-ter yoke Ja-cob's sons and daugh-ters,
All the win-ter of our sins, Long and dark, is fly-ing
Comes to glad Je-ru-sa-lem, Who, with true af-fec-tion,
'Al-le-lu-ia,' with the Son, God the Fa-ther prais-ing;

Led them with un-moist-ened foot Thro' the Red Sea wa-ters.
From his light, to whom we give Laud and praise un-dy-ing.
Wel-comes in un-wea-ried strains Je-sus' res-ur-rec-tion.
'Al-le-lu-ia' yet a-gain To the Spir-it rais-ing. A-men.

The Son of God

163

EASTER FLOWERS. 7. 7. 7. 6. With Refrain

Mary A. Nicholson, 1875

G. Waring Stebbins

UNISON

1. Eas - ter flow'rs are bloom-ing bright, Eas - ter skies pour ra - diant light,
2. An - gels car - oled this sweet lay, When in man - ger rude he lay;
3. He, then born to grief and pain, Now to glo - ry born a - gain,
4. As he ris - eth, rise we too, Tune we heart and voice a - new,

Christ our Lord is risen in might, Glo - ry in the high - est!
Now once more cast grief a - way, Glo - ry in the high - est!
Call - eth forth our glad - dest strain, Glo - ry in the high - est!
Off - 'ring hom - age glad and true, Glo - ry in the high - est!

Refrain

Al - le - lu - ia! Al - le - lu - ia! Christ our Lord is

risen in might, Al - le - lu - ia! A - men.

Resurrection

164

REJOICE. 6. 6. 6. 6. With Refrain

WILLIAM WALSHAM HOW, 1823–1897

T. ALLEN CLEAVER

1. On wings of liv - ing light, At ear - liest dawn of day,
2. The keep - ers watch - ing near, At that dread sight and sound,
3. Then rose from death's dark gloom Un - seen by mor - tal eye,
4. Leave in the grave be - neath The old things passed a - way,

Came down the an - gel bright And rolled the stone a - way.
Fell down with sud - den fear, Like dead men, to the ground.
Tri - um - phant o'er the tomb, The Lord of earth and sky.
Bur - ied with him in death, O live with him to - day.

Refrain

Your voic - es raise with one ac - cord To

bless and praise your ris - en Lord. A - men.

165

VICTORY. 8. 8. 8. With Alleluia

Latin. Translated by
FRANCIS POTT, 1861

Arranged from
PALESTRINA, 1588

Al - le - lu - ia! Al - le - lu - ia! Al - le - lu - ia!

Org.

1. The strife is o'er, the bat - tle done; The vic - to - ry of life is won;
2. The powers of death have done their worst, But Christ their legions hath dispersed;
3. The three sad days are quick - ly sped, He ris - es glo - rious from the dead;
4. Lord, by the stripes which wounded thee, From death's dread sting thy servants free,

D.S.

The song of tri - umph has be - gun;   Al - le - lu - ia!
Let shouts of ho - ly joy out - burst;   Al - le - lu - ia!
All glo - ry to our ris - en Head!   Al - le - lu - ia!
That we may live and sing to thee,   Al - le - lu - ia!   A - men.

166

WALTHAM. L. M.

JOHN MASON NEALE, 1851

J. BAPTISTE CALKIN, 1872

1. Lift up, lift up your voic - es now! The whole wide world re-joic - es now!
2. In vain with stone the cave they barred; In vain the watch kept ward and guard;
3. And all he did, and all he bare, He gives us as our own to share;
4. O Vic - tor, aid us in the fight, And lead thro' death to realms of light;

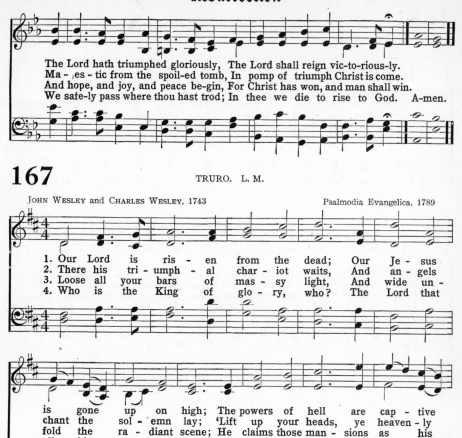

The Lord hath triumphed gloriously, The Lord shall reign vic-to-rious-ly.
Ma - jes - tic from the spoil-ed tomb, In pomp of triumph Christ is come.
And hope, and joy, and peace be-gin, For Christ has won, and man shall win.
We safe-ly pass where thou hast trod; In thee we die to rise to God. A-men.

167

TRURO. L. M.

John Wesley and Charles Wesley, 1743 — Psalmodia Evangelica, 1789

1. Our Lord is ris - en from the dead; Our Je - sus
2. There his tri - umph - al char - iot waits, And an - gels
3. Loose all your bars of mas - sy light, And wide un -
4. Who is the King of glo - ry, who? The Lord that

is gone up on high; The powers of hell are cap - tive
chant the sol - emn lay; 'Lift up your heads, ye heaven - ly
fold the ra - diant scene; He claims those man - sions as his
all his foes o'er-came, The world, sin, death, and hell o'er -

led, Dragged to the por - tals of the sky.
gates, Ye ev - er - last - ing doors, give way.'
right; Re - ceive the King of glo - ry in.
threw; And Je - sus is the Con-queror's name. A - men.

5 Lo! his triumphal chariot waits,
   And angels chant the solemn lay:
'Lift up your heads, ye heavenly gates,
Ye everlasting doors, give way.'

6 Who is the King of glory, who?
   The Lord, of boundless power possessed,
The King of saints and angels too,
God, over all, forever blest.

The Son of God

DIADEMATA. S. M. D.

Matthew Bridges, 1851

George J. Elvey, 1868

1. Crown him with man - y crowns, The Lamb up - on his throne!
2. Crown him the Lord of love! Be - hold his hands and side,
3. Crown him the Lord of peace, Whose power a scep - ter sways
4. Crown him the Lord of years, The Po - ten - tate of time,

Hark how the heaven-ly an - them drowns All mu - sic but its own!
Rich wounds, yet vis - i - ble a - bove, In beau - ty glo - ri - fied.
From pole to pole, that wars may cease, And all be prayer and praise!
Cre - a - tor of the roll - ing spheres, In - ef - fa - bly sub - lime.

A - wake, my soul, and sing Of him who died for thee,
No an - gel in the sky Can ful - ly bear that sight,
His reign shall know no end, And round his pierc - ed feet
All hail, Re - deem - er, hail! For thou hast died for me:

And hail him as thy match-less King Thro' all e - ter - ni - ty.
But down-ward bends his burn-ing eye At mys - ter - ies so bright.
Fair flowers of Par - a - dise ex - tend Their fra-grance ev - er sweet.
Thy praise shall nev - er, nev - er fail Through-out e - ter - ni - ty. A-men.

Ascension and Reign

169

VICTOR'S CROWN. 8. 7. 8. 7. 4. 7.

Thomas Kelly, 1809

Horatio Parker, 1893

1. Look, ye saints! the sight is glo-rious: See the Man of
2. Crown the Sav-iour! an-gels, crown him! Rich the tro-phies
3. Sin-ners in de-ri-sion crowned him, Mock-ing thus the
4. Hark, those bursts of ac-cla-ma-tion! Hark, those loud tri-

Sor-rows now; From the fight re-turned vic-to-rious,
Je-sus brings; In the seat of power en-throne him,
Sav-iour's claim; Saints and an-gels crowd a-round him,
umph-ant chords! Je-sus takes the high-est sta-tion;

Ev-ery knee to him shall bow: Crown him!
While the vault of heav-en rings: Crown him!
Own his ti-tle, praise his name: Crown him!
O what joy the sight af-fords! Crown him!

crown him! Crowns be-come the Vic-tor's brow.
crown him! Crown the Sav-iour King of kings.
crown him! Spread a-broad the Vic-tor's fame.
crown him! King of kings, and Lord of lords! A-men.

The Son of God

ASCENSION. 7. 7. 7. 7. With Alleluia

CHARLES WESLEY, 1739

WILLIAM H. MONK, 1861

1. Hail the day that sees him rise, Al - le - lu - ia!
2. Him tho' high-est heaven re - ceives, Al - le - lu - ia!
3. Still for us his death he pleads; Al - le - lu - ia!
4. Lord, tho' part - ed from our sight, Al - le - lu - ia!

To his throne a - bove the skies; Al - le - lu - ia!
Still he loves the earth he leaves; Al - le - lu - ia!
Prev - a - lent he in - ter - cedes; Al - le - lu - ia!
High a - bove yon az - ure height, Al - le - lu - ia!

Christ, a - while to mor - tals giv'n, Al - le - lu - ia!
Tho' re - turn - ing to his throne, Al - le - lu - ia!
Near him - self pre - pares our place, Al - le - lu - ia!
Grant our hearts may thith - er rise, Al - le - lu - ia!

Re - as - cends his na - tive heaven. Al - le - lu - ia!
Still he calls man-kind his own. Al - le - lu - ia!
Har - bin - ger of hu - man race. Al - le - lu - ia!
Follow-ing thee be - yond the skies. Al - le - lu - ia! A - men.

171

CRUSADER'S HYMN. Irregular

MÜNSTER, 1677
Translated about 1850

Silesian Folk Song
Arranged by RICHARD S. WILLIS, 1850

1. Fair-est Lord Je-sus, Rul-er of all na-ture, O thou of God and man the Son;
2. Fair are the mead-ows, Fairer still the woodlands, Robed in the blooming garb of spring;
3. Fair is the sun-shine, Fair-er still the moonlight, And all the twink-ling, star-ry host;

Thee will I cher-ish, Thee will I hon-or, Thou, my soul's glo-ry, joy and crown.
Je - sus is fair - er, Je - sus is pur-er, Who makes the woe-ful heart to sing.
Jesus shines brighter, Je-sus shines purer Than all the angels heaven can boast. Amen.

172

ORTONVILLE. C. M.

SAMUEL STENNETT, 1787

THOMAS HASTINGS, 1837

1. Ma-jes-tic sweetness sits enthroned Up-on the Sav-iour's brow; His head with radiant
2. No mor-tal can with him com-pare, A-mong the sons of men; Fair-er is he than
3. He saw me plunged in deep distress, He flew to my re-lief; For me he bore the
4. Since from his boun-ty I re-ceive Such proofs of love divine, Had I a thou-sand

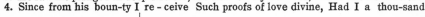

glo-ries crowned, His lips with grace o'er-flow, His lips with grace o'er-flow.
all the fair That fill the heaven-ly train, That fill the heaven-ly train.
shame-ful cross, And car-ried all my grief, And car-ried all my grief.
hearts to give, Lord! they should all be thine! Lord! they should all be thine! A-men.

The Son of God

173

CORONATION. C. M.

EDWARD PERRONET, 1779

OLIVER HOLDEN, 1793

1. All hail the power of Je - sus' name! Let an - gels
2. Crown him, ye mar - tyrs of your God Who from his
3. Ye seed of Is - rael's cho - sen race, Ye ran - somed
4. Let ev - ery kin - dred, ev - ery tribe, On this ter -
5. Oh, that with yon - der sa - cred throng We at his

pros - trate fall; Bring forth the roy - al di - a - dem,
al - tar call; Ex - tol the stem of Jes - se's rod,
of the fall, Hail him who saves you by his grace,
res - trial ball, To him all maj - es - ty as - cribe,
feet may fall, Join in the ev - er - last - ing song,

And crown him Lord of all! Bring forth the roy - al
And crown him Lord of all! Ex - tol the stem of
And crown him Lord of all! Hail him who saves you
And crown him Lord of all! To him all maj - es -
And crown him Lord of all! Join in the ev - er -

di - a - dem, And crown him Lord of all!
Jes - se's rod, And crown him Lord of all!
by his grace, And crown him Lord of all!
ty as - cribe, And crown him Lord of all!
last - ing song, And crown him Lord of all! A - men.

174

MILES' LANE. C. M.

THOMAS KELLY, 1820

WILLIAM SHRUBSOLE, 1779

1. The head that once was crowned with thorns, Is crowned with glo - ry now;
2. The high-est place that heaven af-fords Is his, is his by right,

A roy - al di - a - dem a - dorns The might - y
The King of kings, and Lord of lords, And heaven's e -

Vic - tor's brow, The might - y Vic - tor's brow.
ter - nal Light: And heaven's e - ter - nal Light. A - men.

175

SHELTERING WING. L. M.

JOYCE KILMER (1886–1918)

JOSEPH BARNBY, 1883

1. No lon - ger of him be it said, 'He hath no place to lay his head.'
2. There is no strange and dis-tant place That is not glad-dened by his face.
3. Im-pris-oned for his love of me He makes my spir-it great - ly free.

In ev-ery land a con-stant lamp Flames by his small and might-y camp.
And every na-tion kneels to hail The Splendor shin-ing through its veil.
And thro' my lips that uttered sin The King of Glo - ry en - ters in. A - men.

The Son of God

176

BEECHER. 8. 7. 8. 7. D.

CHARLES WESLEY, 1747

JOHN ZUNDEL, 1870

1. Love Di - vine, all love ex - cell - ing, Joy of heaven, to earth come down;
2. Breathe, O breathe thy lov - ing Spir - it In - to ev - ery troub-led breast;
3. Come, Al - might-y to de - liv - er, Let us all thy life re - ceive;
4. Fin - ish, then, thy new cre - a - tion; Pure and spot - less let us be:

Fix in us thy hum - ble dwell-ing, All thy faith - ful mer-cies crown:
Let us all in thee in - her - it, Let us find the prom-ised rest;
Sud - den - ly re - turn, and nev - er, Nev - er more thy tem-ples leave.
Let us see thy great sal - va - tion Per - fect - ly re - stored in thee;

Je - sus, thou art all com - pas - sion, Pure, un-bound-ed love thou art;
Take a - way the love of sin - ning; Al - pha and O - me - ga be;
Thee we would be al - ways bless-ing, Serve thee as thy hosts a - bove,
Changed from glo - ry in - to glo - ry Till in heaven we take our place,

Vis - it us with thy sal - va - tion, En - ter ev - ery trembling heart.
End of faith, as its be - gin - ning, Set our hearts at lib - er - ty.
Pray, and praise thee with-out ceas-ing, Glo - ry in thy per - fect love.
Till we cast our crowns be-fore thee, Lost in won-der, love and praise. A-men.

The Holy Spirit

177

ST. CUTHBERT. 8. 6. 8. 4.

HARRIET AUBER, 1829

JOHN B. DYKES, 1861

1. Our blest Re-deem-er, ere he breathed His ten-der, last fare-well,
2. He came sweet in-fluence to im-part, A gra-cious, will-ing guest,
3. And his that gen-tle voice we hear, Soft as the breath of even,
4. And ev-ery vir-tue we pos-sess, And ev-ery vic-tory won,
5. Spir-it of pur-i-ty and grace, Our weak-ness, pity-ing, see;

A Guide, a Com-fort-er, bequeathed With us to dwell.
While he can find one hum-ble heart Where-in to rest.
That checks each thought, that calms each fear, And speaks of heaven.
And ev-ery thought of ho-li-ness Are his a-lone.
O make our hearts thy dwell-ing-place, And worth-ier thee. A-men.

178

BRECON. C. M.

ANDREW REED, 1829
Adapted by SAMUEL LONGFELLOW, 1864

NICHOLAS HEINS, 1900

1. Spir-it di-vine, at-tend our prayer, And make our hearts thy home; De-
2. Come as the light! to us re-veal The truth we long to know, Re-
3. Come as the fire! and purge our hearts Like sac-ri-fi-cial flame, Till
4. Come as the dew! and sweet-ly bless This con-se-cra-ted hour, Till
5. Come as the wind, O breath of God! O Pen-te-cost-al grace! Come,

scend with all thy gra-cious power; Come, Ho-ly Spir-it, come.
veal the nar-row path of right, The way of du-ty show.
our whole souls an of-fering be In love's re-deem-ing name.
ev-ery bar-ren place shall own With joy thy quicken-ing power.
make thy great sal-va-tion known Wide as the hu-man race. A-men.

The Holy Spirit

179

BREAD OF HEAVEN. 7. 7. 7. 7. 7. 7.

THOMAS T. LYNCH, 1855

WILLIAM D. MACLAGAN, 1875

1. Gra - cious Spir - it, dwell with me; I my - self would
2. Truth - ful Spir - it, dwell with me; I my - self would
3. Might - y Spir - it, dwell with me; I my - self would
4. Ho - ly Spir - it, dwell with me; I my - self would

gra - cious be; And, with words that help and heal,
truth - ful be; And, with wis - dom kind and clear,
might - y be, Might - y so as to pre - vail
ho - ly be; Sep - a - rate from sin, I would

Would thy life in mine re - veal; And, with ac - tions
Let thy life in mine ap - pear; And, with ac - tions
Where un - aid - ed, man must fail; Ev - er by a
Choose and cher - ish all things good, And what - ev - er

bold and meek, Would for Christ my Sav - iour speak.
broth - er - ly, Speak my Lord's sin - cer - i - ty.
might - y hope, Press - ing on and bear - ing up.
I can be, Give to him who gave me thee! A - men.

146

The Holy Spirit

180

BETHEL. 6. 6. 4. 6. 6. 6. 4.

Latin, about 12th century.
Translated by Ray Palmer, 1858

John H. Cornell, 1872

1. Come, Ho - ly Ghost, in love, Shed on us from a - bove
2. Come, ten - derest Friend and best, Our most de - light - ful guest,
3. Come, Light se - rene and still, Our in - most bos - oms fill,
4. Ex - alt our low de - sires; Ex - tin - guish pas - sion's fires;
5. Come, all the faith - ful bless, Let all who Christ con - fess

Thine own bright ray; Di - vine - ly good thou art;
With sooth - ing power; Rest which the wea - ry know,
Dwell in each breast; We know no dawn but thine,
Heal ev - ery wound: Our stub - born spir - its bend,
His praise em - ploy; Give vir - tue's rich re - ward;

Thy sa - cred gifts im - part To glad - den
Shade 'mid the noon - tide glow, Peace when deep
Send forth thy beams di - vine On our dark
Our ic - y cold - ness end, Our de - vious
Vic - to - rious death ac - cord, And with our

each sad heart; O come to - day!
griefs o'er - flow, Cheer us this hour.
souls to shine, And make us blest.
steps at - tend While heaven - ward bound.
glo - rious Lord, E - ter - nal joy. A - men.

181

GOTTSCHALK. (MERCY.) 7. 7. 7. 7.

ANDREW REED, 1817

Arranged from
LOUIS M. GOTTSCHALK, 1854

1. Ho - ly Ghost, with light di - vine, Shine up - on this
2. Ho - ly Ghost, with power di - vine, Cleanse this guilt - y
3. Ho - ly Ghost, with joy di - vine, Cheer this sad - dened
4. Ho - ly Spir - it, all di - vine, Dwell with - in this

heart of mine; Chase the shades of night a -
heart of mine; Long hath sin, with - out con -
heart of mine; Bid my man - y woes de -
heart of mine; Cast down ev - ery i - dol -

way, Turn my dark - ness in - to day.
trol, Held do - min - ion o'er my soul.
part, Heal my wound - ed, bleed - ing heart.
throne; Reign su - preme— and reign a - lone. A - men.

182

TRENTHAM. S. M.

EDWIN HATCH, 1886

ROBERT JACKSON, 1894

1. Breathe on me, Breath of God, Fill me with life a - new, That I may
2. Breathe on me, Breath of God, Un - til my heart is pure, Un - til with
3. Breathe on me, Breath of God, Till I am whol - ly thine, Till all this
4. Breathe on me, Breath of God, So shall I nev - er die, But live with

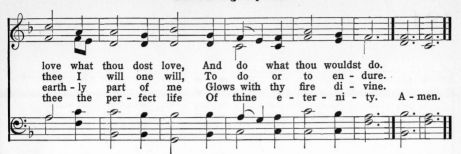

love what thou dost love, And do what thou wouldst do.
thee I will one will, To do or to en - dure.
earth - ly part of me Glows with thy fire di - vine.
thee the per - fect life Of thine e - ter - ni - ty. A - men.

183

HAVEN. 7. 7. 7. 7.

SAMUEL LONGFELLOW, 1864   EDWIN H. LEMARE, 1889

1. Ho - ly Spir - it, Truth di - vine, Dawn up - on this
2. Ho - ly Spir - it, Love di - vine, Glow with - in this
3. Ho - ly Spir - it, Power di - vine, Fill and nerve this
4. Ho - ly Spir - it, Right di - vine, King with - in my

soul of mine; Word of God, and in - ward Light,
heart of mine; Kin - dle ev - ery high de - sire;
will of mine; By thee may I strong - ly live,
con - science reign; Be my law, and I shall be,

Wake my spir - it, clear my sight.
Per - ish self in thy pure fire.
Brave - ly bear, and no - bly strive.
Firm - ly bound, for - ev - er free. A - men.

5 Holy Spirit, Peace divine,
Still this restless heart of mine;
Speak to calm this tossing sea,
Stayed in thy tranquillity.

6 Holy Spirit, Joy divine,
Gladden thou this heart of mine;
In the desert ways I sing,
'Spring, O Well, for ever spring.'

The Holy Spirit

184

MORECAMBE. 10. 10. 10. 10.

GEORGE CROLY, 1854

FREDERICK C. ATKINSON, 1870

1. Spir - it of God, de - scend up - on my heart; Wean it from earth; thro'
2. I ask no dream, no proph - et - ec - sta - sies, No sud - den rend - ing
3. Teach me to feel that thou art al - ways nigh; Teach me the strug - gles
4. Teach me to love thee as thine an - gels love, One ho - ly pas - sion

all its puls - es move; Stoop to my weak-ness, might - y as thou art,
of the veil of clay, No an - gel - vis - i - tant, no open - ing skies;
of the soul to bear, To check the ris - ing doubt, the reb - el sigh;
fill - ing all my frame,—The bap - tism of the heaven-de-scend-ed Dove,

And make me love thee as I ought to love.
But take the dim - ness of my soul a - way.
Teach me the pa - tience of un - an - swered prayer.
My heart an al - tar, and thy love the flame. A - men.

185

ST. VINCENT. L. M.

CECIL F. ALEXANDER, 1858

Adapted from SIGISMUND NEUKOMM
By JAMES UGLOW, 1868

1. Thou Power and Peace, in whom we find All ho - liest strength, all
2. For - ev - er lend thy sov - ereign aid, And urge us on, and
3. Nor let us quench thy sav - ing light; But still with soft - est

pur - - est love, The rush - ing of the might - y
keep us thine; Nor leave the hearts which thou hast
breath ings stir Our way - ward souls, and lead us

wind, The brood - ing of the gen - tle dove!
made Fit tem - ples of thy grace di - vine.
right, O Ho - ly Spir - it, Com - fort - er. A - men.

186
BRACONDALE. C. M.

EBENEZER S. OAKLEY, 1889

JOSIAH BOOTH, (1852——)

1. En - dur - ing Soul of all our life, In whom all be - ings blend,
2. Through thee the worlds, with all they bear, Their might - y cours - es run;
3. The thoughts that move the heart of man And lift his soul on high;
4. These are thy thoughts, Al - might - y Mind, This skill is thine, O Lord,
5. O fill us now, thou liv - ing Power, With en - er - gy di - vine;

Unchanging Peace' mid storm and strife, Our Par-ent, Home, and End:
Thro' thee the heav'ns are passing fair, And splendor clothes the sun.
The skill that teach - es him to plan With wondrous sub - tle - ty,—
Who dost by hid - den influence bind All powers in sweet ac - cord.
Thus shall our wills from hour to hour Be-come not ours, but thine. A - men.

The Holy Spirit

MELITA. 8. 8. 8. 8. 8. 8.

LATIN, about 10th CENTURY
Translated by JOHN DRYDEN, 1693

JOHN B. DYKES, 1861

187

1. Cre - a - tor Spir - it, by whose aid The world's foun - da - tions
2. O Source of un - cre - a - ted light, The Fa - ther's prom - ised
3. Plen-teous of grace, de - scend from high, Rich in thy seven - fold

first were laid, Come, vis - it ev - ery pi - ous mind;
Par - a - clete, Thrice ho - ly fount, thrice ho - ly fire,
en - er - gy; Make us e - ter - nal truths re - ceive,

Come, pour thy joys on hu - man kind; From sin and sor - row
Our hearts with heaven-ly love in - spire; Come, and thy sa - cred
And prac - tice all that we be - lieve; Give us thy - self, that

set us free, And make thy tem - ples worth - y thee.
unc - tion bring To sanc - ti - fy us, while we sing.
we may see The Fa - ther and the Son by thee. A - men.

188

MUNICH. 7. 6. 7. 6. D.

WILLIAM WALSHAM HOW, 1867

Meiningisches Gesang-Buch, 1693

1. O Word of God in-car-nate, O Wis-dom from on high,
2. The Church from her dear Mas-ter Re-ceived the gift di-vine,
3. It float-eth like a ban-ner Be-fore God's host un-furled;
4. O make thy Church, dear Sav-iour, A lamp of pur-est gold,

O Truth un-changed, un-chang-ing, O Light of our dark sky,
And still that light she lift-eth O'er all the earth to shine.
It shin-eth like a bea-con A-bove the dark-ling world:
To bear be-fore the na-tions Thy true light, as of old!

We praise thee for the ra-diance That from the hal-lowed page,
It is the gold-en cas-ket, Where gems of truth are stored;
It is the chart and com-pass That o'er life's surg-ing sea,
O teach thy wan-dering pil-grims By this their path to trace,

A lan-tern to our foot-steps, Shines on from age to age.
It is the heaven-drawn pic-ture Of Christ, the liv-ing Word.
'Mid mists and rocks and dark-ness, Still guides, O Christ, to thee.
Till, clouds and dark-ness end-ed, They see thee face to face! A-men.

189

UXBRIDGE. L. M.

ISAAC WATTS, 1719

LOWELL MASON, 1830

1. The heavens de - clare thy glo - ry, Lord, In
2. Thy no - blest won - ders here we view, In
3. The roll - ing sun, the chang - ing light, And
4. Sun, moon, and stars con - vey thy praise Round
5. Nor shall thy spread - ing gos - pel rest, Till

ev - ery star thy wis - dom shines; But when our eyes be -
souls re - newed, and sins for - given; Lord, cleanse our sins, our
nights and days, thy power con - fess; But the blest vol - ume
the whole earth, and nev - er stand; So, when thy truth be -
thro' the world thy truth has run; Till Christ has all the

hold thy word, We read thy name in fair - er lines.
souls re - new, And make thy word our guide to heaven.
thou didst write, Re - veals thy jus - tice and thy grace.
gan its race, It touched and glanced on ev - ery land.
na - tions blest That see the light, or feel the sun. A - men

190

LAMBETH.. C. M.

BERNARD BARTON, 1836

WILHELM A. F. SCHULTHES, 1871

1. Lamp of our feet, where - by we trace Our path, when wont to stray;
2. Bread of our souls, where - on we feed, True man - na from on high;
3. Pil - lar of fire, through watch - es dark, Or ra - diant cloud by day;
4. Word of the ev - er - liv - ing God, Will of his glo - rious Son;

Stream from the fount of heavenly grace, Brook by the traveler's way.
Our guide and chart, wherein we read Of realms be-yond the sky.
When waves would 'whelm our tossing bark Our anchor and our stay.
Without thee how could earth be trod, Or heaven it - self be won? A - men.

191

ORTONVILLE. C. M.

WILLIAM COWPER, 1779

THOMAS HASTINGS, 1837

1. The Spir - it breathes up - on the word, And brings the truth to
2. A glo - ry gilds the sa - cred page, Ma - jes - tic like the
3. The hand that gave it still sup - plies The gra - cious light and
4. Let ev - er - last - ing thanks be thine, For such a bright dis -
5. My soul re - joic - es to pur - sue The steps of him I

sight; Pre - cepts and prom - is - es af - ford A sanc - ti -
sun; It gives a light to ev - ery age; It gives, but
heat; His truths up - on the na - tions rise; They rise, but
play As makes a world of dark - ness shine With beams of
love, Till glo - ry breaks up - on my view In bright - er

fy - ing light, A sanc - ti - fy - ing light.
bor - rows none, It gives, but bor - rows none.
nev - er set, They rise, but nev - er set.
heaven - ly day, With beams of heaven - ly day.
worlds a - bove, In bright - er worlds a - bove. A - men.

The Holy Scriptures

192

KIRBY BEDON. 6. 6. 4. 6. 6. 6. 4.

THOMAS T. LYNCH, 1855

EDWARD BUNNETT 1887

1. Christ in his word draws near; Hush, moan-ing voice of fear,
2. Ris - ing a - bove thy care, Meet him as in the air,
3. For works of love and praise He brings thee sum - mer days,
4. From the bright sky a - bove, Clad in his robes of love,

He bids thee cease; With songs sin-cere and sweet Let us a -
O wea - ry heart; Put on joy's sa - cred dress; Lo, as he
Warm days and bright; Win - ter is past and gone, Now he, sal -
'Tis he, our Lord! Dim earth it - self grows clear As his light

rise, and meet Him who comes forth to greet Our souls with peace.
comes to bless, Quite from thy wea - ri - ness Set free thou art.
va - tion's Sun, Shin-eth on ev - er - y one With mer-cy's light.
draw - eth near; O let us hush and hear His ho - ly word. A-men.

193

LUCERNA. 6. 6. 6. 6.

HENRY W. BAKER, 1861

FREDERIC F. BULLARD, 1895

1. Lord, thy word a - bid - eth, And our foot - steps guid - eth;
2. When our foes are near us, Then thy word doth cheer us,
3. When the storms are o'er us, And dark clouds be - fore us,
4. Who can tell the pleas - ure, Who re - count the treas - ure,

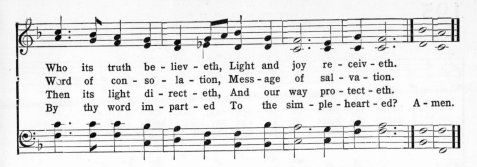

Who its truth be-liev-eth, Light and joy re-ceiv-eth.
Word of con-so-la-tion, Mess-age of sal-va-tion.
Then its light di-rect-eth, And our way pro-tect-eth.
By thy word im-part-ed To the sim-ple-heart-ed? A-men.

5 Word of mercy, giving
  Succor to the living;
  Word of life, supplying
  Comfort to the dying!

6 O that we, discerning
  Its most holy learning,
  Lord, may love and fear thee,
  Evermore be near thee!

194

ROCKINGHAM. NEW. L. M.

BENJAMIN BEDDOME, 1787
THOMAS COTTERILL, 1819

LOWELL MASON, 1830

1. God, in the gos-pel of his Son, Makes his e-ter-nal coun-sels known;
2. Here sin-ners of a hum-ble frame May taste his grace, and learn his Name;
3. The prisoner here may break his chains; The wea-ry rest from all his pains;
4. Here faith re-veals to mor-tal eyes A bright-er world be-yond the skies;
5. O grant us grace, Al-might-y Lord, To read and mark thy ho-ly word;

Where love in all its glo-ry shines, And truth is drawn in fair-est lines.
May read, in char-ac-ters of blood, The wis-dom, power, and grace of God.
The cap-tive feel his bond-age cease; The mourn-er find the way of peace.
Here shines the light which guides our way From earth to realms of endless day.
Its truths with meek-ness to re-ceive, And by its ho-ly pre-cepts live. A-men.

The Christian Life

VOX DILECTI. C. M. D.

HORATIUS BONAR, 1846

JOHN B. DYKES, 1868

1. I heard the voice of Je - sus say, 'Come un - to me and rest;
2. I heard the voice of Je - sus say, 'Be - hold, I free - ly give
3. I heard the voice of Je - sus say, 'I am this dark world's light;

Lay down, thou wea - ry one, lay down Thy head up - on my breast.'
The liv - ing wa - ter! thirst - y one, Stoop down, and drink, and live.'
Look un - to me, thy morn shall rise, And all thy day be bright.'

I came to Je - sus as I was, Wea - ry and worn and sad,
I came to Je - sus, and I drank Of that life - giv - ing stream;
I looked to Je - sus, and I found In him my star, my sun;

I found in him a rest - ing place, And he has made me glad.
My thirst was quenched, my soul revived, And now I live in him.
And in that light of life I'll walk, Till trav - el - ing days are done. A-men.

The Appeal of Christ

COME UNTO ME. 7. 6. 7. 6. D.

WILLIAM C. DIX, 1867

JOHN B. DYKES, 1875

1. 'Come un - to me, ye wea - ry, And I will give you rest:'
2. 'Come un - to me, ye wanderers, And I will give you light:'
3. 'Come un - to me, ye faint - ing, And I will give you life:'
4. 'And who - so - ev - er com - eth, I will not cast him out:'

O bless - ed voice of Je - sus, Which comes to hearts op - pressed,
O lov - ing voice of Je - sus, Which comes to cheer the night,
O cheer - ing voice of Je - sus, Which comes to aid our strife,
O wel - come voice of Je - sus, Which drives a - way our doubt,

It tells of ben - e - dic - tion, Of par - don, grace, and peace,
Our hearts were filled with sad - ness And we had lost our way;
The foe is stern and ea - ger, The fight is fierce and long;
Which calls us, ver - y sin - ners, Un - wor - thy though we be

Of joy that hath no end - ing, Of love which can - not cease.
But he has brought us glad - ness And songs at break of day.
But thou hast made us might - y And strong - er than the strong.
Of love so free and bound - less, To come, dear Lord, to thee. A - men.

159

197

BERA. L. M.

JOSEPH GRIGG, 1765

JOHN E. GOULD, 1849

1. Be - hold a Stran - ger at the door! He gen - tly knocks, has
2. O love - ly at - ti - tude! he stands With melt - ing heart, and
3. Ad - mit him, for the hu - man breast Ne'er en - ter - tained so
4. Sov - ereign of souls, thou Prince of Peace, O may thy gen - tle

knocked be - fore, Has wait - ed long, is wait - ing still;
la - den hands; O match - less kind - ness! and he shows
kind a Guest: The Man of Naz - a - reth, 'tis he,
reign in - crease! Throw wide the door, each will - ing mind;

You treat no oth - er friend so ill.
That match - less kind - ness to his foes.
With gar - ments dyed at Cal - va - ry.
And be his em - pire all man - kind. A - men.

198

GALILEE. 8. 7. 8. 7.

CECIL F. ALEXANDER, 1852

WILLIAM H. JUDE, 1887

1. Je - sus calls us; o'er the tu - mult Of our life's wild, rest - less sea,
2. Je - sus calls us from the wor - ship Of the vain world's gold - en store,
3. In our joys and in our sor - rows, Days of toil and hours of ease,
4. Je - sus calls us: by thy mer - cies, Sav - iour, may we hear thy call,

The Appeal of Christ

Day by day his sweet voice soundeth, Say-ing, 'Christian, follow me.'
From each i-dol that would keep us, Say-ing, 'Christian, love me more.'
Still he calls, in cares and pleas-ures, 'Christian, love me more than these.'
Give our hearts to thine o-be-dience, Serve and love thee best of all. A-men.

199

HORTON. 7. 7. 7. 7.

SAMUEL LONGFELLOW, 1819–1892

XAVIER SCHNYDER, 1826

1. Love for all! and can it be? Can I hope it
2. I, the dis-o-be-dient child, Way-ward, pas-sion-
3. I, who spurned his lov-ing hold, I, who would not
4. To my Fa-ther can I go? At his feet my-
5. See! my Fa-ther wait-ing stands, See! he reach-es

is for me— I, who strayed so long a-
ate and wild; I, who left my Fa-ther's
be con-trolled: I, who would not hear his
self I'll throw; In his house there yet may
out his hands: God is love; I know, I

go; Strayed so far, and fell so low?
home, In for-bid-den ways to roam;
call; I, the wil-ful prod-i-gal.
be Place— a serv-ant's place— for me.
see, Love for me— yes, e-ven me. A-men.

161

The Christian Life

200

ST. HILDA. 7. 6. 7. 6. D.

WILLIAM WALSHAM HOW, 1867

JUSTIN H. KNECHT, 1799
EDWARD HUSBAND, 1871

1. O Je - sus, thou art stand - ing Out - side the fast-closed door,
2. O Je - sus, thou art knock - ing; And lo! that hand is scarred,
3. O Je - sus, thou art plead - ing In ac - cents meek and low,

In low - ly pa - tience wait - ing To pass the thresh-old o'er:
And thorns thy brow en - cir - cle, And tears thy face have marred:
'I died for you, my chil - dren, And will ye treat me so?'

We bear the name of Chris - tians, His name and sign we bear,
O love that pass - eth knowl - edge, So pa - tient - ly to wait!
O Lord, with shame and sor - row, We o - pen now the door;

O shame, thrice shame up - on us, To keep him stand - ing there!
O sin that hath no e - qual, So fast to bar the gate!
Dear Sav - iour, en - ter, en - ter, And leave us nev - er - more! A - men.

162

201

WOODWORTH. 8. 8. 8. 6.

CHARLOTTE ELLIOTT, 1836

WILLIAM B. BRADBURY, 1849

1. Just as I am, with-out one plea, But that thy blood was shed for me, And
2. Just as I am, and wait-ing not To rid my soul of one dark blot, To
3. Just as I am, tho' tossed a-bout With many a conflict, many a doubt, Fight-
4. Just as I am, poor, wretched, blind; Sight, riches, heal-ing of the mind, Yea,
5. Just as I am! thou wilt re-ceive, Wilt welcome, pardon, cleanse, relieve; Be-

that thou biddest me come to thee, O Lamb of God, I come, I come.
thee whose blood can cleanse each spot, O Lamb of God, I come, I come.
ings and fears with-in, with-out, O Lamb of God, I come, I come.
all I need, in thee to find, O Lamb of God, I come, I come.
cause thy prom-ise I be-lieve, O Lamb of God, I come, I come. A-men.

202

JUST AS I AM. 8. 8. 8. 6.

MARIANNE HEARN, 1887

JOSEPH BARNBY, 1893

1. Just as I am, thine own to be, Friend of the young, who lov-est me,
2. In the glad morn-ing of my day, My life to give, my vows to pay,
3. I would live ev-er in the light, I would work ev-er for the right,
4. Just as I am, young, strong, and free, To be the best that I can be

UNISON

To con-se-crate my-self to thee, O Je-sus Christ, I come.
With no re-serve and no de-lay, With all my heart I come.
I would serve thee with all my might; There-fore, to thee I come.
For truth, and right-eous-ness, and thee, Lord of my life, I come. A-men.

203

STEPHANOS. 8. 5. 8. 3.

John Mason Neale, 1862

Henry W. Baker, 1868

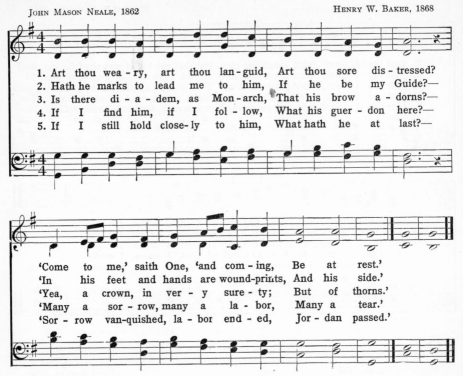

1. Art thou wea-ry, art thou lan-guid, Art thou sore dis-tressed?
2. Hath he marks to lead me to him, If he be my Guide?—
3. Is there di-a-dem, as Mon-arch, That his brow a-dorns?—
4. If I find him, if I fol-low, What his guer-don here?—
5. If I still hold close-ly to him, What hath he at last?—

'Come to me,' saith One, 'and com-ing, Be at rest.'
'In his feet and hands are wound-prints, And his side.'
'Yea, a crown, in ver-y sure-ty; But of thorns.'
'Many a sor-row, many a la-bor, Many a tear.'
'Sor-row van-quished, la-bor end-ed, Jor-dan passed.'

6 If I ask him to receive me,
  Will he say me nay?—
'Not till earth, and not till heaven
  Pass away.'

7 Finding, following, keeping, struggling,
  Is he sure to bless?—
'Saints, apostles, prophets, martyrs,
  Answer, Yes.'

204

BULLINGER. 8. 5. 8. 3.

Frances R. Havergal, 1874

Ethelbert W. Bullinger, 1877

1. I am trust-ing thee, Lord Je-sus, Trust-ing on-ly thee!
2. I am trust-ing thee for par-don, At thy feet I bow,
3. I am trust-ing thee to guide me; Thou a-lone shalt lead,
4. I am trust-ing thee, Lord Je-sus; Nev-er let me fall;

The Appeal of Christ

Trust - ing thee for full sal - va - tion, Great and free.
For thy grace and ten - der mer - cy, Trust - ing now.
Ev - ery day and hour sup - ply - ing All my need.
I am trust - ing thee for - ev - er, And for all. A - men.

205　　QUEM PASTORES LAUDAVERE. 8. 7. 8. 7.

RAY PALMER, 1864　　　　　　　　German Melody, Fifteenth Century

1. Take me, O my Fa - ther, take me; Take me, save me,
2. Long from thee my foot - steps stray - ing, Thorn - y proved the
3. Fruit - less years with grief re - call - ing, Hum - bly I con -
4. Free - ly now to thee I prof - fer This re - lent - ing
5. Fath - er, take me; all for - giv - ing, Fold me to thy

thro' thy Son; That which thou wouldst have me,
way I trod; Wea - ry come I now, and
fess my sin; At thy feet, O Fa - ther
heart of mine; Free - ly life and soul I
lov - ing breast; In thy love for - ev - er

make me; Let thy will in me be done.
pray - ing, Take me to thy love, my God.
fall - ing, To thy house - hold take me in.
of - fer, Gift un - worth - y love like thine.
liv - ing I must be for - ev - er blest. A - men.

165

206

HERVEY'S LITANY. 7. 7. 7. 6.

Thomas B. Pollock, 1875

Frederic A. J. Hervey, 1875

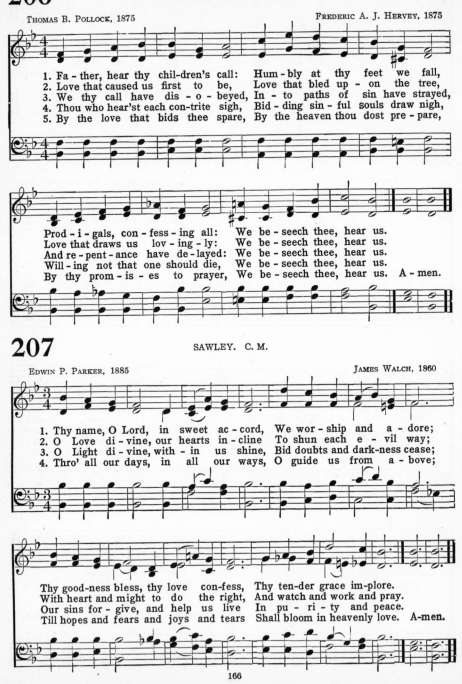

1. Fa - ther, hear thy chil-dren's call: Hum - bly at thy feet we fall,
2. Love that caused us first to be, Love that bled up - on the tree,
3. We thy call have dis - o - beyed, In - to paths of sin have strayed,
4. Thou who hear'st each con-trite sigh, Bid - ding sin - ful souls draw nigh,
5. By the love that bids thee spare, By the heaven thou dost pre - pare,

Prod - i - gals, con - fess - ing all: We be - seech thee, hear us.
Love that draws us lov - ing - ly: We be - seech thee, hear us.
And re - pent - ance have de - layed: We be - seech thee, hear us.
Will - ing not that one should die, We be - seech thee, hear us.
By thy prom - is - es to prayer, We be - seech thee, hear us. A - men.

207

SAWLEY. C. M.

Edwin P. Parker, 1885

James Walch, 1860

1. Thy name, O Lord, in sweet ac - cord, We wor - ship and a - dore;
2. O Love di - vine, our hearts in - cline To shun each e - vil way;
3. O Light di - vine, with - in us shine, Bid doubts and dark-ness cease;
4. Thro' all our days, in all our ways, O guide us from a - bove;

Thy good-ness bless, thy love con-fess, Thy ten-der grace im-plore.
With heart and might to do the right, And watch and work and pray.
Our sins for - give, and help us live In pu - ri - ty and peace.
Till hopes and fears and joys and tears Shall bloom in heavenly love. A-men.

208

CONSOLATION. 11. 10. 11. 10.

Thomas Moore, 1816

Samuel Webbe, 1792

1. Come, ye dis-con-so-late, wher-e'er ye lan-guish,
Come to the mer-cy-seat, fer-vent-ly kneel:
Here bring your wound-ed hearts, here tell your an-guish;
Earth has no sor-row that heaven can-not heal.

2. Joy of the des-o-late, light of the stray-ing,
Hope of the pen-i-tent, fade-less and pure,
Here speaks the Com-fort-er, ten-der-ly say-ing,
'Earth has no sor-row that heaven can-not cure.'

3. Here see the Bread of Life; see wa-ters flow-ing
Forth from the throne of God, pure from a-bove;
Come to the feast pre-pared; come, ev-er know-ing
'Earth has no sor-rows but heaven can re-move.' A-men.

209

GOLDEN GROVE. 10. 10. 10. 10.

Francis Turner Palgrave, 1824–1897

Ernest Littlewood

1. Christ in his heaven - ly gar - den walks all day,
2. 'How long, un - wise, will ye pur - sue your woe?
3. ''Tis not from earth - ly paths I bid you flee,
4. 'Still by the gate I stand as on ye stray;

And calls to souls up - on the world's high - way;
Here from the throne sweet wa - ters ev - er go;
But light - er in my ways] your feet will be;
Turn your steps hith - er; am not I the Way?

Wea - ried with tri - fles, maimed and sick with sin,
Here the white lil - ies shine like stars a - bove;
'Tis not to sum - mon you from hu - man mirth,
The sun is fall - ing fast, the night is nigh;

Christ by the gate stands, and in - vites them in.
Here in the red rose burns the face of Love.'
But add a depth and sweet-ness not of earth.'
Why will ye wan - der, where - fore will ye die?' A - men.

The Appeal of Christ

210

ST. HELEN'S. 8.5.8.3.

CHARLES A. DICKINSON, 1900

ROBERT P. STEWART, 1825-1894

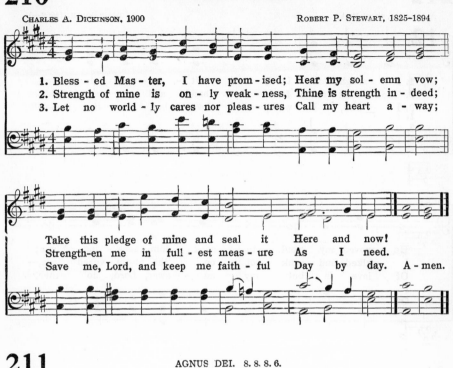

1. Bless - ed Mas - ter, I have prom - ised; Hear my sol - emn vow;
2. Strength of mine is on - ly weak - ness, Thine is strength in - deed;
3. Let no world - ly cares nor pleas - ures Call my heart a - way;

Take this pledge of mine and seal it Here and now!
Strength-en me in full - est meas - ure As I need.
Save me, Lord, and keep me faith - ful Day by day. A - men.

211

AGNUS DEI. 8. 8. 8. 6.

JANE CREWDSON, 1864

WILLIAM BLOW, 1881

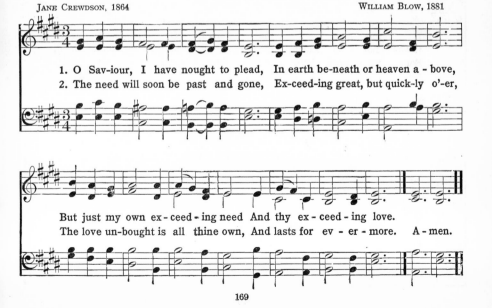

1. O Sav-iour, I have nought to plead, In earth be-neath or heaven a - bove,
2. The need will soon be past and gone, Ex-ceed-ing great, but quick-ly o'-er,

But just my own ex - ceed - ing need And thy ex - ceed - ing love.
The love un-bought is all thine own, And lasts for ev - er - more. A - men.

The Christian Life

212

TRANQUILLITY. 10. 10. 10. 6.

Anonymous, about 1904

JOSIAH BOOTH, (1852—)

1. I sought the Lord, and aft - er - ward I knew
2. Thou didst reach forth thy hand and mine en - fold;
3. I find, I walk, I love, but, O the whole

He moved my soul to seek him, seek - ing me;
I walked and sank not on the storm - vexed sea,—
Of love is but my an - swer, Lord, to thee,

It was not I that found, O Sav - iour true;
'Twas not so much that I on thee took hold,
For thou wert long be - fore - hand with my soul,

No, I was found of thee.
As thou, dear Lord, on me.
Al - ways thou lov - edst me. A - men.

170

213

ARTAVIA. 10. 10. 10. 6.

Sarah Williams, 1868

Edward J. Hopkins, 1818–1901

1. Be - cause I knew not when my life was good,
2. Be - cause I held up - on my self - ish road,
3. Be - cause I spent the strength thou gav - est me,
4. Be - cause I was im - pa - tient, would not wait,
5. Be - cause thou hast borne with me all this while,

And when there was a light up - on my path,
And left my broth - er wound - ed by the way,
In strug - gle which thou nev - er didst or - dain,
But thrust my im - pious hand a - cross thy threads,
Hast smit - ten me with love un - til I weep,

But turned my soul per - verse - ly to the
And called am - bi - tion du - ty, and pressed
And have but dregs of life to of - fer
And marred the pat - tern drawn out for my
Hast called me as a moth - er calls her

dark, O Lord, I do re - pent.
on, O Lord, I do re - pent.
thee, O Lord, I do re - pent.
life, O Lord, I do re - pent.
child, O Lord, I do re - pent. A - men.

The Christian Life

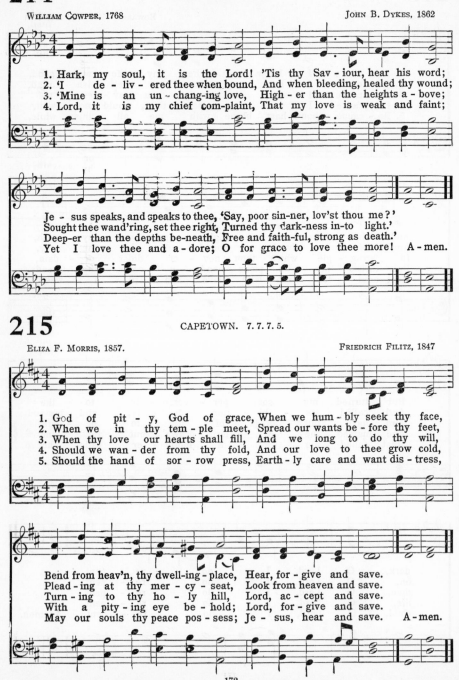

214 ST. BEES. 7.7.7.7.

WILLIAM COWPER, 1768

JOHN B. DYKES, 1862

1. Hark, my soul, it is the Lord! 'Tis thy Sav-iour, hear his word;
2. 'I de-liv-ered thee when bound, And when bleeding, healed thy wound;
3. 'Mine is an un-chang-ing love, High-er than the heights a-bove;
4. Lord, it is my chief com-plaint, That my love is weak and faint;

Je-sus speaks, and speaks to thee, 'Say, poor sin-ner, lov'st thou me?'
Sought thee wand'ring, set thee right, Turned thy dark-ness in-to light.'
Deep-er than the depths be-neath, Free and faith-ful, strong as death.'
Yet I love thee and a-dore; O for grace to love thee more! A-men.

215 CAPETOWN. 7.7.7.5.

ELIZA F. MORRIS, 1857.

FRIEDRICH FILITZ, 1847

1. God of pit-y, God of grace, When we hum-bly seek thy face,
2. When we in thy tem-ple meet, Spread our wants be-fore thy feet,
3. When thy love our hearts shall fill, And we long to do thy will,
4. Should we wan-der from thy fold, And our love to thee grow cold,
5. Should the hand of sor-row press, Earth-ly care and want dis-tress,

Bend from heav'n, thy dwell-ing-place, Hear, for-give and save.
Plead-ing at thy mer-cy-seat, Look from heaven and save.
Turn-ing to thy ho-ly hill, Lord, ac-cept and save.
With a pity-ing eye be-hold; Lord, for-give and save.
May our souls thy peace pos-sess; Je-sus, hear and save. A-men.

Penitence and Prayer

216

STOCKWELL. 8.7.8.7

'A. N.', in 'The Scottish Hymnal,' 1884

DARIUS E. JONES, 1851

1. Lord, thy mer - cy now en - treat-ing, Low be - fore thy throne we fall;
2. Sin - ful thoughts and words un-lov - ing Rise a - gainst us one by one;
3. Hearts that far from thee were stray-ing, While in prayer we bowed the knee;
4. Pre - cious mo - ments i - dly wast - ed, Pre - cious hours in fol - ly spent;
5. Lord, thy mer - cy still en - treat-ing, We with shame our sins would own;

Our mis-deeds to thee con - fess-ing, On thy name we hum-bly call.
Acts un-wor-thy, deeds un-think-ing, Good that we have left un-done;
Lips that, while thy prais-es sounding, Lift - ed not the soul to thee;
Christian vow and fight un-heed-ed; Scarce a thought to wis-dom lent.
From henceforth, the time redeeming, May we live to thee a - lone. A - men.

217

ALMSGIVING. 8.8.8.4.

CHARLOTTE ELLIOTT, 1838

JOHN B. DYKES, 1875

1. My God, is a - ny hour so sweet, From blush of morn to eve-ning star,
2. Blest is that tran-quil hour of morn, And blest that sol - emn hour of eve,
3. Then is my strength by thee re-newed; Then are my sins by thee for-given;
4. No words can tell what sweet re - lief Here for my ev - ery want I find,

As that which calls me to thy feet, The hour of prayer?
When, on the wings of prayer up - borne, The world I leave.
Then dost thou cheer my sol - i - tude With hopes of heaven.
What strength for war-fare, balm for grief, What peace of mind. A - men.

173

218

TOPLADY. 7. 7. 7. 7. 7. 7.

AUGUSTUS M. TOPLADY, 1776

THOMAS HASTINGS, 1830

1. Rock of A - ges, cleft for me, Let me hide my - self in thee;
2. Could my zeal no res - pite know, Could my tears for - ev - er flow,
3. While I draw this fleet - ing breath, When my eye - lids close in death,

Let the wa - ter and the blood, From thy riv - en side which flowed,
All for sin could not a - tone, Thou must save, and thou a - lone;
When I soar to worlds un-known, See thee on thy judg-ment throne,—

Be of sin the dou - ble cure, Cleanse me from its guilt and power.
Noth-ing in my hand I bring, Sim - ply to thy cross I cling.
Rock of A - ges, cleft for me, Let me hide my - self in thee. A - men.

219

FLAVIAN. C. M.

HENRY W. BAKER, 1875

BARBER'S Psalm Tunes.

1. I am not wor - thy, ho - ly Lord, That thou shouldst come to me;
2. I am not wor - thy; cold and bare The lodg - ing of my soul;
3. O come, in this sweet morn-ing hour, Feed me with food di - vine;

Penitence and Prayer

Speak but the word, one gra-cious word Can set the sin - ner free.
How canst thou deign to en - ter there? Lord, speak, and make me whole.
And fill with all thy love and power This worth-less heart of mine. A-men.

220

OLIVET. 6. 6. 4. 6. 6. 6. 4.

Ray Palmer, 1830

Lowell Mason, 1832

1. My faith looks up to thee, Thou Lamb of Cal - va - ry,
2. May thy rich grace im - part Strength to my faint - ing heart,
3. While life's dark maze I tread, And griefs a - round me spread,
4. When ends life's tran-sient dream, When death's cold, sul - len stream

Sav - iour di - vine! Now hear me while I pray, Take all my
My zeal in - spire; As thou hast died for me, O may my
Be thou my guide; Bid dark - ness turn to day; Wipe sor - row's
Shall o'er me roll; Blest Sav - iour, then, in love, Fear and dis -

guilt a - way, O let me from this day Be whol - ly thine.
love to thee, Pure, warm, and changeless be, A liv - ing fire.
tears a - way, Nor let me ev - er stray From thee a - side.
trust re - move; O bear me safe a - bove, A ran-somed soul! A-men.

175

The Christian Life

221

INTERCESSION, NEW. 7. 5. 7. 5. D. With Refrain

HORATIUS BONAR, 1866

WILLIAM H. CALLCOTT, 1867
Last two lines from MENDELSSOHN, 1846

1. When the wea - ry, seek - ing rest, To thy good-ness flee; When the
2. When the strang-er asks a home, All his toils to end; When the
3. When the world-ling, sick at heart, Lifts his soul a - bove; When the

heav - y - la - den cast All their load on thee; When the troub - led,
hun - gry crav - eth food, And the poor a friend, When the sail - or
prod - i - gal looks back To his Fath - er's love; When the proud man,

seek - ing peace, On thy name shall call; When the sin - ner, seek - ing life,
on the wave Bows the fer - vent knee; When the sol - dier on the field
from his pride, Stoops to seek thy face; When the bur-dened brings his guilt

Refrain

At thy feet shall fall: ....
Lifts his heart to thee: .... } Hear then in love, O
To thy throne of grace: ....

Lord, the cry In heaven, thy dwell-ing-place on high. A-men.

222

FLEMMING. 11. 11. 11. 5.

Berwick Hymnal, 1886

FRIEDRICH F. FLEMMING, 1811

1. Fa - ther Al - might - y, bless us with thy bless - ing, An - swer in
2. Shep - herd of souls, who bring - est all who seek thee To pas - tures
3. Fa - ther of mer - cy, from thy watch and keep - ing No place can

love thy chil - dren's sup - pli - ca - tion: Hear thou our prayer, the
green, be - side the peace - ful wa - ters; Ten - der - est Guide, in
part, nor hour of time re - move us: Give us thy good, and

spo - ken and un - spo - ken; Hear us, our Fa - ther.
ways of cheer - ful du - ty, Lead us, good Shep - herd.
save us from our e - vil, In - fi - nite Spir - it! A - men.

The Christian Life

223

RETREAT. L. M.

HUGH STOWELL, 1828

THOMAS HASTINGS, 1842

1. From ev - ery storm - y wind that blows, From
2. There is a place where Je - sus sheds The
3. There is a spot where spir - its blend, Where
4. There, there, on ea - gle's wing we soar, And

ev - ery swell - ing tide of woes, There is a calm, a
oil of glad - ness on our heads, A place than all be -
friend holds fel - low-ship with friend; Tho' sun - dered far, by
time and sense seem all no more, And heaven comes down, our

sure re - treat; 'Tis found be - neath the mer - cy - seat.
side more sweet; It is the blood-bought mer - cy - seat.
faith they meet A - round one com - mon mer - cy - seat.
souls to greet, And glo - ry crowns the mer - cy - seat. A - men.

224

BYEFIELD. C. M.

JAMES MONTGOMERY, 1818

THOMAS HASTINGS, 1840

1. Prayer is the soul's sin-cere de - sire, Un - ut - tered or ex-pressed;
2. Prayer is the sim - plest form of speech That in - fant lips can try;
3. Prayer is the Christian's vi - tal breath, The Christian's na - tive air;
4. O thou, by whom we come to God, The Life, the Truth, the Way!

178

The mo-tion of a hid-den fire That trem-bles in the breast.
Prayer the sub-lim-est strains that reach The Ma-jes-ty on high.
His watch-word at the gates of death: He en-ters heaven with prayer.
The path of prayer thy-self hast trod; Lord, teach us how to pray. A-men.

225

SOUTHAMPTON. Irregular

CHARLES G. AMES, 1828–1912

Anonymous, 1870

1. Fa-ther in heav-en, Hear us to-day; Hal-lowed thy name be;
2. Fa-ther in heav-en, Hear us to-day; Hal-lowed thy name be;
3. Fa-ther in heav-en, Hear us to-day; Hal-lowed thy name be;

Hear us, we pray! O let thy king-dom come, O let thy
Hear us, we pray! Giv-er of dai-ly food, Foun-tain of
Hear us, we pray! Lead us in paths of right, Save us from

will be done, By all be-neath the sun, As in the skies.
truth and good, Be all our hearts im-bued With love like thine.
sin and blight, King of all love and might, Glo-rious for aye. A-men.

226

DENNIS. S. M.

PHILIP DODDRIDGE, 1702–1751

Arranged from HANS G. NAEGELI, 1768–1836
by LOWELL MASON, 1845

1. How gen - tle God's com-mands! How kind his pre - cepts are!
2. Be - neath his watch - ful eye His saints se - cure - ly dwell;
3. Why should this anx - ious load Press down your wea - ry mind?
4. His good - ness stands ap-proved, Un-changed from day to day;

Come, cast your bur-dens on the Lord, And trust his con-stant care.
That hand, which bears all na - ture up, Shall guide his chil-dren well.
Haste to your heaven-ly Fa-ther's throne, And sweet re-fresh-ment find.
I'll drop my bur-den at his feet, And bear a song a-way. A-men.

227

ST. ANDREW. S. M.

JOHN S. B. MONSELL, 1862

JOSEPH BARNBY, 1866

1. Sweet is thy mer - cy, Lord; Be - fore thy mer - cy - seat
2. Wher - e'er thy name is blest, Wher-e'er thy peo - ple meet,
3. Light thou my wea - ry way, Lead thou my wan - dering feet,
4. Thus shall the heaven-ly host Hear all my songs re - peat

My soul a - dor-ing, pleads thy word, And owns thy mer-cy sweet.
There I de-light in thee to rest, And find thy mer-cy sweet.
That while I stay on earth I may Still find thy mer-cy sweet.
To Fa-ther, Son, and Ho - ly Ghost, My joy, thy mer-cy sweet. A - men.

228

BELMONT. C. M.

JOSEPH D. CARLYLE, 1802　　　　　　　　　　WILLIAM GARDINER, 1812

1. Lord, when we bend be - fore thy throne, And our con - fes - sions pour,
2. Our bro - ken spir - it pity - ing see; True pen - i - tence im - part;
3. When we dis-close our wants in prayer May we our wills re - sign;
4. May faith each meek pe - ti - tion fill And waft it to the skies,

Teach us to feel the sins we own, And hate what we de - plore.
Then let a kind-ling glance from thee Beam hope up - on the heart.
And not a thought our bos - om share That is not whol - ly thine.
And teach our hearts 'tis good-ness still That grants it or de - nies. A - men.

229

HOLY CROSS. C. M.

JOHN GREENLEAF WHITTIER, 1807–1892　　　　　　　JAMES C. WADE, 1865

1. The harp at na - ture's ad - vent strung Has nev - er ceased to play:
2. And prayer is made, and praise is given By all things near and far:
3. The green earth sends her in - cense up From many a moun-tain shrine:
4. The blue sky is the tem - ple's arch, Its tran-sept, earth and air;
5. So na - ture keeps the rever - ent frame With which her years be - gan;

The song the stars of morn-ing sung Has nev - er died a - way.
The o - cean look-eth up to heaven And mir-rors ev - ery star:
From fold - ed leaf and dew - y cup She pours her sa - cred wine.
The mu - sic of its star - ry march, The cho - rus of a prayer.
And all her signs and voi - ces shame The prayer-less heart of man. A - men.

The Christian Life

230

ERIE. 8.7.8.7. D.

JOHN SCRIVEN, 1855

CHARLES C. CONVERSE, 1868

1. What a friend we have in Je-sus, All our sins and griefs to bear;
2. Have we tri-als and temp-ta-tions? Is there troub-le an-y-where?
3. Are we weak and heav-y-la-den, Cum-bered with a load of care?

What a priv-i-lege to car-ry Ev-ery-thing to God in prayer!
We should nev-er be dis-cour-aged: Take it to the Lord in prayer!
Pre-cious Sav-iour, still our ref-uge, Take it to the Lord in prayer!

O what peace we oft-en for-feit, O what need-less pain we bear,
Can we find a friend so faith-ful, Who will all our sor-rows share?
Do thy friends de-spise, for-sake thee? Take it to the Lord in prayer!

All be-cause we do not car-ry Ev-ery-thing to God in prayer.
Je-sus knows our ev-ery weak-ness—Take it to the Lord in prayer!
In his arms he'll take and shield thee, Thou wilt find a sol-ace there. A-men.

182

231

BEATITUDO. C. M.

WILLIAM COWPER, 1772

JOHN B. DYKES, 1875

1. O for a clos-er walk with God, A calm and heaven-ly frame,
2. Re-turn, O ho-ly dove, re-turn, Sweet mes-sen-ger of rest!
3. The dear-est i-dol I have known, What-e'er that i-dol be,
4. So shall my walk be close with God, Calm and se-rene my frame;

A light to shine up-on the road That leads me to the Lamb!
I hate the sins that made thee mourn, And drove thee from my breast.
Help me to tear it from thy throne, And wor-ship on-ly thee.
So pur-er light shall mark the road That leads me to the Lamb. A-men.

232

NAOMI. C. M.

Arranged from JOHANN G. NAEGELI
by LOWELL MASON, 1836

ANNE STEELE, 1760

1 Fa-ther, what-e'er of earth-ly bliss Thy sov-ereign will de-nies,
2. Give me a calm, a thank-ful heart, From ev-ery mur-mur free;
3. Let the sweet hope that thou art mine My life and death at-tend:

Ac-cept-ed at thy throne of grace Let this pe-ti-tion rise.
The bless-ings of thy grace im-part, And make me live to thee.
Thy presence through my journey shine, And crown my jour-ney's end. A-men.

233

STRENGTH AND STAY. 11. 10. 11. 10.

SAMUEL JOHNSON, 1846

JOHN B. DYKES, 1875

1. Fa - ther, in thy mys - te - rious pres - ence kneel - ing,
2. Lord, we have wan - dered forth thro' doubt and sor - row,
3. Now, Fa - ther, now in thy dear pres - ence kneel - ing,

Fain would our souls feel all thy kind - ling love;
And thou hast made each step an on - ward one;
Our spir - its yearn to feel thy kin - dling love;

For we are weak, and need some deep re - veal - ing
And we will ev - er trust each un - known mor - row;
Now make us strong; we need thy deep re - veal - ing

Of trust, and strength, and calm-ness from a - bove.
Thou wilt sus - tain us till its work is done.
Of trust, and strength, and calm - ness from a - bove. A - men.

Inner Strength and Peace

BURLEIGH. 10. 10. 10. 10.

WILLIAM H. BURLEIGH, 187*]*

JOSEPH BARNBY, 1883

1. Lead us, O Fa - ther, in the paths of peace;
2. Lead us, O Fa - ther, in the paths of right;
3. Lead us, O Fa - ther, to thy heaven - ly rest,

With - out thy guid - ing hand we go a - stray,
Blind - ly we stum - ble when we walk a - lone,
How - ev - er rough and steep the path may be,

And doubts ap - pall, and sor - rows still in - crease;
In - volved in shad - ows of a dark - some night;
Through joy or sor - row, as thou deem - est best,

Lead us through Christ, the true and liv - ing way.
On - ly with thee we jour - ney safe - ly on.
Un - til our lives are per - fect - ed in thee. A - men.

235

PENITENCE. 6. 5. 6. 5. D.

JAMES MONTGOMERY, 1834.

SPENCER LANE, 1879

1. In the hour of tri - al, Je - sus plead for me,
2. With for - bid - den pleas - ures Would this vain world charm;
3. Should thy mer - cy send me Sor - row, toil, and woe;
4. When my last hour com - eth, Fraught with strife and pain,

Lest by base de - ni - al I de - part from thee;
Or its sor - did treas - ures Spread to work me harm;
Or should pain at - tend me On my path be - low;
When my dust re - turn - eth To the dust a - gain;

When thou see'st me wav - er, With a look re - call,
Bring to my re - mem - brance Sad Geth - sem - a - ne,
Grant that I may nev - er Fail thy hand to see;
On thy truth re - ly - ing, Through that mor - tal strife,

Nor, for fear or fa - vor, Suf - fer me to fall.
Or, in dark - er sem - blance, Cross-crowned Cal - va - ry.
Grant that I may ev - er Cast my care on thee.
Je - sus, take me, dy - ing, To e - ter - nal life. A - men.

Inner Strength and Peace

236

LYNDHURST. 6. 5. 6. 5. D.

Anonymous

Anonymous in
Church Praise, 1883

1. Pu - rer yet and pu - rer, I would be in mind,
2. Calm - er yet and calm - er, In the hour of pain,
3. High - er yet and high - er Out of clouds and night,
4. Swift - er yet and swift - er Ev - er on - ward run,

Dear - er yet and dear - er Ev - ery du - ty find;
Sur - er yet and sur - er Peace at last to gain;
Near - er yet and near - er Ris - ing to the light;—
Firm - er yet and firm - er Step as I go on:

Hop - ing still and trust - ing God with - out a fear,
Suf - f'ring still and do - ing, To his will re - signed,
Light se - rene and ho - ly, Where my soul may rest,
Oft these ear - nest long - ings Swell with - in my breast,

Pa - tient - ly be - liev - ing He will make all clear.
And to God sub - du - ing Heart and will and mind.
Pu - ri - fied and low - ly, Sanc - ti - fied and blest.
Yet their in - ner mean - ing Ne'er can be ex - pressed. A - men.

The Christian Life

237

SANDON. 10. 4. 10. 4. 10. 10.

STOPFORD A. BROOKE, 1881

CHARLES H. PURDAY, 1860

1. Im - mor - tal love, with - in whose right-eous will Is al - ways peace,
2. The days are gone, when far and wide my will Drove me a - stray;
3. What-e'er of pain thy lov - ing hand al - lot I glad - ly bear;
4. So may I, far a - way, when eve - ning falls On life and love,

O pit - y me, storm-tossed on waves of ill; Let pas - sion cease;
And now I fain would climb the ar - duous hill, That nar - row way,
On - ly, O Lord, let peace be not for - got, Nor yet thy care,
Ar - rive at last the ho - ly, hap - py halls, With thee a - bove;

Come down in power with - in my heart to reign,
Which leads through mists and rocks to thine a - bode,
Free - dom from storms, and wild de - sires with - in,
Wound - ed yet healed, sin - lad - en yet for - given,

For I am weak, and striv - ing has been vain.
Toil - ing for man, and thee, Al - might - y God.
Peace from the fierce op - pres - sion of my sin.
And sure that good - ness is my on - ly heaven. A - men.

Inner Strength and Peace

238

LUX BEATA. 10. 4. 10. 4. 10. 10.

JOHN, DUKE OF ARGYLL, 1877

ALBERT L. PEACE, 1885

1. Un - to the hills a - round do I lift up
   My long-ing eyes: O whence for me shall my sal-va-tion come,
   From whence a - rise? From God the Lord doth come my cer-tain aid,
   From God the Lord, who heaven and earth hath made.

2. He will not suf - fer that thy foot be moved:
   Safe shalt thou be. No care-less slum - ber shall his eye - lids close
   Who keep-eth thee. Be - hold, our God, the Lord, he slum-b'reth ne'er
   Who keep-eth Is - rael in his ho - ly care.

3. Je - ho - vah is him - self thy Keep - er true,
   Thy change-less Shade; Je - ho - vah thy de - fense on thy right hand
   Him - self hath made: And thee no sun by day shall ev - er smite;
   No moon shall harm thee in the si - lent night.

4. From ev - ery e - vil shall he keep thy soul,
   From ev - ery sin: Je - ho - vah shall pre - serve thy go - ing out,
   Thy com - ing in: A - bove thee watch-ing, he whom we a - dore
   Shall keep thee hence-forth, yea, for - ev - er - more. A - men.

The Christian Life

239

AMESBURY. C. M. D.

JOHN GREENLEAF WHITTIER, 1865

UZZIAH C. BURNAP, 1895

1. I bow my fore-head to the dust, I veil mine eyes for shame,
2. Yet, in the maddening maze of things, And tossed by storm and flood,
3. I know not what the fu-ture hath Of mar-vel or sur-prise,
4. And so be-side the Si-lent Sea I wait the muf-fled oar;

And urge, in trem-bling self-dis-trust, A prayer with-out a claim.
To one fixed stake my spir-it clings; I know that God is good.
As-sured a-lone that life and death His mer-cy un-der-lies.
No harm from him can come to me On o-cean or on shore.

I see the wrong that round me lies, I feel the guilt with-in;
I dim-ly guess from bless-ings known Of great-er out of sight,
And if my heart and flesh are weak To bear an un-tried pain,
I know not where his is-lands lift Their frond-ed palms in air:

I hear, with groan and tra-vail-cries, The world con-fess its sin;
And, with the chastened Psalmist, own His judgments too are right.
The bruis-ed reed he will not break, But strengthen and sus-tain.
I on-ly know I can-not drift Be-yond his love and care. A-men.

Inner Strength and Peace

WESSEX. 8. 6. 8. 6. 8. 8.

Samuel Longfellow, 1864

Edward J. Hopkins, 1867

1. I look to thee in ev - ery need, And nev - er look in vain; I feel thy strong and ten - der love, And all is well a - gain; The thought of thee is might - ier far Than sin and pain and sor - row are.

2. Dis - cour - aged in the work of life, Dis - heart - ened by its load, Shamed by its fail - ures or its fears, I sink be - side the road; But let me on - ly think of thee, And then new heart springs up in me.

3. Thy calm - ness bends se - rene a - bove, My rest - less - ness to still; A - round me flows thy quicken - ing life, To nerve my falter - ing will; Thy pres - ence fills my sol - i - tude; Thy prov - i - dence turns all to good.

4. Em - bos - omed deep in thy dear love, Held in thy law, I stand; Thy hand in all things I be - hold, And all things in thy hand; Thou lead - est me by un - sought ways, And turn'st my mourn - ing in - to praise. A - men.

241 FEDERAL STREET. L. M.

WILLIAM T. MATSON, 1866   HENRY K. OLIVER, 1832

1. O bless-ed Life! the heart at rest, When all with-
2. O bless-ed Life! the mind that sees, What-ev-er
3. O bless-ed Life! the soul that soars When sense of
4. O Life! how bless-ed!— how di-vine!— High Life, the

out tu-mul-tuous seems: That trusts a high-er Will, and
change the years may bring, A mer-cy still in ev-ery-
mor-tal sight is dim, Be-yond the sense— be-yond, to
ear-nest of a higher: Sav-iour! ful-fill my deep de-

deems That high-er Will, not mine, the best.
thing, And shin-ing through all mys-ter-ies.
him Whose love un-locks the heaven-ly doors.
sire, And let this bless-ed Life be mine. A-men.

242 SCHUMANN. S. M.

PAULUS GERHARDT, 1656
Translated by JOHN WESLEY, 1739   Cantica Laudis, 1850

1. Give to the winds thy fears; Hope and be un-dis-mayed;
2. Still heav-y is thy heart? Still sink thy spir-its down?
3. Com-mit thou all thy griefs And ways in-to his hands,
4. Who points the clouds their course, Whom winds and seas o-bey,
5. Leave to his sover-eign will To choose and to com-mand:

Inner Strength and Peace

God hears thy sighs and counts thy tears, God shall lift up thy head.
Cast off the weight, let fear de - part, And ev - ery care be gone.
To his sure truth and ten - der care, Who earth and heaven commands.
He shall di - rect thy wan-dering feet, He shall pre-pare thy way.
With won-der filled, thou then shalt own How wise, how strong his hand. A-men.

243

BROMLEY. L. M.

ROSALIE M. CODY, 1920

JEREMIAH CLARK, 1700

1. Al - might - y one, whose ten - der thought Bends down to
2. The power that spreads the arch of blue Where sun and
3. Je - ho - vah, Lord, thy strength is mine; I am of

paint the low - liest flower, Thy child can sure - ly trust
moon in glo - ry ride, Will hold me safe - ly, lift -
thee a ver - y part; Mine is the shield of thy

that love To light - en sor - row's dark - est hour.
ed high A - bove pain's deep and drag - ging tide.
right arm, And mine the shel - ter of thy heart. A-men.

The Christian Life

244
PAX TECUM. 10.10

EDWARD H. BICKERSTETH, 1870

GEORGE T. CALDBECK, 1878

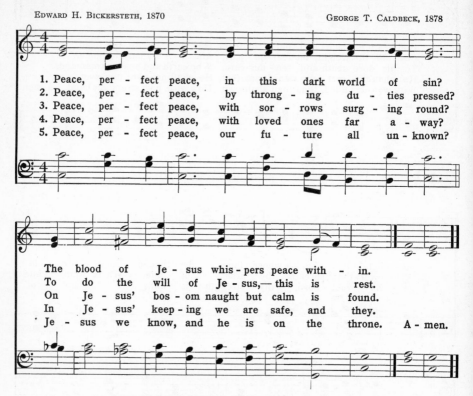

1. Peace, per - fect peace, in this dark world of sin?
2. Peace, per - fect peace, by throng - ing du - ties pressed?
3. Peace, per - fect peace, with sor - rows surg - ing round?
4. Peace, per - fect peace, with loved ones far a - way?
5. Peace, per - fect peace, our fu - ture all un - known?

The blood of Je - sus whis - pers peace with - in.
To do the will of Je - sus,— this is rest.
On Je - sus' bos - om naught but calm is found.
In Je - sus' keep - ing we are safe, and they.
Je - sus we know, and he is on the throne. A - men.

6 Peace, perfect peace, death shadowing us and ours?
   Jesus has vanquished death and all its powers.

7 It is enough; earth's struggles soon shall cease,
   And Jesus call us to heaven's perfect peace.

245
ST. DENYS. 6. 6. 6. 6.

HORATIUS BONAR, 1861

FRANK S. SPINNEY, 1850–1888

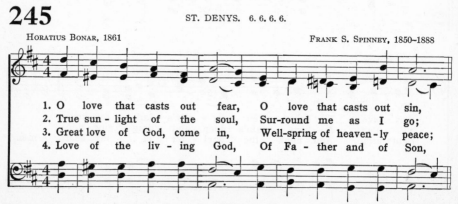

1. O love that casts out fear, O love that casts out sin,
2. True sun - light of the soul, Sur - round me as I go;
3. Great love of God, come in, Well-spring of heaven - ly peace;
4. Love of the liv - ing God, Of Fa - ther and of Son,

194

Inner Strength and Peace

Tar - ry no more with - out, But come and dwell with - in.
So shall my way be safe, My feet no stray - ing know.
Thou liv - ing wa - ter, come, Spring up, and nev - er cease.
Love of the Ho - ly Ghost, Fill thou each need - y one. A - men.

246　　　　　　　FLEMMING. 8. 8. 8. 6.

CHARLOTTE ELLIOTT, 1834　　　　　　　FRIEDRICH F. FLEMMING, 1810

1. O ho - ly Sav - iour, Friend un - seen, Since on thine
2. What though the world de - ceit - ful prove, And earth - ly
3. Though faith and hope may long be tried, I ask not,

arm thou bidd'st me lean, Help me, through-out life's
friends and joys re - move, With pa - tient, un - com -
need not aught be - side; How safe, how calm, how

va - rying scene, By faith to cling to thee.
plain - ing love Still would I cling to thee.
sat - is - fied, The souls that cling to thee! A - men.

195

247

HESPERUS. L. M.

OLIVER WENDELL HOLMES, 1859

HENRY BAKER, 1866

1. O Love di - vine, that stooped to share Our sharp - est
2. Tho' long the wea - ry way we tread, And sor - row
3. When droop - ing pleas - ure turns to grief, And tremb - ling
4. On thee we fling our bur - dening woe, O Love di -

pang, our bit - terest tear, On thee we cast each earth - born
crown each ling - ering year, No path we shun, no dark - ness
faith is changed to fear, The mur - muring wind, the quiv - ering
vine, for ev - er dear, Con - tent to suf - fer while we

care, We smile at pain while thou art near.
dread, Our hearts still whisper - ing, thou art near.
leaf, Shall soft - ly tell us thou art near.
know, Liv - ing and dy - ing, thou art near. A - men.

248

BEATITUDO. C. M.

HELEN M. WILLIAMS, 1786

JOHN B. DYKES, 1875

1. While thee I seek, pro - tect - ing Power, Be my vain wish - es stilled:
2. Thy love the powers of thought be-stowed; To thee my thoughts would soar:
3. In each e - vent of life, how clear Thy rul - ing hand I see;
4. In ev - ery joy that crowns my days, In ev - ery pain I bear,

And may this con - se - crat - ed hour With bet - ter hopes be filled.
Thy mer - cy o'er my life has flowed; That mer - cy I a - dore.
Each bless-ing to my soul more dear Be-cause con-ferred by thee.
My heart shall find de - light in praise, Or seek re - lief in prayer. A-men.

249   HARVARD. 8. 6. 8. 6. 8. 8.

Lucy Larcom, 1824–1893   Arthur Berridge

1. In Christ I feel the heart of God, Throb-bing from heaven thro' earth;
2. In Christ I touch the hand of God, From his pure height reached down,
3. Hold-ing his hand, my stead - ied feet May walk the air, the seas;
4. Not my Christ on - ly; he is ours: Hu - man - i - ty's close bond;

Life stirs a - gain with - in the clod, Re-newed in beauteous birth; The soul springs
By bless-ed ways be - fore un - trod, To lift us to our crown; Vic - t'ry that
On life and death his smile falls sweet, Lights up all mys - ter - ies; Strang-er nor
Key to its vast, un - o-pened pow'rs, Dream of our dreams be-yond. What yet we

up, a flower of prayer, Breath-ing his breath out on the air.
on - ly per - fect is Thro' lov-ing sac - ri - fice, like his.
ex - ile can I be In new worlds where he lead-eth me.
shall be none can tell; Now are we his, and all is well. A - men.

250

WHITTIER. (REST). 8. 6. 8. 8. 6.

JOHN G. WHITTIER, 1872

FREDERICK C. MAKER, 1887

1. Dear Lord and Fa-ther of man-kind, For-give our fev-erish ways;
2. In sim-ple trust like theirs who heard, Be-side the Syr-ian sea,
3. O Sab-bath rest by Gal-i-lee! O calm of hills a-bove!
4. Drop thy still dews of qui-et-ness, Till all our striv-ings cease;
5. Breathe through the heats of our de-sire Thy cool-ness and thy balm;

Re-clothe us in our right-ful mind; In pur-er lives thy
The gra-cious call-ing of the Lord, Let us, like them, with-
Where Je-sus knelt to share with thee The si-lence of e-
Take from our souls the strain and stress, And let our or-dered
Let sense be dumb, let flesh re-tire; Speak through the earth-quake,

serv-ice find, In deep-er rev-erence, praise.
out a word, Rise up and fol-low thee.
ter-ni-ty, In-ter-pret-ed by love.
lives con-fess The beau-ty of thy peace.
wind, and fire, O still small voice of calm! A-men.

251

ST. CECILIA. 6. 6. 6. 6.

HORATIUS BONAR, 1857

LEIGHTON G. HAYNE, 1863

1. Thy way, not mine, O Lord, How-ev-er dark it be:
2. Smooth let it be or rough, It will be still the best;
3. I dare not choose my lot; I would not, if I might;
4. The king-dom that I seek Is thine: so let the way
5. Not mine, not mine the choice In things or great or small;

Inner Strength and Peace

Lead me by thine own hand, Choose out the path for me.
Wind - ing or straight, it leads Right on - ward to thy rest.
Choose thou for me, my God, So shall I walk a - right.
That leads to it be thine, Else I must sure - ly stray.
Be thou my guide, my strength, My wis - dom, and my all. A - men.

252 NEED. 6. 4. 6. 4. With Refrain

ANNIE S. HAWKES, 1872 ROBERT LOWRY, 1872

1. I need thee ev-ery hour, Most gra-cious Lord; No ten-der voice like thine
2. I need thee ev-ery hour, Stay thou near by; Temp-ta-tions lose their power
3. I need thee ev-ery hour, In joy or pain; Come quick-ly and a - bide,
4. I need thee ev-ery hour, Teach me thy will; And thy rich prom-is - es,
5. I need thee ev-ery hour, Most ho - ly one; O make me thine in-deed,

Refrain

Can peace af - ford.
When thou art nigh.
Or life is vain. } I need thee, O I need thee, Ev - ery hour I
In me ful - fill.
Thou bless - ed Son.

need thee, O bless me now, my Sav-iour, I come to thee. A - men.

The Christian Life

253

PENITENTIA. 10. 10. 10. 10.

EDWARD H. BICKERSTETH, 1825–1906

EDWARD DEARLE, 1874

1. Come ye your-selves a - part and rest a - while,
2. Come, tell me all that ye have said and done,
3. Come ye, and rest; the jour - ney is too great,
4. Then, fresh from con - verse with your Lord, re - turn

Wea - ry, I know it, of the press and throng,
Your vic - tor - ies and fail - ures, hopes and fears,
And ye will faint be - side the way and sink:
And work till day - light soft - ens in - to even;

Wipe from your brow the sweat and dust of toil,
I know how hard - ly souls are wooed and won;
The bread of life is here for you to eat,
The brief hours are not lost in which ye learn

And in my qui - et strength a - gain be strong.
My choic - est wreaths are al - ways wet with tears.
And here for you the wine of love to drink.
More of your Mas - ter and his rest in heaven. A - men.

Inner Strength and Peace

254

CLIFTON. 11. 10. 11. 10.

HARRIET BEECHER STOWE, 1812–1896

UZZIAH C. BURNAP, 1834–1900

1. When winds are rag - ing o'er the up - per o - cean,
2. Far, far be - neath, the noise of tem - pests di - eth,
3. So to the heart that knows thy love, O Pur - est,
4. Far, far a - way, the noise of pas - sion di - eth,

And bil - lows wild con - tend with an - gry roar,
And sil - ver waves chime ev - er peace - ful - ly;
There is a tem - ple, peace - ful ev - er - more;
And lov - ing thoughts rise ev - er peace - ful - ly;

'Tis said, far down be - neath the wild com - mo - tion
And no rude storm, how fierce so - e'er it fli - eth,
And all the bab - ble of life's an - gry voic - es
And no rude storm, how fierce so - e'er it fli - eth,

That peace - ful still - ness reign - eth ev - er - more.
Dis - turbs the Sab - bath of that deep - er sea.
Dies in hushed still - ness at its sac - red door.
Dis - turbs that deep - er rest, O Lord, in thee. A - men.

The Christian Life

255

HANFORD. 8. 8. 8. 4.

CHARLOTTE ELLIOTT, 1834

ARTHUR S. SULLIVAN, 1874

1. My God, and Fa - ther, while I stray Far from my home in
2. What though in lone - ly grief I sigh For friends be - loved, no
3. If thou shouldst call me to re - sign What most I prize, it
4. Re - new my will from day to day, Blend it with thine, and
5. Then, when on earth I breathe no more The prayer oft mixed with

life's rough way, O teach me from my heart to say, 'Thy will be done!'
long - er nigh, Sub - mis-sive still would I re - ply, 'Thy will be done!'
ne'er was mine; I on - ly yield thee what is thine; 'Thy will be done!'
take a - way All that now makes it hard to say, 'Thy will be done!'
tears be - fore, I'll sing up - on a hap-pier shore, 'Thy will be done!' A-men.

256

PLEYEL'S HYMN. 7. 7. 7. 7.

JOHN CENNICK, 1742

Arranged from
IGNACE PLEYEL, 1790

1. Chil - dren of the heaven-ly King, As ye jour - ney, sweet-ly sing;
2. We are trav - eling home to God, In the way the fa - thers trod:
3. Lift your eyes, ye sons of light, Zi - on's cit - y is in sight:
4. Fear not, breth-ren; joy - ful stand On the bor - ders of your land;
5. Lord, o - be - dient - ly we go, Glad - ly leav - ing all be - low;

Sing your Sav-iour's worth-y praise, Glo-rious in his works and ways.
They are hap - py now, and we Soon their hap-pi - ness shall see.
There our end-less home shall be, There our Lord we soon shall see.
Je - sus Christ, your Fa-ther's Son, Bids you un - dis-mayed go on.
On - ly thou our Lead - er be, And we still will fol - low thee. A-men.

202

Inner Strength and Peace

257

ST. BARNABAS. 11. 10. 11. 10.

FREDERICK HOSMER, 1881.

JOHN B. DYKES, 1875

1. Fa - ther, to thee we look in all our sor - row,
2. When fond hopes fail and skies are dark be - fore us,
3. Nought shall af - fright us on thy good - ness lean - ing,
4. Pa - tient, O heart, though heav - y be thy sor - rows!

Thou art the foun - tain whence our heal - ing flows;
When the vain cares that vex our life in - crease,—
Low in the heart faith sing - eth still her song;
Be not cast down, dis - qui - et - ed in vain;

Dark though the night, joy com - eth with the mor - row;
Comes with its calm the thought that thou art o'er us,
Chast - ened by pain we learn life's deep - er mean - ing,
Yet shalt thou praise him when these dark - ened fur - rows,

Safe - ly they rest who on thy love re - pose.
And we grow qui - et, fold - ed in thy peace.
And in our weak - ness thou dost make us strong.
Where now he plow - eth, wave with gold - en grain. A - men.

203

The Christian Life

258

MARTYN. 7. 7. 7. 7. D.

Charles Wesley, 1740

Simeon B. Marsh, 1834

1. Je - sus, Lov - er of my soul, Let me to thy bos - om fly,
2. Oth - er ref - uge have I none; Hangs my help-less soul on thee;
3. Thou, O Christ, art all I want; More than all in thee I find:
4. Plenteous grace with thee is found, Grace to cov - er all my sin;

While the near - er wa - ters roll, While the tem - pest still is high:
Leave, ah, leave me not a - lone, Still sup - port and com - fort me.
Raise the fall - en, cheer the faint, Heal the sick, and lead the blind.
Let the heal-ing streams a-bound; Make and keep me pure with - in.

Hide me, O my Sav - iour! hide, Till the storm of life is past;
All my trust on thee is stayed, All my help from thee I bring;
Just and ho - ly is thy name; I am all un - right-eous - ness;
Thou of life the foun - tain art, Free-ly let me take of thee;

Safe in - to the ha - ven guide; O re-ceive my soul at last!
Cov - er my de-fense-less head With the shad-ow of thy wing;
False and full of sin I am, Thou art full of truth and grace.
Spring thou up with-in my heart! Rise to all e - ter - ni - ty.

A-men.

Illumination and Guidance

259

.BRYANT.   8. 6. 8. 6. 8. 8.

HENRY VAN DYKE, 1922

WALTER G. ALCOCK, (1861——)

1. O   Mak - er   of   the   Might - y   Deep   Where - on   our
2. We   know   not   where   the   se - cret   tides   Will   help   us
3. When out - ward   bound   we   bold - ly   sail   And   leave   the
4. When home-ward   bound   we   glad - ly   turn,   O   bring   us
5. Be - yond   the   cir - cle   of   the   sea,   When   voy - age -

ves - sels   fare,   A - bove   our   life's   ad - ven - ture   keep
or   de - lay,   Nor   where   the   lurk - ing   tem - pest   hides,
friend - ly   shore,   Let   not   our   heart   of   cour - age   fail
safe - ly   there,   Where har - bor - lights   of   friend - ship   burn
ing   is   past,   We   seek   our   fi - nal   port   in   thee;

Thy   faith - ful   watch   and   care,   In   thee   we   trust, what -
Nor   where   the   fogs   are   gray.   We   trust   in   thee, what -
Un - til   the   voyage   is   o'er.   We   trust   in   thee, what -
And   peace   is   in   the   air.   We   trust   in   thee, what -
O   bring   us   home   at   last.   In   thee   we   trust, what -

e'-er   be - fall;   Thy   sea   is   great,   our   boats   are   small.   A - men.

260

PILOT. 7. 7. 7. 7. 7. 7.

EDWARD HOPPER, 1871

JOHN E. GOULD, 1871

1. Je - sus, Sav - iour, pi - lot me   O - ver life's tem - pest-uous sea;
2. As a moth - er stills her child,   Thou canst hush the o - cean wild;
3. When at last I near the shore, And the fear - ful break-ers roar

Un - known waves be-fore me roll,   Hid - ing rock and treach'rous shoal;
Bois -t'rous waves o - bey thy will   When thou say'st to them, 'Be still.'
'Twixt me and the peace-ful rest,   Then, while lean - ing on thy breast,

Chart and com-pass come from thee: Je - sus, Sav - iour, pi - lot me.
Won-drous Sov-'reign of the sea,   Je - sus, Sav - iour, pi - lot me.
May I hear thee say to me,   'Fear not, I will pi - lot thee.' A - men.

261

NOX PRÆCESSIT. C. M.

BERNARD BARTON, 1826

J. BAPTISTE CALKIN, 1875

1. Walk in the light; so shalt thou know That fel - low-ship of love
2. Walk in the light; and thou shalt find Thy heart made tru - ly his,
3. Walk in the light; and thou shalt own Thy dark - ness passed a - way,
4. Walk in the light; and thine shall be A path, though thorn - y, bright;

His spir - it on - ly can be-stow, Who reigns in light a - bove.
Who dwells in cloudless light enshrined, In whom no dark - ness is.
Be-cause that light hath on thee shone In which is per - fect day.
For God, by grace, shall dwell in thee, And God him - self is light   A - men.

262

WESTON. 5. 5. 8. 8. 5. 5.

Nicolaus L. von Zinzendorf, 1721
Translated by Jane Borthwick, 1846

Josiah Booth (1852- —)

1. Je - sus   still   lead   on,   Till   our   rest   be   won:
2. If   the   way   be   drear,   If   the   foe   be   near,
3. When   we   seek   re - lief   For   a   long - felt   grief;
4. Je - sus,   still   lead   on,   Till   our   rest   be   won;

And, al - though the way be cheer - less   We will fol - low, calm and
Let not faith - less fears o'er - take us,   Let not faith   and hope for -
When temp - ta - tions come al - lur - ing,   Make us pa - tient and en -
Heaven-ly Lead - er, still di - rect us,   Still sup - port, con - sole, pro -

fear - less;   Guide us by thy hand   To our Fa - ther - land.
sake us;   For, through man-y a foe,   To our home we   go.
dur - ing;   Show us that bright shore   Where we weep no   more.
tect us,   Till   we safe - ly stand   In our Fa - ther - land.   A - men.

The Christian Life

263

SICILIAN MARINERS. 8. 7. 8. 7. 4. 7.

James Edmeston, 1821

Sicilian Melody, 1794

1. Lead us, heaven-ly Fa-ther, lead us O'er the world's tem-
pest-uous sea; Guard us, guide us, keep us, feed us,
For we have no help but thee; Yet pos-sess-ing
Ev - ery bless-ing, If our God our Fa-ther be.

2. Sav - iour, breathe for - give-ness o'er us, All our weak-ness
thou dost know; Thou did'st tread this earth be - fore us,
Thou didst feel its keen-est woe; Lone and drear - y,
Faint and wea - ry, Through the des - ert thou did'st go.

3. Spir - it of our God, de - scend-ing, Fill our hearts with
heaven-ly joy, Love with ev - ery pas - sion blend-ing,
Pleas - ure that can nev - er cloy; Thus pro - vid - ed,
Par - doned, guid - ed, Noth-ing can our peace de - stroy. A-men.

Illumination and Guidance

264

SEGUR. 8.7.8.7.4.7.

WILLIAM WILLIAMS, 1745

JOSEPH P. HOLBROOK, 1865

1. Guide me, O thou great Je - ho - vah, Pil - grim
2. O - pen now the crys - tal foun - tain, Whence the
3. When I tread the verge of Jor - dan, Bid my

through this bar - ren land; I am weak, but thou art might - y,
heal - ing stream doth flow; Let the fire and cloud - y pil - lar
anx - ious fears sub - side; Death of deaths and hell's de - struc - tion,

Hold me with thy power - ful hand: Bread of heav - en,
Lead me all my jour - ney through: Strong De - liv - 'rer,
Land me safe on Ca - naan's side: Songs of prais - es,

Bread of heav - en, Feed me till I want no more.
Strong De - liv - 'rer, Be thou still my strength and shield.
Songs of prais - es, I will ev - er give to thee. A - men.

265

WATCHWORD. 6. 5. 6. 5. D. With Refrain

HENRY ALFORD, 1871

HENRY SMART, 1872

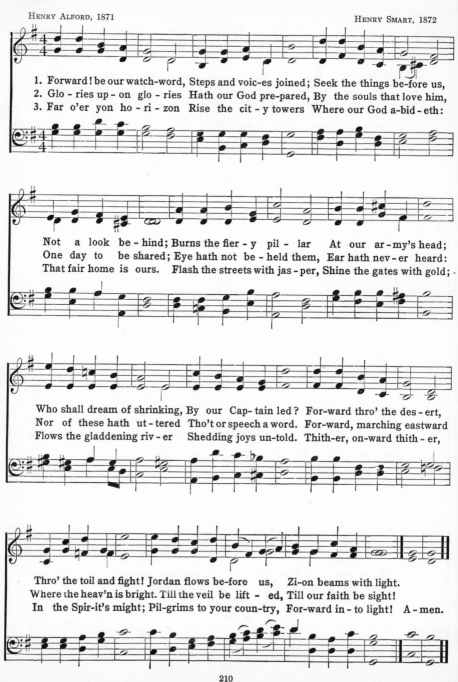

1. Forward! be our watch-word, Steps and voic-es joined; Seek the things be-fore us,
2. Glo - ries up - on glo - ries Hath our God pre-pared, By the souls that love him,
3. Far o'er yon ho - ri - zon Rise the cit - y towers Where our God a-bid - eth:

Not a look be - hind; Burns the fier - y pil - lar At our ar-my's head;
One day to be shared; Eye hath not be - held them, Ear hath nev - er heard:
That fair home is ours. Flash the streets with jas - per, Shine the gates with gold;

Who shall dream of shrinking, By our Cap- tain led? For-ward thro' the des - ert,
Nor of these hath ut - tered Tho't or speech a word. For-ward, marching eastward
Flows the gladdening riv - er Shedding joys un-told. Thith-er, on-ward thith - er,

Thro' the toil and fight! Jordan flows be-fore us, Zi-on beams with light.
Where the heav'n is bright. Till the veil be lift - ed, Till our faith be sight!
In the Spir-it's might; Pil-grims to your coun-try, For-ward in - to light! A - men.

266

ST. ASAPH. 8.7.8.7. D.

BERNHARDT S. INGEMANN, 1825
Translated by SABINE BARING-GOULD, 1867

WILLIAM S. BAMBRIDGE, 1872

1. Through the night of doubt and sor - row On - ward goes the pil-grim band,
2. One the light of God's own pres-ence O'er his ran-somed peo- ple shed,
3. One the strain that lips of thou-sands Lift as from the heart of one;

Sing - ing songs of ex - pec - ta - tion, March-ing to the prom-ised land.
Chas- ing far the gloom and ter - ror, Brightening all the path we tread;
One the con - flict, one the per - il, One the march in God be - gun;

Clear be - fore us through the dark-ness Gleams and burns the guid-ing light;
One the ob - ject of our jour-ney, One the faith which nev - er tires,
One the glad-ness of re - joic-ing On the far e - ter - nal shore,

Broth-er clasps the hand of broth - er, Stepping fearless through the night.
One the ear - nest look-ing for-ward, One the hope our God in - spires;
Where the one Al - might-y Fa - ther Reigns in love for - ev - er-more. A - men.

211

267

LUX BENIGNA. 10. 4. 10. 4. 10. 10.

JOHN H. NEWMAN, 1833

JOHN B. DYKES, 1868

1. Lead, kind-ly Light, a-mid th'en-cir-cling gloom,   Lead thou me on.
2. I was not ev - er thus, nor prayed that thou   Shouldst lead me on;
3. So long thy power hath blest me, sure it still   Will lead me on,

The night is dark, and I am far from home,—   Lead thou me on.
I loved to choose and see my path; but now   Lead thou me on.
O'er moor and fen, o'er crag and tor - rent, till   The night is gone;

Keep thou my feet; I do not ask to see
I loved the gar - ish day, and, spite of fears,
And with the morn those an - gel fa - ces smile

The dis - tant scene,— one step e - nough for me.
Pride ruled my will; re - mem - ber not past years.
Which I have loved long since, and lost a - while. A - men.

268

FELIX. 11. 10. 11. 10.

Anna B. Warner, 1858

Felix Mendelssohn, 1809–1847

1. We would see Je - sus; for the shad - ows length - en
2. We would see Je - sus, the great rock foun - da - tion
3. We would see Je - sus— oth - er lights are pal - ing,
4. We would see Je - sus; sense is all too bind - ing,
5. We would see Je - sus; this is all we're need - ing;

A - cross this lit - tle land - scape of our life;
Where - on our feet were set by sov - ereign grace:
Which for long years we have re - joiced to see;
And heaven ap - pears too dim, too far a - way;
Strength, joy, and will - ing - ness come with the sight;

We would see Je - sus, our weak faith to strength - en,
Nor life nor death, with all their ag - i - ta - tion,
The bless - ings of our pil - grim - age are fail - ing,
We would see thee, thy - self our hearts re - mind - ing
We would see Je - sus, dy - ing, ris - en, plead - ing;

For the last wea - ri - ness, the fi - nal strife.
Can thence re - move us, if we see his face.
We would not mourn them, for we go to thee.
What thou hast suf - fered, our great debt to pay.
Then wel - come day, and fare - well mor - tal night. A - men.

The Christian Life

269

BETHANY. 6. 4. 6. 4. 6. 6. 4.

SARAH F. ADAMS, 1841

LOWELL MASON, 1856

1. Near - er, my God, to thee, Near - er to thee!
2. Though like the wan - der - er, The sun gone down,
3. There let the way ap - pear Steps un - to heaven;
4. Then, with my wak - ing tho'ts Bright with thy praise,
5. Or if on joy - ful wing, Cleav - ing the sky,

E'en though it be a cross That rais - eth me;
Dark - ness be o - ver me, My rest a stone;
All that thou send - est me In mer - cy given;
Out of my ston - y griefs, Beth - el I'll raise;
Sun, moon, and stars for - got, Up - ward I fly,

Still all my song shall be, Near - er, my God, to thee,
Yet in my dreams I'd be Near - er, my God, to thee,
An - gels to beck - on me Near - er, my God, to thee,
So by my woes to be Near - er, my God, to thee,
Still all my song shall be, Near - er, my God, to thee,

Near - er, my God, to thee, Near - er to thee! A - men.

214

Illumination and Guidance

270

HE LEADETH ME. L. M. With Refrain

JOSEPH H. GILMORE, 1859

WILLIAM B. BRADBURY, 1864

1. He lead-eth me; O bless-ed thought! O words with heavenly comfort fraught!
2. Sometimes 'mid scenes of deepest gloom, Sometimes where Eden's bowers bloom,
3. Lord, I would clasp thy hand in mine, Nor ev - er mur - mur nor re-pine;
4. And when my task on earth is done, When, by thy grace, the vic-t'ry's won,

What-e'er I do, wher-e'er I be, Still 'tis God's hand that lead-eth me.
By wa - ters calm, o'er troubled sea,—Still 'tis his hand that lead-eth me.
Con - tent, what-ev - er lot I see, Since 'tis my God that lead-eth me.
E'en death's cold wave I will not flee, Since God thro' Jor - dan lead-eth me.

Refrain

He lead-eth me, he lead-eth me, By his own hand he lead-eth me:

His faith-ful fol-lower I would be, For by his hand he lead-eth me. A-men.

271

EDENGROVE. 7. 6. 7. 6.

ANNA L. WARING, 1850

SAMUEL SMITH, 1874

1. In heaven-ly love a-bid-ing, No change my heart shall fear;
2. Wher-ev-er he may guide me, No want shall turn me back;
3. Green pas-tures are be-fore me, Which yet I have not seen;

And safe is such con-fid-ing, For noth-ing chan-ges here.
My Shep-herd is be-side me, And noth-ing can I lack.
Bright skies will soon be o'er me, Where dark-est clouds have been.

The storm may roar with-out me, My heart may low be laid,
His wis-dom ev-er wak-eth, His sight is nev-er dim,
My hope I can-not meas-ure, My path to life is free,

But God is 'round a-bout me, And can I be dis-mayed?
He knows the way he tak-eth, And I will walk with him.
My Sav-iour has my treas-ure, And he will walk with me. A-men.

272

ST. KEVIN. 7.6.7.6. D.

Mary Butler, 1881

Arthur S. Sullivan, 1872

1. Look-ing up-ward ev-ery day, Sun-shine on our fa - ces;
2. Walk-ing ev-ery day more close To our El - der Broth - er;
3. Leav-ing ev-ery day be - hind Some-thing which might hin - der;

Press - ing on-ward ev-ery day Toward the heaven-ly pla - ces;
Grow - ing ev-ery day more true Un - to one an - oth - er;
Run - ning swift-er ev-ery day, Grow-ing pur - er, kind - er,—

Grow - ing ev-ery day in awe, For thy name is ho - ly;
Ev - ery day more grate-ful - ly Kind-ness - es re - ceiv - ing;
Lord, so pray we ev-ery day, Hear us in thy pit - y,

Learn-ing ev-ery day to love With a love more low-ly;
Ev - ery day more read-i - ly In - ju - ries for-giv - ing;
That we en-ter in at last To the ho - ly cit - y. A-men.

273

BRADBURY. 8. 7. 8. 7. D.

'Hymns for the Young,' 1836

WILLIAM B. BRADBURY, 1859

1. Sav-iour, like a shep-herd lead us, Much we need thy ten-der care;
2. We are thine, do thou be-friend us; Be the guard-ian of our way;
3. Thou hast prom-ised to re - ceive us, Poor and sin - ful tho' we be;
4. Ear - ly let us seek thy fa - vor, Ear - ly let us do thy will;

In thy pleas-ant pas-tures feed us, For our use thy folds pre- pare:
Keep thy flock, from sin de - fend us, Seek us when we go a - stray:
Thou hast mer - cy to re - lieve us, Grace to cleanse, and power to free:
Bless-ed Lord and on - ly Sav - iour, With thy love our bo-soms fill:

Bless-ed Je - sus, bless-ed Je - sus, Thou hast bought us, thine we are,
Bless-ed Je - sus, bless-ed Je - sus, Hear the chil - dren when they pray,
Bless-ed Je - sus, bless-ed Je - sus, Ear - ly let us turn to thee,
Bless-ed Je - sus, bless-ed Je - sus, Thou hast loved us, love us still,

Bless-ed Je-sus, bless-ed Je - sus, Thou hast bought us, thine we are.
Bless-ed Je-sus, bless-ed Je - sus, Hear the children when they pray.
Bless-ed Je-sus, bless-ed Je - sus, Ear - ly let us turn to thee.
Bless-ed Je-sus, bless-ed Je - sus, Thou hast loved us, love us still. A-men.

Illumination and Guidance

274

KIRBY BEDON. 6. 6. 4. 6. 6. 6. 4.

CLEMENT OF ALEXANDRIA, about 200 A.D.
Translated by HENRY M. DEXTER, 1846

EDWARD BUNNETT, 1887

1. Shep - herd of ten - der youth, Guid - ing in love and
2. Thou art the great High Priest; Thou hast pre - pared the
3. Ev - er be thou our Guide, Our Shep - herd and our
4. So now, and till we die, Sound we thy prais - es

truth, Through de - vious ways; Christ our tri -
feast Of heaven - ly love; In all our
Pride, Our Staff and Song; Je - sus, thou
high, And joy - ful sing; Let all the

um - phant King, We come thy name to sing,
mor - tal pain None call on thee in vain;
Christ of God, By thy per - en - nial word,
ho - ly throng Who to thy Church be - long,

And here our chil - dren bring To shout thy praise.
Help thou did'st not dis - dain, Help from a - bove.
Lead us where thou hast trod, Make our faith strong.
U - nite and swell the song To Christ our King! A - men.

219

The Christian Life

275

ST. CATHERINE. 8. 8. 8. 8. 8. 8.

PAUL GERHARDT, 1653
Translated by JOHN WESLEY, 1739

HENRI F. HEMY and
JAMES G. WALTON, 1874

1. Je - sus, thy bound - less love to me
   No thought can reach, no tongue de - clare; O knit my thank - ful heart to thee,
   And reign with - out a ri - val there: Thine whol - ly, thine a - lone, I am, Be thou a - lone my con - stant Flame.

2. O grant that noth - ing in my soul
   May dwell, but thy pure love a - lone; O may thy love pos - sess me whole,
   My joy, my treas - ure, and my crown: Strange fires far from my soul re - move; My ev - ery act, word, thought, be love.

3. O love, how cheer - ing is thy ray!
   All pain be - fore thy pres - ence flies: Care, an - guish, sor - row, melt a - way,
   Wher - e'er thy heal - ing beams a - rise. O Je - sus, noth - ing may I see, Noth - ing de - sire, or seek, but thee.

4. Still let thy love point out my way;
   What wondrous things thy love hath wrought! Still lead me, lest I go a - stray;
   Di - rect my work, in - spire my thought; And if I fall, soon may I hear Thy voice, and know that love is near.

5. In suf - fering, be thy love my peace;
   In weak - ness, be thy love my power; And when the storms of life shall cease,
   Je - sus, in that e - vent - ful hour, In death, as life, be Guide and Friend, That I may love thee with - out end. A - men.

220

Love and Gratitude

276

ST. CHRYSOSTOM. 8. 8. 8. 8. 8. 8.

HENRY COLLINS, 1854, Altered

JOSEPH BARNBY, 1871

1. Je - sus, my Lord, my God, my all, Hear me blest Sav - iour,
2. Je - sus, too late I thee have sought; How can I love thee
3. Je - sus, what didst thou find in me That thou hast dealt so
4. Je - sus, of thee shall be my song; To thee my heart and

when I call; Hear me, and from thy dwell - ing - place Pour
as I ought? And how ex - tol thy match - less fame, The
lov - ing - ly? How great the joy that thou hast brought! O
soul be - long: All that I am or have is thine; And

down the rich - es of thy grace. Je - sus, my Lord, I
glo - rious beau - ty of thy Name? Je - sus, my Lord, I
far ex - ceed - ing hope or thought! Je - sus, my Lord, I
thou, my Sav - iour, thou art mine. Je - sus, my Lord, I

thee a - dore; O make me love thee more and more! A - men.

221

The Christian Life

277

JAMES G. SMALL, 1866

CONSTANCE. 8. 7. 8. 7. D.

ARTHUR S. SULLIVAN, 1875

1. I've found a Friend; O such a Friend! He loved me ere I knew him;
2. I've found a Friend; O such a Friend! He bled, he died to save me;
3. I've found a Friend; O such a Friend! So kind and true and ten - der!

He drew me with the cords of love, And thus he bound me to him;
And not a - lone the gift of life, But his own self he gave me.
So wise a Coun - sel - lor and Guide, So might - y a De - fend - er!

And round my heart still close - ly twine Those ties which naught can sev - er,
Naught that I have, mine own I call, I'll hold it for the Giv - er,
From him who loves me now so well What power my soul shall sev - er?

For I am his and he is mine, For - ev - er and for - ev - er.
My heart, my strength, my life, my all, Are his, and his for - ev - er.
Shall life or death, shall earth or hell? No: I am his for - ev - er. A - men.

222

Love and Gratitude

GREENLAND. 7. 6. 7. 6. D.

278

Frances R. Havergal, 1870

J. Michael Haydn, 1737–1806

1. O Sav-iour, pre-cious Sav-iour, Whom yet un-seen we love,
2. O bring-er of sal-va-tion, Who won-drous-ly hast wrought,
3. In thee all ful-ness dwell-eth, All grace and power di-vine;
4. O grant the con-sum-ma-tion Of this our song a-bove,

O Name of might and fa-vor, All oth-er names a-bove!
Thy-self the rev-e-la-tion Of love be-yond our thought,
The glo-ry that ex-cell-eth, O Son of God, is thine;
In end-less ad-o-ra-tion, And ev-er-last-ing love;

We wor-ship thee, we bless thee, To thee, O Christ, we sing;
We wor-ship thee, we bless thee, To thee, O Christ, we sing;
We wor-ship thee, we bless thee, To thee, O Christ, we sing;
Then shall we praise and bless thee Where per-fect prais-es ring,

We praise thee, and con-fess thee Our ho-ly Lord and King.
We praise thee, and con-fess thee Our gra-cious Lord and King.
We praise thee, and con-fess thee Our glo-rious Lord and King.
And ev-er-more con-fess thee Our Sav-iour and our King. A-men.

The Christian Life

279

DOMINUS REGIT ME. 8. 7. 8. 7.

HENRY W. BAKER, 1868

JOHN B. DYKES, 1868

1. The King of love my Shep - herd is, Whose
2. Where streams of liv - ing wa - ter flow, My
3. Per - verse and fool - ish oft I strayed, But
4. In death's dark vale I fear no ill With
5. And so through all the length of days, Thy

good - ness fail - eth nev - er; I noth - ing lack if
ran - somed soul he lead - eth, And, where the ver - dant
yet in love he sought me, And on his shoul - der
thee, dear Lord, be - side me; Thy rod and staff my
good - ness fail - eth nev - er; Good Shep - herd, may I

I am his, And he is mine for - ev - er.
pas - tures grow, With food ce - les - tial feed - eth.
gen - tly laid, And home, re - joic - ing, brought me.
com - fort still, Thy cross be - fore to guide me.
sing thy praise With - in thy house for - ev - er. A - men.

280

POSEN. 7. 7. 7. 7.

JANE E. LEESON, 1842

GEORGE C. STRATTNER, 1691

1. Sav - iour, teach me, day by day, Love's sweet les - son to o - bey;
2. With a child - like heart of love, At thy bid - ding may I move;
3. Teach me all thy steps to trace, Strong to fol - low in thy grace;
4. Love in lov - ing finds em - ploy, In o - be - dience all her joy;
5. Thus may I re - joice to show That I feel the love I owe;

Love and Gratitude

Sweet-er les-son can-not be, Lov-ing him who first loved me.
Prompt to serve and fol-low thee, Lov-ing him who first loved me.
Learn-ing how to love from thee; Lov-ing him who first loved me.
Ev-er new that joy will be, Lov-ing him who first loved me.
Sing-ing, till thy face I see, Of his love who first loved me. A-men.

281

ST. MARGARET. 8. 8. 8. 8. 6.

GEORGE MATHESON, 1882   ALBERT PEACE, 1885

1. O Love that wilt not let me go, I rest my wea-ry
2. O Light that fol-lowest all my way, I yield my flick-ering
3. O Joy that seek-est me through pain, I can-not close my
4. O Cross that lift-est up my head, I dare not ask to

soul in thee; I give thee back the life I owe,
torch to thee; My heart re-stores its bor-rowed ray,
heart to thee; I trace the rain-bow through the rain,
fly from thee; I lay in dust life's glo-ry dead,

That in thine o-cean depths its flow May rich-er, full-er be.
That in thy sun-shine's blaze its day May bright-er, fair-er be.
And feel the prom-ise is not vain That morn shall tearless be.
And from the ground there blossoms red Life that shall end-less be. A-men.

225

The Christian Life

282

SAWLEY. C. M.

RAY PALMER, 1859

JAMES WALCH, 1860

1. Je - sus, these eyes have nev - er seen That ra - diant form of thine;
2. I see thee not, I hear thee not, Yet art thou oft with me;
3. Yet, though I have not seen, and still Must rest in faith a - lone,
4. When death these mor-tal eyes shall seal, And still this throb-bing heart.

The veil of sense hangs dark be-tween Thy bless-ed face and mine.
And earth hath ne'er so dear a spot As where I meet with thee.
I love thee, dear - est Lord,—and will, Un-seen, but not un-known.
The rend-ing veil shall thee re - veal, All glo-rious as thou art! A - men.

283

ST. AGNES. C. M.

BERNARD OF CLAIRVAUX, 1091–1153
Translated by EDWARD CASWALL

JOHN B. DYKES, 1866

1. Je - sus, the ver - y thought of thee With sweet-ness fills my breast;
2. Nor voice can sing, nor heart can frame, Nor can the mem-ory find
3. O Hope of ev - ery con - trite heart, O Joy of all the meek,
4. But what to those who find? Ah, this—Nor tongue nor pen can show;
5. Je - sus, our on - ly joy be thou, As thou our prize wilt be;

But sweet-er far thy face to see, And in thy pres - ence rest.
A sweet-er sound than thy blest name, O Sav-iour of man-kind!
To those that fall, how kind thou art! How good to those who seek!
The love of Je - sus, what it is None but his loved ones know.
Je - sus, be thou our glo - ry now, And through e - ter - ni - ty. A - men.

Love and Gratitude

284
ST. PETER. C. M.

JOHN NEWTON, 1779

ALEXANDER R. REINAGLE, 1826

1. How sweet the name of Je - sus sounds In a be - liev - er's ear!
2. It makes the wound-ed spir - it whole, And calms the troub - led breast;
3. Dear Name, the rock on which I build, My shield and hid - ing - place,
4. Je - sus! my Shep-herd, Guardian, Friend, My Proph- et, Priest and King!
5. Weak is the ef - fort of my heart, And cold my warm- est thought;

It soothes his sorrows, heals his wounds, And drives a-way his fear.
'Tis man - na to the hun -gry soul, And to the wea - ry, rest.
My nev - er - fail - ing treas-ury, filled With boundless stores of grace.
My Lord, my Life, my Way, my End! Ac - cept the praise I bring.
But when I see thee as thou art, I'll praise thee as I ought. A - men.

285
AZMON. C. M.

CHARLES WESLEY, 1739

CARL G. GLASER, 1828
Arranged by LOWELL MASON, 1839

1. O for a thou - sand tongues to sing My dear Re - deem-er's praise,
2. My gra - cious Mas - ter and my God, As - sist me to pro - claim,
3. Je - sus, the name that charms our fears, That bids our sor - rows cease;
4. He breaks the power of reign - ing sin, He sets the pris - oner free;
5. He speaks, and, list - ening to his voice, New life the dead re - ceive;

The glo - ries of my God and King, The tri - umphs of his grace!
To spread thro' all the earth a-broad, The hon - ors of thy name.
'Tis mu - sic in the sin - ner's ears, 'Tis life, and health, and peace.
His blood can make the foulest clean, His blood a - vailed for me.
The mournful, bro-ken hearts rejoice; The hum-ble poor be - lieve. A - men.

286

ILIFF. 8. 8. 8. 2. 7.

John S. Blackie, 1876

Lindsay B. Longacre, 1912

1. Lord of might, and Lord of glo - ry, On my
2. Grop - ing dim, and bend - ing low - ly, Mor - tal
3. In the deed that no man know - eth, Where no
4. In the work that no gold pay - eth, Where he
5. In his name, who meek and low - ly, Died to

knees I bow be - fore thee; With my whole heart I a -
vi - sion catch - eth slow - ly Glimp - ses of the pure and
praise - ful trump - et blow - eth, Where he may not reap who
speed - eth best who pray - eth, Do - eth most who lit - tle
make poor sin - ners ho - ly, Stum - bling oft, and creep - ing

dore thee; Great Lord, Lis - ten to my cry, O Lord!
ho - ly; Now, Lord, O - pen thou mine eyes, O Lord!
sow - eth, There, Lord, Let my heart serve thee, O Lord!
say - eth, There, Lord, Let me work thy will, O Lord!
slow - ly, Great Lord, Guide me by thy truth, O Lord! A - men.

287

SUBMISSION. 10. 4. 10. 4.

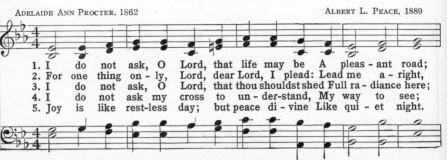

Adelaide Ann Procter, 1862

Albert L. Peace, 1889

1. I do not ask, O Lord, that life may be A pleas - ant road;
2. For one thing on - ly, Lord, dear Lord, I plead: Lead me a - right,
3. I do not ask, O Lord, that thou shouldst shed Full ra - diance here;
4. I do not ask my cross to un - der - stand, My way to see;
5. Joy is like rest - less day; but peace di - vine Like qui - et night.

Love and Gratitude

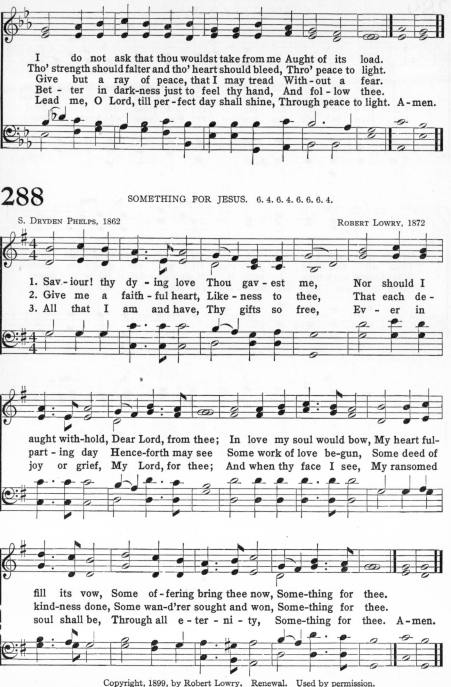

I   do not ask that thou wouldst take from me Aught of its   load.
Tho' strength should falter and tho' heart should bleed, Thro' peace to   light.
Give   but   a   ray   of   peace, that I may tread With - out a   fear.
Bet - ter   in   dark-ness just to feel thy hand, And fol - low   thee.
Lead   me, O Lord, till per -fect day shall shine, Through peace to light. A - men.

288   SOMETHING FOR JESUS. 6. 4. 6. 4. 6. 6. 6. 4.

S. DRYDEN PHELPS, 1862   ROBERT LOWRY, 1872

1. Sav.-iour! thy dy - ing love Thou gav - est   me,   Nor should I
2. Give me a   faith - ful heart, Like - ness to   thee,   That each de -
3. All that I am and have, Thy gifts so free,   Ev - er in

aught with-hold, Dear Lord, from thee; In love my soul would bow, My heart ful-
part - ing day Hence-forth may see   Some work of love be-gun, Some deed of
joy   or grief, My Lord, for thee; And when thy face I see, My ransomed

fill   its vow, Some of - fering bring thee now, Some-thing for   thee.
kind-ness done, Some wan-d'rer sought and won, Some-thing for   thee.
soul shall be, Through all e - ter - ni - ty, Some-thing for   thee. A - men.

289

HANKEY. 7. 6. 7. 6. D. With Refrain

KATHERINE HANKEY, 1874

WILLIAM G. FISCHER, 1869

1. I love to tell the sto - ry Of un - seen things a - bove,
2. I love to tell the sto - ry; More won - der - ful it seems
3. I love to tell the sto - ry; 'Tis pleas - ant to re - peat
4. I love to tell the sto - ry; For those who know it best

Of Je - sus and his glo - ry, Of Je - sus and his love.
Than all the gold - en fan - cies Of all our gold - en dreams,
What seems, each time I tell it, More won - der - ful - ly sweet.
Seem hun - ger - ing and thirst - ing To hear it, like the rest.

I love to tell the sto - ry, Be - cause I know 'tis true;
I love to tell the sto - ry, It did so much for me;
I love to tell the sto - ry, For some have nev - er heard
And when, in scenes of glo - ry, I sing the new, new song,

It sat - is - fies my long - ings As noth - ing else could do.
And that is just the rea - son I tell it now to thee.
The mes - sage of sal - va - tion From God's own ho - ly word.
'Twill be the old, old sto - ry That I have loved so long.

230

Love and Gratitude

Refrain

I love to tell the sto-ry, 'Twill be my theme in glo-ry,

To tell the old, old sto-ry, Of Je-sus and his love. A-men.

290

MORE LOVE TO THEE. 6. 4. 6. 4. 6. 6. 4.

ELIZABETH P. PRENTISS, 1869

WILLIAM H. DOANE, 1868

1. More love to thee, O Christ! More love to thee; Hear thou the
2. Once earth-ly joy I craved, Sought peace and rest; Now thee a-
3. Let sor-row do its work, Come grief or pain; Sweet are thy
4. Then shall my lat-est breath Whis-per thy praise, This be the

prayer I make On bend-ed knee; This is my ear-nest plea,
lone I seek, Give what is best: This all my prayer shall be,
mes-sen-gers, Sweet their re-frain, When they can sing with me,
part-ing cry My heart shall raise; This still its prayer shall be:

More love, O Christ, to thee, More love to thee, More love to thee! A-men.

291

MORLEY. 6. 5. 6. 5. D.

GODFREY THRING, 1862

THOMAS MORLEY, 1865

1. Sav - iour, bless - ed Sav - iour, Lis - ten while we sing;
2. Near - er, ev - er near - er, Christ, we draw to thee,
3. Bright - er still, and bright - er, Glows the gold - en sun,
4. On - ward, ev - er on - ward, Jour - neying o'er the road
5. Great and ev - er great - er Are thy mer - cies here,

Hearts and voic - es rais - ing Prais - es to our King.
Deep in ad - o - ra - tion Bend - ing low the knee;
Shed - ding all its glad - ness O'er our work be - gun;
Worn by saints be - fore us, Jour - neying on to God;
True and ev - er - last - ing Are thy glo - ries there;

All we have to of - fer, All we hope to be,
Life has lost its shad - ows, Pure the light with - in;
Ev - ery day that pass - eth, Ev - ery hour that flies,
Leav - ing all be - hind us, May we has - ten on,
Where no pain, nor sor - row, Toil or care is known,

Bod - y, soul and spir - it, All we yield to thee.
Thou hast shed thy ra - diance On a world of sin.
Tells of love in - car - nate, Love that nev - er dies.
Back - ward nev - er look - ing Till the prize be won.
Where the an - gel le - gions Cir - cle round thy throne. A - men.

Love and Gratitude

292

ELLACOMBE. C. M. D.

Horatius Bonar, 1866

Gesang Buch der Herzogl, 1784

1. Fill thou my life, O Lord, my God In ev-ery part with praise,
2. Praise in the com-mon words I speak, Life's com-mon looks and tones,
3. So shall each fear, each fret, each care, Be turn-ed in-to song,

That my whole be-ing may pro-claim Thy be-ing and thy ways;
In in-ter-course at hearth or board With my be-lov-ed ones,—
And ev-ery wind-ing of the way The ech-o shall pro-long;

Not for the lip of praise a-lone, Nor e'en the prais-ing heart
En-dur-ing wrong, re-proach, or loss With sweet and stead-fast will,
So shall no part of day or night From sa-cred-ness be free,

I ask, but for a life made up Of praise in ev-ery part.
Lov-ing and bless-ing those who hate, Re-turn-ing good for ill.
But all my life, in ev-ery step, Be fel-low-ship with thee. A-men.

233

293

ST. CRISPIN. L. M.

ALFRED TENNYSON, 1850

GEORGE J. ELVEY, 1862

1. Strong Son of God, im - mor - tal Love, Whom we, that
2. Thou seem - est hu - man and di - vine, The high - est,
3. Our lit - tle sys - tems have their day; They have their
4. We have but faith: we can - not know, For knowl - edge
5. Let knowl - edge grow from more to more, But more of

have not seen thy face, By faith, and faith a -
ho - liest man - hood, thou: Our wills are ours, we
day and cease to be; They are but bro - ken
is of things we see; And yet we trust it
rev - erence in us dwell; That mind and soul, ac -

lone, em - brace, Be - liev - ing where we can - not prove;
know not how; Our wills are ours, to make them thine.
lights of thee, And thou, O Lord, art more than they.
comes from thee, A beam in dark - ness: let it grow.
cord - ing well, May make one mu - sic as be - fore. A - men.

294

ST. BERNARD C. M.

Ascribed to FRANCIS XAVIER, 1546
Translated by EDWARD CASWALL, 1849

Cologne, 1741

1. My God, I love thee, not be - cause I hope for heaven there - by;
2. But, O my Je - sus, thou didst me Up - on the cross em - brace;
3. Then why, O bless - ed Je - sus Christ, Should I not love thee well?
4. Not with the hope of gain - ing aught, Not seek - ing a re - ward;
5. E'en so I love thee, and will love, And in thy praise will sing;

234

Love and Gratitude

Nor yet be-cause, if I love not, I must for-ev-er die.
For me didst bear the nails, and spear, And man-i-fold dis-grace.
Not for the hope of win-ning heaven, Nor of es-cap-ing hell;
But as thy-self hast lov-ed me, O ev-er-lov-ing Lord!
Sole-ly be-cause thou art my God, And my e-ter-nal King. A-men.

295

BRADFORD. C. M.

CHARLES WESLEY, 1707–1788   GEORGE F. HANDEL, 1685–1759

1. I know that my Re - deem - er lives, And
2. I find him lift - ing up my head; He
3. He wills that I should ho - ly be: What
4. Je - sus, I hang up - on thy word: I

ev - - er prays for me: A to - ken of his
brings sal - va - tion near: His pres - ence makes me
can with - stand his will? The coun - sel of his
stead - fast - ly be - lieve Thou wilt re - turn and

love he gives, A pledge of lib - er - ty.
free in - deed, And he will soon ap - pear.
grace in me He sure - ly shall ful - fill.
claim me, Lord, And to thy - self re - ceive. A - men.

235

The Christian Life

296

LEOMINSTER. S. M. D.

George W. Martin, 1862
Harmonized by Arthur Sullivan, 1874

George Matheson, 1842–1906

1. Make me a cap-tive, Lord, And then I shall be free; Force
2. My heart is weak and poor Un-til it mas-ter find: It
3. My power is faint and low Till I have learned to serve, It
4. My will is not my own Till thou hast made it thine; If

me to ren-der up my sword, And I shall con-q'ror be.
has no spring of ac-tion sure— It va-ries with the wind:
wants the need-ed fire to glow, It wants the breeze to nerve;
it would reach a mon-arch's throne It must its crown re-sign:

I sink in life's a-larms When by my-self I stand; Im-
It can-not free-ly move Till thou hast wrought its chain; En-
It can-not drive the world Un-til it-self be driven; Its
It on-ly stands un-bent A-mid the clash-ing strife, When

pris'n me in thy might-y arms, And strong shall be my hand.
slave it with thy match-less love, And death-less it shall reign.
flag can on-ly be un-furled When thou shalt breathe from heaven.
on thy bos-om it has leant, And found in thee its life. A-men.

Consecration and Obedience

297

ST. BEDE. 8. 6. 8. 6. 8. 6.

ANNA L. WARING, 1848, Arranged

JOHN B. DYKES, 1867

1. Fa - ther, I know that all my life Is por - tioned
2. I ask thee for a thought - ful love, Through con - stant
3. I would not have the rest - less will That hur - ries
4. I ask thee for the dai - ly strength To none that
5. In serv - ice which thy will ap - points There are no

out for me; The chan - ges that are sure to come
watch - ing wise, To meet the glad with joy - ful smiles,
to and fro, Seek - ing for some great thing to do,
ask de - nied, A mind to blend with out - ward life,
bonds for me; My in - most heart is taught the truth

I do not fear to see: I ask thee for a
And wipe the weep - ing eyes, A heart at leis - ure
Or se - cret thing to know; I would be treat - ed
While keep - ing at thy side; Con - tent to fill a
That makes thy chil - dren free: A life of self - re -

pres - ent mind, In - tent on pleas - ing thee.
from it - self To soothe and sym - pa - thize.
as a child, And guid - ed where I go.
lit - tle space, If thou be glo - ri - fied.
nounc - ing love Is one of lib - er - ty. A - men.

237

298

JEWETT. 6. 6. 6. 6. D

Benjamin Schmolck, 1716
Translated by Jane Borthwick, 1853

Arranged from
Carl M. von Weber

1. My Je - sus, as thou wilt! O may thy will be mine;
2. My Je - sus, as thou wilt! Tho' seen through many a tear,
3. My Je - sus, as thou wilt! All shall be well for me;

In - to thy hand of love I would my all re - sign.
Let not my star of hope Grow dim or dis - ap - pear.
Each chang - ing fu - ture scene I glad - ly trust with thee.

Through sor - row, or through joy, Con - duct me as thine own;
Since thou on earth hast wept And sor - rowed oft a - lone,
Straight to my home a - bove I trav - el calm - ly on,

And help me still to say, My Lord, thy will be done.
If I must weep with thee, My Lord, thy will be done.
And sing, in life or death, My Lord, thy will be done. A - men.

Consecration and Obedience

299

ELLESDIE. 8. 7. 8. 7. D.

HENRY F. LYTE, 1824

Arranged from MOZART
By HUBERT P. MAIN, 1873

1. Je - sus, I my cross have tak - en, All to leave and fol - low thee;
2. Take, my soul, thy full sal - va - tion, Rise o'er sin, and fear and care,
3. Haste, then, on from grace to glo - ry, Armed by faith and winged by prayer;

Des - ti - tute, de - spised, for - sak - en, Thou, from hence, my all shalt be:
Joy to find in ev - ery sta - tion Some-thing still to do or bear!
Heaven's e - ter - nal day's be - fore thee, God's own hand shall guide thee there:

Per - ish ev - ery fond am - bi - tion, All I've sought, and hoped, or known;
Think what Spir-it dwells with - in thee, What a Fa - ther's smile is thine,
Soon shall close thy earth - ly mis-sion, Swift shall pass thy pil - grim days,

Yet how rich is my con-di -tion, God and heaven are still my own!
What a Sav-iour died to win thee,—Child of heaven, shouldst thou repine?
Hope shall change to glad fru- i- tion, Faith to sight, and prayer to praise. A-men.

300

ANGEL'S STORY. 7. 6. 7. 6. D

JOHN E. BODE, 1869

ARTHUR H. MANN, 1881

1. O Je - sus, I have prom - ised To serve thee to the end;
2. O let me feel thee near me! The world is ev - er near;
3. O let me hear thee speak - ing In ac - cents clear and still;
4. O Je - sus, thou hast prom - ised To all who fol - low thee,

Be thou for - ev - er near me, My Mas - ter and my Friend;
I see the sights that daz - zle, The tempt - ing sounds I hear:
A - bove the storms of pas - sion, The mur - murs of self - will!
That where thou art in glo - ry There shall thy ser - vant be;

I shall not fear the bat - tle If thou art by my side,
My foes are ev - er near me, A - round me and with - in;
O speak to re - as - sure me, To has - ten or con - trol!
And, Je - sus, I have prom - ised To serve thee to the end;

Nor wan - der from the path-way, If thou wilt be my Guide.
But, Je - sus, draw thou near - er, And shield my soul from sin.
O speak, and make me lis - ten, Thou Guard-ian of my soul!
O give me grace to fol - low, My Mas - ter and my Friend. A - men.

Consecration and Obedience

301

CONSECRATION. 7.7.7.7. D.

Frances R. Havergal, 1874

Anonymous

1. Take my life, and let it be Con-se-crat-ed, Lord, to thee.
2. Take my voice, and let me sing Al-ways, on-ly, for my King.
3. Take my will, and make it thine; It shall be no long-er mine.

Take my mo-ments and my days; Let them flow in cease-less praise.
Take my lips, and let them be Filled with mes-sa-ges from thee.
Take my heart, it is thine own; It shall be thy roy-al throne.

Take my hands, and let them move At the im-pulse of thy love.
Take my sil-ver and my gold; Not a mite would I with-hold.
Take my love; my Lord, I pour At thy feet its treas-ure-store.

Take my feet, and let them be Swift and beau-ti-ful for thee.
Take my in-tel-lect, and use Ev-ery power as thou shalt choose.
Take my-self, and I will be Ev-er, on-ly, all for thee. A-men.

302

HOLLEY. L. M.

Frank W. Gunsaulus, 1856–1921

George Hews, 1835

1. O God, would I might bring to thee Of ri - pened
2. I take thy prom - ise to my heart; 'Thy pla - ces
3. My waste of time, Im - mor - tal One, A - lone e -
4. My waste of power—thy wis - dom, Lord, Will show me
5. The waste that sin has wrought in me, Be - neath thy

grain an au - tumn yield; But midst my har - vest
waste I will re - store.' Nev - er shall hope or
ter - ni - ty may take, And bind my loss - es
things worth while at length; Then will I bat - tle
cross is all re - stored; My time, my power, my

sheaves I see The pla - ces waste with - in my field.
joy de - part If love so tri - umph ev - er - more.
to thy throne, To make them gains for love's dear sake.
in ac - cord With love's un - fold - ing arm of strength.
heart to thee, My life re - newed I give thee, Lord. A - men.

303

RADIANT MORN. 8. 8. 8. 4.

Frederic Smith, 1870

Charles F. Gounod, 1872

1. O God, not on - ly in dis - tress, In pain and want and wea - ri - ness,
2. But often-er on the wings of peace And girt a - bout with ten-der - ness,
3. In all that na - ture hath sup-plied, In flowers a - long the coun - try side,
4. And when the burdened heart can bring Its sor-rows to thy feet, and cling
5. Thy will is pure, O Lord, and just; And we, frail crea-tures of the dust,

Consecration and Obedience

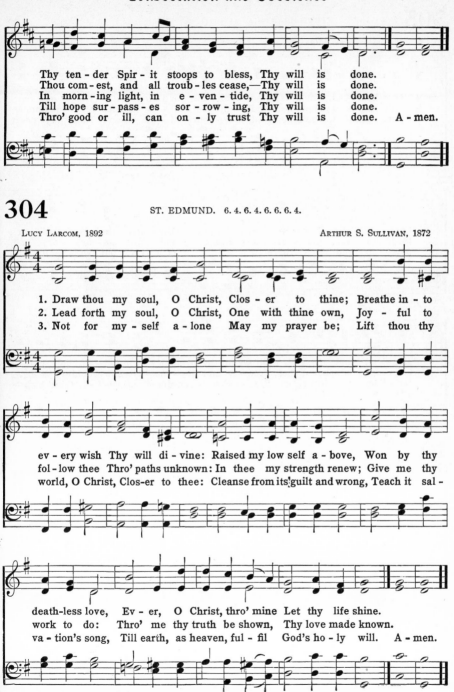

Thy ten - der Spir - it stoops to bless, Thy will is done.
Thou com - est, and all troub - les cease,—Thy will is done.
In morn - ing light, in e - ven - tide, Thy will is done.
Till hope sur - pass - es sor - row - ing, Thy will is done.
Thro' good or ill, can on - ly trust Thy will is done. A - men.

304

ST. EDMUND. 6.4.6.4.6.6.6.4.

Lucy Larcom, 1892

Arthur S. Sullivan, 1872

1. Draw thou my soul, O Christ, Clos - er to thine; Breathe in - to
2. Lead forth my soul, O Christ, One with thine own, Joy - ful to
3. Not for my - self a - lone May my prayer be; Lift thou thy

ev - ery wish Thy will di - vine: Raised my low self a - bove, Won by thy
fol - low thee Thro' paths unknown: In thee my strength renew; Give me thy
world, O Christ, Clos - er to thee: Cleanse from its guilt and wrong, Teach it sal -

death-less love, Ev - er, O Christ, thro' mine Let thy life shine.
work to do: Thro' me thy truth be shown, Thy love made known.
va - tion's song, Till earth, as heaven, ful - fil God's ho - ly will. A - men.

The Christian Life

305

TRUE-HEARTED. 11. 10. 11. 10. With Refrain

FRANCES R. HAVERGAL, 1874

GEORGE C. STEBBINS, 1890

1. True-heart-ed, whole-heart-ed, faith-ful and loy-al, King of our
2. True-heart-ed, whole-heart-ed, full-est al-le-giance Yield-ing hence-
3. True-heart-ed, whole-heart-ed, Sav-iour all-glo-rious! Take thy great

lives, by thy grace we will be; Un-der the stand-ard ex-
forth to our glo-ri-ous King; Val-iant en-deav-or and
pow-er and reign there a-lone, O-ver our wills and af-

alt-ed and roy-al, Strong in thy strength we will bat-tle for thee.
lov-ing o-be-dience, Free-ly and joy-ous-ly now would we bring.
fec-tions vic-to-rious, Free-ly sur-ren-dered and whol-ly thine own.

Refrain

Peal out the watch-word! si-lence it nev-er! Song of our
Peal out the watch-word! si-lence it nev-er! Song of our

spir-its, re-joic-ing and free; Peal out the watch-word! loy-al for-
spir-its, re-joic-ing and free; Peal out the watch-word! loy-al for-

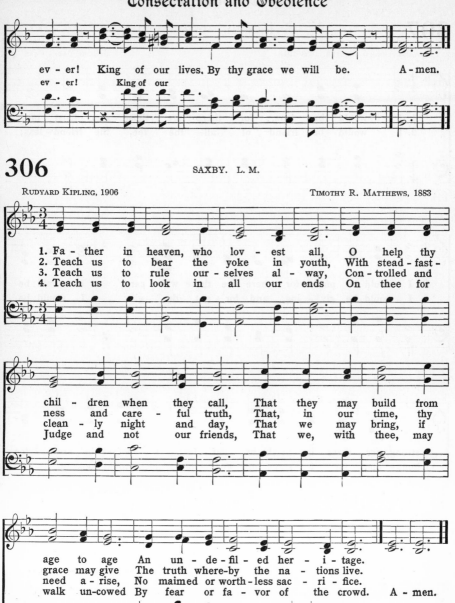

ev - er! King of our lives. By thy grace we will be. A - men.

ev - er! King of our

306

SAXBY. L. M.

RUDYARD KIPLING, 1906

TIMOTHY R. MATTHEWS, 1883

1. Fa - ther in heaven, who lov - est all, O help thy
2. Teach us to bear the yoke in youth, With stead - fast -
3. Teach us to rule our - selves al - way, Con - trolled and
4. Teach us to look in all our ends On thee for

chil - dren when they call, That they may build from
ness and care - ful truth, That, in our time, thy
clean - ly night and day, That we may bring, if
Judge and not our friends, That we, with thee, may

age to age An un - de - fil - ed her - i - tage.
grace may give The truth where-by the na - tions live.
need a - rise, No maimed or worth - less sac - ri - fice.
walk un-cowed By fear or fa - vor of the crowd. A - men.

5 Teach us the strength that cannot seek,
   By deed or thought, to hurt the weak,
   That, under thee, we may possess
   Man's strength to comfort man's distress.

6 Teach us delight in simple things,
   And mirth that has no bitter springs,
   Forgiveness free of evil done,
   And love to all men 'neath the sun.

The Christian Life

PEEK. 11. 10. 11. 10.

HOWARD ARNOLD WALTER, 1883-1918

JOSEPH YATES PEEK

1. I would be true, for there are those who trust me;
2. I would be friend of all— the foe, the friend - less;

I would be pure, for there are those who care; I would be
I would be giv - ing, and for - get the gift; I would be

strong, for there is much to suf - fer; I would be brave, for
hum - ble, for I know my weak - ness; I would look up, and

there is much to dare, I would be brave, for there is much to dare.
laugh, and love, and lift, I would look up, and laugh, and love, and lift. A-men.

Used by permission of J. Yates Peek

Consecration and Obedience

308

ARMAGEDDON. 6. 5. 6. 5. 12 lines

Frances R. Havergal, 1877

Arranged by
John Goss, 1871

1. Who is on the Lord's side? Who will serve the King? Who will be his help-ers
2. Not for weight of glo - ry, Not for crown and palm, En - ter we the ar - my,
3. Je - sus, thou hast bought us, Not with gold or gem, But with thine own life-blood,
4. Fierce may be the con - flict, Strong may be the∙ foe, But the King's own ar - my

Oth - er lives to bring? Who will leave the world's side? Who will face the foe?
Raise the war-rior psalm; But for love that claim - eth Lives for whom he died:
For thy di - a - dem: With thy bless-ing fill - ing Each who comes to thee,
None can o - ver - throw: Round his stan-dard rang-ing, Vic - tory is se - cure;

Who is on the Lord's side? Who for him will go? By thy call of mer - cy,
He whom Je - sus nam - eth, Must be on his side. By thy love con-strain-ing,
Thou hast made us will - ing, Thou hast made us free. By thy grand re-demp-tion,
For his truth un-chang-ing Makes the tri-umph sure. Joy-ful - ly en - list - ing

By thy grace di - vine, We are on the Lord's side, Saviour, we are thine. A-men.

The Christian Life

309

CARTER. 8.7.8.7.

Love M. Willis, 1859

Edmund S. Carter, 1874

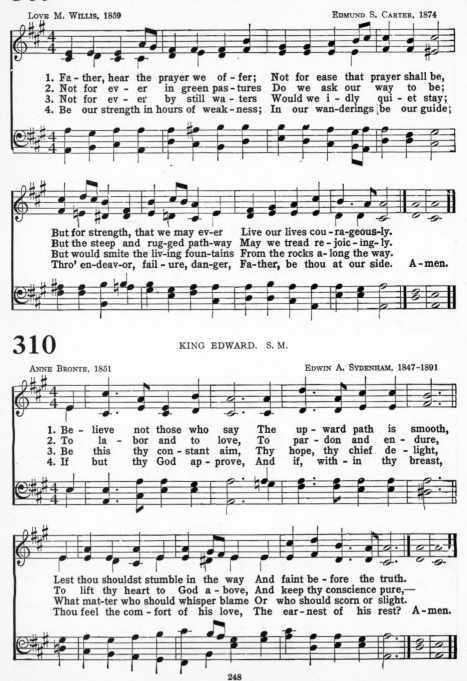

1. Fa - ther, hear the prayer we of - fer; Not for ease that prayer shall be,
2. Not for ev - er in green pas - tures Do we ask our way to be;
3. Not for ev - er by still wa - ters Would we i - dly qui - et stay;
4. Be our strength in hours of weak - ness; In our wan-derings be our guide;

But for strength, that we may ev-er Live our lives cou - ra-geous-ly.
But the steep and rug-ged path-way May we tread re - joic-ing-ly.
But would smite the liv-ing foun-tains From the rocks a- long the way.
Thro' en-deav-or, fail - ure, dan-ger, Fa-ther, be thou at our side. A-men.

310

KING EDWARD. S. M.

Anne Bronte, 1851

Edwin A. Sydenham, 1847-1891

1. Be - lieve not those who say The up - ward path is smooth,
2. To la - bor and to love, To par - don and en - dure,
3. Be this thy con - stant aim, Thy hope, thy chief de - light,
4. If but thy God ap - prove, And if, with - in thy breast,

Lest thou shouldst stumble in the way And faint be - fore the truth.
To lift thy heart to God a - bove, And keep thy conscience pure,—
What mat-ter who should whisper blame Or who should scorn or slight.
Thou feel the com - fort of his love, The ear - nest of his rest? A-men.

311

SILVER STREET. S. M.

Samuel Johnson, 1846

Isaac Smith, 1770

1. God of the ear - nest heart, The trust as - sured and still,
2. Up - on that pain - ful road By saints se - rene - ly trod,
3. 'Gainst doubt and shame and fear In hu - man hearts to strive,
4. To draw thy bless - ing down, And bring the wronged re - dress,

Thou who our strength for-ev - er art,—We come to do thy will.
Where-on their hallowing in-fluence flowed, Would we go forth, O God,—
That all may learn to love and bear, To con - quer self, and live,—
And give this glo - rious world its crown Of truth and righteousness. A-men.

312

VIGILATE. 7. 7. 7. 3.

Charlotte Elliott, 1839

William H. Monk, 1868

1. Chris-tian, seek not yet re - pose, Cast thy dreams of ease a - way;
2. Gird thy heaven-ly ar - mor on, Wear it ev - er, night and day;
3. Hear the vic - tors who o'er - came; Still they mark each war-rior's way;
4. Hear, a - bove all, hear thy Lord, Him thou lov - est to o - bey;
5. Watch, as if on that a - lone Hung the is - sue of the day;

Thou art in the midst of foes: Watch and pray!
Am - bushed lies the e - vil one: Watch and pray!
All with one sweet voice ex - claim: 'Watch and pray!'
Hide with - in thy heart his word: 'Watch and pray!'
Pray that help may be sent down: Watch and pray! A - men.

313

CHRISTMAS. C. M.

PHILIP DODDRIDGE, 1702–1751

GEORGE F. HANDEL, 1728

1. A - wake, my soul, stretch ev - ery nerve, And press with vig - or
2. A cloud of wit - ness - es a - round Hold thee in full sur -
3. 'Tis God's all - an - i - mat - ing voice That calls thee from on
4. Blest Sav - iour, in - tro - duced by thee, Have I my race be -

on! A heaven-ly race de - mands thy zeal, And
vey; For - get the steps al - read - y trod, And
high; 'Tis his own hand pre - sents the prize To
gun; And, crowned with vic - tory, at thy feet I'll

an im - mor - tal crown, And an im - mor - tal crown.
on - ward urge thy way, And on - ward urge thy way.
thine as - pir - ing eye, To thine as - pir - ing eye.
lay my hon - ors down, I'll lay my hon - ors down. A - men.

314

MARLOW. C. M.

ISAAC WATTS, 1723

JOHN CHELTHAM, 1718

1. Am I a sol - dier of the cross, A fol - low'r of the Lamb?
2. Must I be car - ried to the skies On flow-ery beds of ease,
3. Are there no foes for me to face? Must I not stem the flood?
4. Sure I must fight, if I would reign; In - crease my cour - age, Lord;

Conflict and Heroism

And shall I fear to own his cause, Or blush to speak his name?
While others fought to win the prize, And sailed through bloody seas?
Is this vile world a friend to grace, To help me on to God?
I'll bear the toil, en-dure the pain, Sup-port-ed by thy word. A-men.

315

PENTECOST. L. M.

John S. B. Monsell, 1863

William Boyd, 1868

1. Fight the good fight with all thy might! Christ is thy
2. Run the straight race through God's good grace, Lift up thine
3. Cast care a-side, up-on thy Guide Lean, and his
4. Faint not nor fear, his arms are near, He chang-eth

strength, and Christ thy right; Lay hold on life, and it shall
eyes, and seek his face; Life with its way be-fore us
mer-cy will pro-vide; Lean, and the trust-ing soul shall
not and thou art dear; On-ly be-lieve, and thou shalt

be Thy joy and crown e-ter-nal-ly.
lies, Christ is the path, and Christ the prize.
prove Christ is its life, and Christ its love.
see That Christ is all in all to thee. A-men.

316

LABAN. S. M.

George Heath, 1781

Lowell Mason, 1830

1. My soul, be on thy guard, Ten thou-sand foes a-rise; The
2. O watch, and fight, and pray; The bat-tle ne'er give o'er; Re -
3. Ne'er think the vic-tory won, Nor lay thine ar-mor down; Thine
4. Fight on, my soul, till death Shall bring thee to thy God; He'll

hosts of sin are press-ing hard To draw thee from the skies.
new it bold-ly ev-ery day, And help di-vine im-plore.
ar-duous work will not be done Till thou ob-tain thy crown.
take thee, at thy part-ing breath, Up to his blest a-bode. A-men.

317

BOYLSTON. S. M.

Charles Wesley, 1762

Lowell Mason, 1832

1. A charge to keep I have, A God to glo-ri-fy,
2. To serve the pres-ent age, My call-ing to ful-fill;
3. Arm me with jeal-ous care, As in thy sight to live,
4. Help me to watch and pray, And on thy-self re-ly,

A nev-er-dy-ing soul to save, And fit it for the sky.
O may it all my powers en-gage, To do my Mas-ter's will!
And O, thy serv-ant, Lord, pre-pare, A strict ac-count to give!
As-sured, if I my trust be-tray, I shall for-ev-er die. A-men.

Conflict and Heroism

318

UNIVERSITY COLLEGE. 7. 7. 7. 7.

HENRY K. WHITE, 1806

HENRY J. GAUNTLETT, 1848

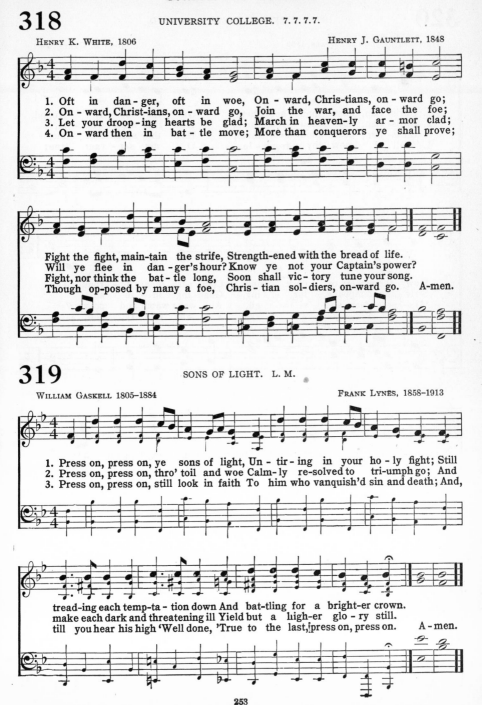

1. Oft in dan-ger, oft in woe, On-ward, Chris-tians, on-ward go;
2. On-ward, Christ-ians, on-ward go, Join the war, and face the foe;
3. Let your droop-ing hearts be glad; March in heaven-ly ar-mor clad;
4. On-ward then in bat-tle move; More than conquerors ye shall prove;

Fight the fight, main-tain the strife, Strength-ened with the bread of life.
Will ye flee in dan-ger's hour? Know ye not your Captain's power?
Fight, nor think the bat-tle long, Soon shall vic-tory tune your song.
Though op-posed by many a foe, Chris-tian sol-diers, on-ward go. A-men.

319

SONS OF LIGHT. L. M.

WILLIAM GASKELL 1805–1884

FRANK LYNES, 1858–1913

1. Press on, press on, ye sons of light, Un-tir-ing in your ho-ly fight; Still
2. Press on, press on, thro' toil and woe Calm-ly re-solved to tri-umph go; And
3. Press on, press on, still look in faith To him who vanquish'd sin and death; And,

tread-ing each temp-ta-tion down And bat-tling for a bright-er crown.
make each dark and threatening ill Yield but a high-er glo-ry still.
till you hear his high 'Well done, 'True to the last, press on, press on. A-men.

The Christian Life

320

ST. ANDREW OF CRETE. 6. 5. 6. 5. D.

ANDREW OF CRETE, 660-732
Translated by JOHN M. NEALE, 1862

JOHN B. DYKES, 1868

1. Chris- tian, dost thou see them On the ho - ly ground,
2. Chris- tian, dost thou feel them, How they work with - in,
3. Chris-'tian, dost thou hear them, How they speak thee fair,—
4. 'Well I know thy troub - le, O my ser - vant true;

How the powers of dark - ness Com - pass thee a - round?
Striv - ing, tempt-ing, lur - ing, Goad-ing in - to sin?
'Al - ways fast and vi - gil, Al - ways watch and prayer?'
Thou art ver - y wea - ry, I was wea-ry, too;

Chris - tian, up and smite them, Count - ing gain but loss,
Chris - tian, nev - er trem - ble, Nev - er be down - cast;
Chris - tian, an - swer bold - ly,— 'While I breathe I pray!'
But that toil shall make thee Some day all mine own,

In the strength that com - eth By the ho - ly cross!
Gird thee for the bat - tle, Watch and pray and fast.
Peace shall fol - low bat - tle, Night shall end in day.
And the end of sor - row Shall be near my throne.' A - men.

254

Conflict and Heroism

321

PORTUGUESE HYMN. 11. 11. 11. 11.

RIPPON'S SELECTION, 1787

WADE'S Cantus Diversi, 1751

1. How firm a foun-da-tion, ye saints of the Lord, Is laid for your faith in his ex-cel-lent word! What more can he say than to you he hath said, To you who for ref-uge to Je-sus have fled? To you who for ref-uge to Je-sus have fled?

2. 'Fear not, I am with thee, O be not dis-mayed; For I am thy God, I will still give thee aid: I'll strength-en thee, help thee, and cause thee to stand, Up-held by my right-eous, om-nip-o-tent hand, Up-held by my right-eous, om-nip-o-tent hand.

3. 'When thro' the deep wa-ters I call thee to go, The riv-ers of sor-row shall not o-ver-flow; For I will be near thee, thy troub-les to bless, And sanc-ti-fy to thee thy deep-est dis-tress, And sanc-ti-fy to thee thy deep-est dis-tress.

4. 'When thro' fi-ery tri-als thy path-way shall lie, My grace, all-suf-fi-cient, shall be thy sup-ply; The flame shall not hurt thee; I on-ly de-sign Thy dross to con-sume, and thy gold to re-fine. Thy dross to con-sume, and thy gold to re-fine.

5. 'The soul that on Je-sus hath leaned for re-pose, I will not, I will not de-sert to his foes; That soul, tho' all hell should en-deav-or to shake, I'll nev-er, no, nev-er, no nev-er for-sake, I'll nev-er, no, nev-er, no, nev-er for-sake!' A-men.

The Christian Life

DIADEMATA. S. M. D.

322

CHARLES WESLEY, 1749

GEORGE J. ELVEY, 1868

1. Sol - diers of Christ, a - rise, And put your ar - mor on,
2. Stand, then, in his great might, With all his strength en - dued;
3. Leave no un-guard - ed place, No weak - ness of the soul,

Strong in the strength which God sup - plies Through his e - ter - nal Son,
And take, to arm you for the fight, The pan - o - ply of God!
Take ev - ery vir - tue, ev - ery grace, And for - ti - fy the whole.

Strong in the Lord of Hosts, And in his might - y power,
That, hav - ing all things done, And all your con - flicts past,
From strength to strength go on; Wres - tle, and fight, and pray;

Who in the strength of Je - sus trusts Is more than con - quer - or.
Ye may o'er - come thro' Christ a - lone, And stand en - tire at last.
Tread all the powers of dark-ness down, And win the well-fought day! A-men.

323

CHENIES. 7. 6. 7. 6. D.

James Montgomery, 1822

Timothy R. Matthews, 1855

1. God is my strong sal - va - tion; What foe have I to fear?
2. Place on the Lord re - li - ance, My soul, with cour - age wait,

In dark - ness and temp - ta - tion, My light, my help is near.
His truth be thine af - fi - ance, When faint and des - o - late.

Though hosts en - camp a - round me, Firm to the fight I stand.
His might thy heart shall strength - en, His love thy joy in - crease,

What ter - ror can con - found me With God at my right hand?
Mer - cy thy days shall length-en, The Lord will give thee peace. A-men.

324

ST. GERTRUDE. 6. 5. 6. 5. D. With Refrain

Sabine Baring-Gould, 1865

Arthur S. Sullivan, 1871

1. On - ward, Chris - tian sol - diers, March - ing as to war,
2. Like a might - y ar - my Moves the church of God:
3. Crowns and thrones may per - ish, King - doms rise and wane,
4. On - ward, then, ye peo - ple, Join our hap - py throng,

With the cross of Je - sus Go - ing on be - fore!
Broth - ers, we are tread - ing Where the saints have trod:
But the church of Je - sus Con - stant will re - main;
Blend with ours your voi - ces In the tri - umph song,—

Christ, the roy - al Mas - ter, Leads a - gainst the foe:
We are not di - vid - ed, All one bod - y we,
Gates of hell can nev - er 'Gainst that church pre - vail;
'Glo - ry, laud, and hon - or Un - to Christ the King!'

For - ward in - to bat - tle See his ban - ners go.
One in hope and doc - trine, One in char - i - ty.
We have Christ's own prom - ise, And that can - not fail.
This thro' count - less a - ges Men and an - gels sing.

Conflict and Heroism

Refrain

On - ward, Chris - tian sol - diers, March - ing as to war,

With the cross of Je - sus Go - ing on be - fore! A - men.

325 MIRFIELD. C. M.

SAMUEL LONGFELLOW, 1864 ARTHUR COTTMAN, 1872

1. God's trum - pet wakes the slum-bering world: Now each man to his post!
2. He who in feal - ty to the truth, And count-ing all the cost,
3. He who, no an - ger on his tongue, Nor an - y i - dle boast,
4. He who, with calm, un - daunt - ed will, Ne'er counts the bat - tle lost,
5. He who is read - y for the cross, The cause de-spised loves most,

The red - cross ban - ner is un - furled: Who joins the glo-rious host?
Doth con - se - crate his gen-erous youth, He joins the no - ble host.
Bears steadfast witness 'gainst the wrong, He joins the sa - cred host.
But, though de-feat - ed, bat - tles still, He joins the faith - ful host.
And shuns not pain or shame or loss, He joins the mar-tyr host. A - men.

326

WEBB. 7. 6. 7. 6. D.

GEORGE DUFFIELD, 1858

GEORGE J. WEBB, 1837

1. Stand up, stand up for Je - sus, Ye sol - diers of the cross;
2. Stand up, stand up for Je - sus, The trump - et call o - bey;
3. Stand up, stand up for Je - sus, Stand in his strength a - lone;
4. Stand up, stand up for Je - sus, The strife will not be long;

Lift high his roy - al ban - ner, It must not suf - fer loss;
Forth to the might - y con - flict In this his glo - rious day:
The arm of flesh will fail you, Ye dare not trust your own;
This day the noise of bat - tle, The next the vict - or's song:

From vic - tory un - to vic - tory His ar - my he shall lead,
Ye that are men now serve him A - gainst un - num - bered foes;
Put on the gos - pel ar - mor, Each piece put on with prayer,
To him that o - ver - com - eth A crown of life shall be;

Till ev - ery foe is van - quished, And Christ is Lord in - deed.
Let cour - age rise with dan - ger, And strength to strength oppose.
Where du - ty calls, or dan - ger, Be nev - er want - ing there.
He with the King of Glo - ry Shall reign e - ter - nal - ly. A - men.

Conflict and Heroism

327

MISSION. 7. 6. 7. 6. D.

LAWRENCE TUTTIETT, 1861

HORATIO PARKER, 1894

1. Go for-ward, Chris-tian sol-dier, Be-neath his ban-ner true!
2. Go for-ward, Chris-tian sol-dier! Fear not the se-cret foe;
3. Go for-ward, Christ-ian sol-dier! Nor dream of peace-ful rest,
4. Go for-ward, Christ-ian sol-dier! Fear not the gath-ering night:

The Lord him-self, thy Lead-er, Shall all thy foes sub-due.
Far more o'er thee are watch-ing Than hu-man eyes can know:
Till Sa-tan's host is van-quished And heaven is all pos-sessed!
The Lord has been thy shel-ter; The Lord will be thy light.

His love fore-tells thy tri-als; He knows thine hour-ly need;
Trust on-ly Christ, thy Cap-tain; Cease not to watch and pray;
Till Christ him-self shall call thee To lay thine ar-mor by,
When morn his face re-veal-eth, Thy dan-gers all are past:

He can with bread of heav-en Thy faint-ing spir-it feed.
Heed not the treacherous voic-es That lure thy soul a-stray.
And wear in end-less glo-ry The crown of vic-to-ry.
O pray that faith and vir-tue May keep thee to the last! A-men.

The Christian Life

328

ALL SAINTS. C. M. D.

REGINALD HEBER, 1827

HENRY S. CUTLER, 1872

1. The Son of God goes forth to war, A king-ly crown to gain;
2. The mar-tyr first, whose ea-gle eye Could pierce be-yond the grave,
3. A glo-rious band, the cho-sen few On whom the Spir-it came,
4. A no-ble ar-my, men and boys, The ma-tron and the maid,

His blood-red ban-ner streams a-far; Who fol-lows in his train?
Who saw his Mas-ter in the sky, And called on him to save;
Twelve val-iant saints, their hope they knew, And mocked the cross and flame;
A-round the Sav-iour's throne re-joice, In robes of light ar-rayed:

Who best can drink his cup of woe Tri-umph-ant o-ver pain,
Like him, with par-don on his tongue, In midst of mor-tal pain,
They met the ty-rant's brandished steel, The li-on's go-ry mane;
They climbed the steep as-cent of heaven Through per-il, toil, and pain:

Who pa-tient bears his cross be-low,—He fol-lows in his train.
He prayed for them that did the wrong: Who fol-lows in his train?
They bowed their necks the stroke to feel; Who fol-lows in their train?
O God, to us may grace be given To fol-low in their train. A-men.

Conflict and Heroism

329

ST. THERESA. 6. 5. 6. 5. D. With Refrain.

THOMAS J. POTTER, 1860

ARTHUR S. SULLIVAN, 1874

1. Bright - ly gleams our ban - ner, Point - ing to the sky, Wav - ing
2. Je - sus, Lord and Mas - ter, At thy sa - cred feet, Here with
3. All our days di - rect us In the way we go; Lead us
4. Then with saints and an - gels May we join a - bove, Of - fering

on Christ's sol - diers To their home on high. March-ing thro' the des - ert,
hearts re - joic - ing See thy chil-dren meet; Of - ten have we left thee,
on vic - to - rious O - ver ev - ery foe; Bid thine an - gels shield us
prayers and prais-es At thy throne of love; When the toil is o - ver,

Glad - ly thus we pray, Still with hearts u - nit - ed Sing-ing on our way.
Of - ten gone a - stray; Keep us, might-y Sav - iour, In the nar-row way.
When the storm-clouds lower; Par-don, Lord, and save us In the last dread hour.
Then come rest and peace; Je - sus in his beau - ty, Songs that nev-er cease.

Refrain

'Bright - ly gleams our ban - ner, Point - ing to the sky,

Wav - ing on Christ's sol - diers To their home on high.' A - men.

330

INNOCENTS. 7. 7. 7. 7.

F. A. ROLLO RUSSELL, 1893

GEORGE F. HANDEL, 1728
Arranged by WILLIAM H. MONK, 1823–1889

1. Chris-tian, rise, and act thy creed, Let thy prayer be in thy deed;
2. Hearts a-round thee sink with care; Thou canst help their load to bear,
3. Let thine alms be hope and joy, And thy wor-ship God's em-ploy;
4. Come then, Law di-vine, and reign, Fre-est faith as-sailed in vain,

Seek the right, per-form the true, Raise thy work and life a-new.
Thou canst bring in-spir-ing light, Arm their fal-tering wills to fight.
Give him thanks in hum-ble zeal, Learn-ing all his will to feel.
Per-fect love be-reft of fear, Born in heaven and ra-diant here. A-men.

331

ORIENTIS PARTIBUS. 7. 7. 7. 7.

WILLIAM WALSHAM HOW, 1864

PIERRE DE CORBEIL, (——1222)

1. Sol-diers of the cross, a-rise, Gird you with your ar-mor bright:
2. Mid the homes of want and woe, Stran-gers to the liv-ing word,
3. To the wea-ry and the worn Tell of realms where sor-rows cease!
4. Guard the help-less! seek the strayed! Com-fort troub-les! ban-ish grief!
5. Be the ban-ner still un-furled, Still un-sheathed the Spir-it's sword,

Might-y are your en-e-mies, Hard the bat-tle ye must fight.
Let the Sav-iour's her-ald go! Let the voice of hope be heard!
To the out-cast and for-lorn Speak of mer-cy and of peace!
In the might of God ar-rayed, Scat-ter sin and un-be-lief!
Till the king-doms of the world Are the king-dom of the Lord! A-men.

332
FAITH. C. M.

Thomas W. Freckleton, 1884

John B. Dykes, 1867

1. O God, who work-est hith-er-to, Work-ing in all we see,
2. The toil of brain, or heart, or hand, Is man's ap-point-ed lot;
3. Toil is no thorn-y crown of pain, Bound round man's brow for sin;
4. Our skill of hand, and strength of limb, Are not our own, but thine;
5. Wher-e'er thou send-est we will go, Nor an-y ques-tion ask,

Fain would we be, and bear, and do, As best it pleas-eth thee.
He who thy call can un-der-stand, Will work, and mur-mur not.
True souls from it all strength may gain, High man-li-ness may win.
We link them to the work of him Who made all life di-vine.
And what thou bid-dest we will do, What-ev-er be the task. A-men.

333
BRACONDALE. C. M.

John Ellerton, 1870

Josiah Booth, (1852——)

1. Be-hold us, Lord, a lit-tle space From dai-ly tasks set free;
2. Yet these are not the on-ly walls Where-in thou mayest be sought;
3. Thine is the loom, the forge, the mart, The wealth of land and sea,
4. Then let us prove our heaven-ly birth, In all we do and know;
5. Work shall be prayer, if all be wrought As thou wouldst have it done,

And met with-in thy ho-ly place To rest a-while with thee.
On home-liest work thy bless-ing falls, In truth and pa-tience wrought.
The worlds of sci-ence and of art Revealed and ruled by thee.
And claim the king-dom of the earth For thee and not thy foe.
And prayer, by thee in-spired and taught, It-self with work be one. A-men.

The Reign of Righteousness

334

WELWYN. 11. 10. 11. 10.

SHEPHERD KNAPP, 1907

A. SCOTT-GATTY

1. Lord God of Hosts, whose pur-pose, nev - er swerv - ing,
2. Strong Son of God, whose work was his that sent thee,
3. O Prince of peace, thou bring - er of good tid - ings,
4. Lord God, whose grace has called us to thy serv - ice,

Leads toward the day of Je - sus Christ thy Son,
One with the Fa - ther, thought and deed and word,
Teach us to speak thy word of hope and cheer,—
How good thy thoughts toward us, how great their sum!

Grant us to march a - mong thy faith - ful le - gions,
One make us all, true com - rades in thy serv - ice,
Rest for the soul, and strength for all man's striv - ing,
We work with thee, we go where thou wilt lead us,

Armed with thy cour - age, till the world is won.
And make us one in thee with God the Lord.
Light for the path of life, and God brought near.
Un - til in all the earth thy king - dom come. A - men.

Human Service and Brotherhood

335

FIELD. 10. 10. 10. 10.

CALVIN W. LAUFER, 1919

CALVIN W. LAUFER, 1919

1. We thank thee, Lord, thy paths of serv - ice lead
2. We've sought and found thee in the se - cret place
3. We've felt thy touch in sor - row's dark - ened way
4. We've seen thy glo - ry like a man - tle spread

To bla - zoned heights and down the slopes of need;
And mar - velled at the ra - diance of thy face;
A - bound with love and sol - ace for the day;
O'er hill and dale in saf - fron flame and red;

They reach thy throne, en - com - pass land and sea,
But of - ten in some far off Gal - i - lee
And, 'neath the bur - dens there, thy sov - 'reign - ty
But in the eyes of men, re - deemed and free,

And he who jour - neys in them, walks with thee.
Be - held thee fair - er yet, while serv - ing thee.
Has held our hearts en - thralled, while serv - ing thee.
A splen - dor great - er yet, while serv - ing thee. A - men.

336

MARYTON. L. M.

Washington Gladden, 1879

H. Percy Smith, 1874

1. O Mas-ter, let me walk with thee In low-ly paths
2. Help me the slow of heart to move By some clear, win-
3. Teach me thy pa-tience; still with thee In clos-er, dear-
4. In hope that sends a shin-ing ray Far down the fu-

of serv-ice free; Tell me thy se-cret; help me
ning word of love; Teach me the way-ward feet to
er com-pa-ny, In work that keeps faith sweet and
ture's broad-ening way; In peace that on-ly thou canst

bear The strain of toil, the fret of care.
stay, And guide them in the home-ward way.
strong, In trust that tri-umphs o-ver wrong;
give,— With thee, O Mas-ter, let me live. A-men.

337

BEULAH. C. M.

Samuel Longfellow, 1864

George M. Garrett, 1889

1. O still in ac-cents sweet and strong Sounds forth the an-cient word,
2. We hear the call; in dreams no more In self-ish ease we lie,
3. Where prophets' word, and martyrs' blood, And prayers of saints were sown,
4. O thou whose call our hearts has stirred! To do thy will we come;

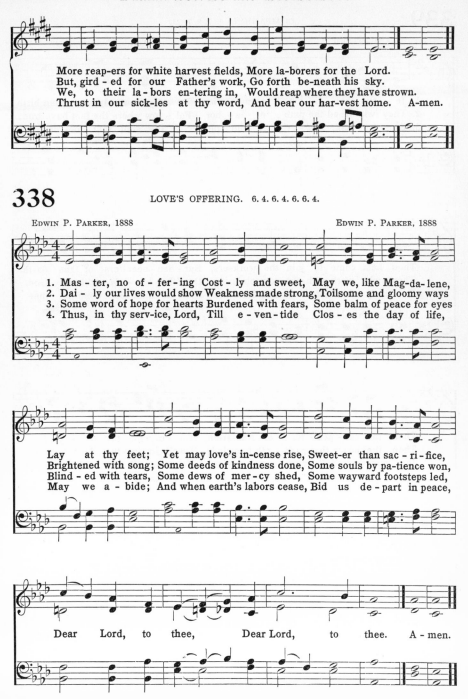

More reap-ers for white harvest fields, More la-borers for the Lord.
But, gird - ed for our Father's work, Go forth be-neath his sky.
We, to their la - bors en-tering in, Would reap where they have strown.
Thrust in our sick-les at thy word, And bear our har-vest home. A-men.

338   LOVE'S OFFERING. 6. 4. 6. 4. 6. 6. 4.

EDWIN P. PARKER, 1888   EDWIN P. PARKER, 1888

1. Mas - ter, no of - fer-ing Cost - ly and sweet, May we, like Mag-da-lene,
2. Dai - ly our lives would show Weakness made strong, Toilsome and gloomy ways
3. Some word of hope for hearts Burdened with fears, Some balm of peace for eyes
4. Thus, in thy serv-ice, Lord, Till e - ven-tide Clos - es the day of life,

Lay at thy feet; Yet may love's in-cense rise, Sweet-er than sac - ri - fice,
Brightened with song; Some deeds of kindness done, Some souls by pa-tience won,
Blind - ed with tears, Some dews of mer - cy shed, Some wayward footsteps led,
May we a - bide; And when earth's labors cease, Bid us de - part in peace,

Dear Lord, to thee, Dear Lord, to thee. A - men.

The Reign of Righteousness

339

COMPANION. 8. 7. 8. 7. D.

Henry Van Dyke, 1909

J. Arthur Demuth, (1848——)

1. Je - sus, thou di - vine com-pan-ion, By thy low - ly hu - man birth
2. They who tread the path of la - bor Fol - low where thy feet have trod;
3. Ev - ery task, how-ev - er sim - ple, Sets the soul that does it free;

Thou hast come to join the work-ers, Bur - den - bear - ers of the earth.
They who work with-out com-plain-ing Do the ho - ly will of God.
Ev - ery deed of love and kind-ness Done to man is done to thee.

Thou, the car - pen - ter of Naz-areth, Toil - ing for thy dai - ly food,
Thou, the peace that pass - eth knowledge, Dwell-est in the dai - ly strife;
Je - sus, thou di - vine com-pan - ion, Help us all to work our best;

By thy pa-tience and thy cour-age, Thou hast taught us toil is good.
Thou, the bread of heaven, art bro-ken In the sac - ra-ment of life.
Bless us in our dai - ly la - bor, Lead us to our Sab-bath rest. A-men.

340

RICHARDS. 8. 7. 8. 7. D.

John G. Adams, 1846

Arranged from Emmelar

1. Heaven is here, where hymns of glad-ness Cheer the toil - ers' rug - ged way,
2. Where the sad, the poor, de - spair-ing, Are up - lift - ed, cheered and blest,

In this world, where clouds of sad - ness Of - ten change our night to day:
Where in oth - ers' la - bors shar-ing, We can find our sur - est rest;

Heaven is here, where mis-ery light-ened Of its heav - y load is seen,
Where we heed the voice of du - ty, Tread the path that Je - sus trod,—

Where the face of sor - row, brightened By the deeds of love hath been;
This is heaven, its peace, its beau-ty Ra-diant with the love of God. A - men.

341

HUMILITY. L. M.

Charles S. Newhall, 1913

Samuel P. Tuckerman, 1848

1. O Je - sus, Mas - ter, when to - day I meet a -
long the crowd - ed way My bur - dened broth - ers— mine and
thine— May then through me thy Spir - it shine;

2. To cheer them in their on - ward way, Till eve - ning
ends the var - ied day— To kin - dle so a grow - ing
light Where else might be but gloom and night.

3. Grant too that they my need may know As side by
side we on - ward go— An e - qual need of kind - ly
thought, And love like that which thou hast taught.

4. Then give our hands a touch di - vine, And to our
voi - ces tones like thine, As side by side we on - ward
go, Nor need each oth - er's names to know. A - men.

342

MAINZER. L. M.

William Cullen Bryant, 1859

Joseph Mainzer, about 1845

1. Look from thy sphere of end - less day, O God of mer - cy and of might!
2. In peo - pled vale, in lone - ly glen, In crowd - ed mart, by stream or sea,
3. Send forth thy her - alds, Lord, to call The thoughtless young, the hardened old,
4. Send them thy might - y word to speak Till faith shall dawn and doubt de-part,
5. Then all these wastes, a drear - y scene On which, with sorrowing eyes, we gaze,

Human Service and Brotherhood

In pit - y look on those who stray, Be-night-ed in this land of light.
How man - y of the sons of men Hear not the message sent from thee.
A wandering flock, and bring them all To the Good Shepherd's peaceful fold.
To awe the bold, to stay the weak, And bind and heal the broken heart.
Shall grow with liv-ing wa-ters green, And lift to heaven the voice of praise. A-men.

343

RIVAULX. L. M.

OCTAVIUS B. FROTHINGHAM, 1846   JOHN B. DYKES, 1866

1. Thou, Lord of Hosts, whose guid - ing hand Has brought us
2. And now with hymn and prayer we stand To give our
3. Send us wher - e'er thou wilt, O Lord, Through rug - ged
4. Send down thy con - stant aid, we pray; Be thy pure

here be - fore thy face, Our spir - its wait for
strength to thee, great God, We would re - deem thy
toil and wea - rying fight; Thy con - quering love shall
an - gels with us still; Thy truth, be that our

thy com - mand, Our si - lent hearts im - plore thy peace.
ho - ly land, That land which sin so long has trod.
be our sword, And faith in thee our tru - est might.
firm - est stay; Our on - ly rest, to do thy will. A - men.

273

344

MENDON. L. M.

SAMUEL LONGFELLOW, 1886

German Melody
Arranged by SAMUEL DYER, 1814

1. Thou Lord of life, our sav - ing health, Who makest thy
2. As on the riv - er's ris - ing tide Flow strength and
3. To heal the wound, to still the pain, And strength to
4. Bless thou the gifts our hands have brought; Bless thou the

suf - fering ones our care, Our gifts are still our
cool - ness from the sea, So, through the ways our
fail - ing puls - es bring, Un - til the lame shall
work our hearts have planned: Ours is the faith, the

tru - est wealth, To serve thee our sin - cer - est prayer.
hands pro - vide, May quick-ening life flow in from thee.
leap a - gain, And the parched lips with glad - ness sing.
will, the thought; The rest, O God, is in thy hand. A - men.

345

STOCKWELL. 8. 7. 8. 7.

THOMAS HASTINGS, 1836

DARIUS E. JONES, 1851

1. He that go - eth forth with weep - ing, Bear - ing pre-cious seed in love,
2. Soft de-scend the dews of heav - en, Bright the rays ce - les - tial shine;
3. Sow thy seed, be nev - er wea - ry, Let no fears thy soul an-noy;
4. Lo, the scene of ver - dure bright-ening, See the ris - ing grain ap-pear;

Nev-er tir-ing, nev-er sleep-ing, Find-eth mer-cy from a-bove.
Pre-cious fruits will thus be giv-en, Through an influence all di-vine.
Be the pros-pect ne'er so drear-y, Thou shalt reap the fruits of joy.
Look a-gain; the fields are whitening, For the har-vest-time is near. A-men.

346

ERNAN. L. M.

HORATIUS BONAR, 1843

LOWELL MASON, 1850

1. Go, la-bor on; spend and be spent, Thy joy to
2. Go, la-bor on; 'tis not for naught, Thine earth-ly
3. Toil on, faint not, keep watch, and pray; Be wise the
4. Toil on, and in thy toil re-joice; For toil comes

do the Fa-ther's will; It is the way the
loss is heaven-ly gain; Men heed thee, love thee,
err-ing soul to win; Go forth in-to the
rest, for ex-ile home; Soon shalt thou hear the

Mas-ter went; Should not the serv-ant tread it still?
praise thee not; The Mas-ter prais-es; what are men?
world's high-way, Com-pel the wan-derer to come in.
Bride-groom's voice, The mid-night peal, 'Be-hold, I come!' A-men.

347

MINISTRY. 8. 4. 8. 4. 8. 8.

ROBERT DAVIS, 1908

JOHN H. GOWER, 1909

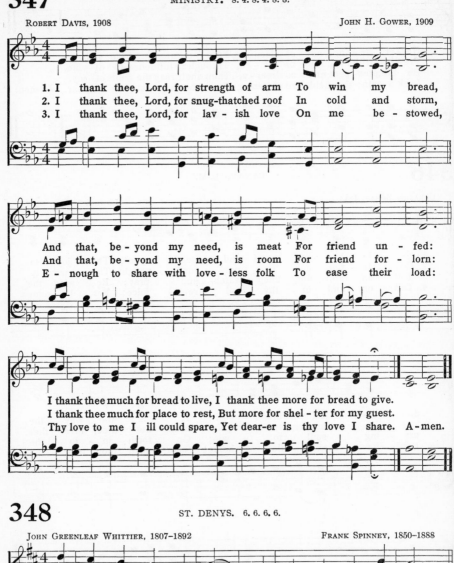

1. I thank thee, Lord, for strength of arm To win my bread,
2. I thank thee, Lord, for snug-thatched roof In cold and storm,
3. I thank thee, Lord, for lav - ish love On me be - stowed,

And that, be - yond my need, is meat For friend un - fed:
And that, be - yond my need, is room For friend for - lorn:
E - nough to share with love - less folk To ease their load:

I thank thee much for bread to live, I thank thee more for bread to give.
I thank thee much for place to rest, But more for shel - ter for my guest.
Thy love to me I ill could spare, Yet dear - er is thy love I share. A - men.

348

ST. DENYS. 6. 6. 6. 6.

JOHN GREENLEAF WHITTIER, 1807–1892

FRANK SPINNEY, 1850–1888

1. Sweet - er than an - y song, My songs that found no tongue;
2. Oth - ers shall sing the song, Oth - ers shall right the wrong,
3. What mat - ter I, or they? Mine or an - oth - er's day,

No - bler than an - y fact My wish that failed of act.
Fin - ish what I be - gin, And all I fail I win.
So the right word be said, And life the sweet - er made? A - men.

349

GRACE CHURCH. L. M.

EMILY V. CLARK, 1891

IGNAZ J. PLEYEL, 1815

1. O God of mer - cy! heark - en now: Be - fore thy
2. We seek thee where thou dwell'st on high; Be - yond the
3. O let the heal - ing wa - ters spring, Touched by thy
4. Where pov - er - ty in pain must lie, Where lit - tle

throne we hum - bly bow; With heart and voice to
glitter - ing star - ry sky: We find thee where thou
pity - ing an - gel's wing; With quicken - ing power new
suffer - ing chil - dren cry, Bid us haste forth as

thee we cry For all on earth who suf - fering lie.
dwell'st be - low Be - side the beds of want and woe.
strength im - part To pal - sied will, to with - ered heart.
called by thee, And in thy poor, thy - self to see. A - men.

350

ELLESDIE. 8.7.8.7. D.

Daniel March, 1868, Altered

Arranged from Mozart
by Hubert P. Main, 1873

1. Hark! the voice of Jesus calling, 'Who will go and work to-day?
2. If you cannot cross the ocean, And far mission lands explore,
3. Let none hear you idly saying, 'There is nothing I can do,'

Fields are white, and harvests waiting, Who will bear the sheaves away?'
You can find the needy nearer, You can help them at your door;
While the souls of men are dying, And the Master calls for you.

Earnestly the Master calleth, Rich reward he offers free;
If you cannot give your thousands, You can serve with willing might;
Take the task he gives you gladly; Let his work your pleasure be;

Who will answer, gladly saying, 'Here am I, O Lord, send me'?
And what-e'er you do for Jesus Will be precious in his sight.
Answer quickly when he calleth, 'Here am I, O Lord, send me.' A-men.

351

WORK SONG. 7. 6. 7. 5. D.

Anna L. Coghill, 1860

Lowell Mason, 1864

1. Work, for the night is com - ing, Work through the morn - ing hours;
2. Work, for the night is com - ing, Work through the sun - ny noon;
3. Work, for the night is com - ing, Un - der the sun - set skies;

Work while the dew is spark - ling, Work 'mid spring - ing flowers;
Fill bright - est hours with la - bor, Rest comes sure and soon:
While their bright tints are glow - ing, Work, for day - light flies;

Work while the day grows bright - er, Un - der the glow - ing sun;
Give ev - ery fly - ing min - ute Some-thing to keep in store;
Work, till the last beam fad - eth, Fad - eth to shine no more;

Work, for the night is com - ing, When man's work is done.
Work, for the night is com - ing, When man works no more.
Work, while night is dark-'ning, When man's work is o'er. A-men.

352

BULLINGER. 8. 5. 8. 3.

THEODORE CHICKERING WILLIAMS, 1891

ETHELBERT W. BULLINGER, 1877

1. When thy heart with joy o'er-flow-ing, Sings a thank-ful prayer,
2. When the har-vest sheaves in-gath-ered, Fill thy barns with store,
3. If thy soul, with power up-lift-ed, Yearn for glo-rious deed,
4. Share with him thy bread of bless-ing, Sor-row's bur-den share:

In thy joy, O let thy broth-er With thee share.
To thy God and to thy broth-er Give the more.
Give thy strength to serve thy broth-er In his need.
When thy heart en-folds a broth-er God is there. A-men.

353

CHISELHURST. S. M.

HARRY L. CRAIN, 1906

JOSEPH BARNBY, 1887

1. O bless-ed Son of God, In love and faith we plead, That thou wouldst
2. Our Eld-er Broth-er thou, Whose her-i-tage we share, Our kin-dred
3. Thou didst the will of him Who sent thee from a-bove; Thou send-est
4. To serve thy king-dom, Lord, To qui-et sin's tur-moil, Do thou or-
5. Thou Man of Gal-i-lee, O wilt thou live a-gain, A-bide with-

bind our minds and hearts In Broth-er-hood of need.
lives we of-fer thee, In Broth-er-hood of prayer.
us, as he sent thee, In Broth-er-hood of love.
dain and con-se-crate Our Broth-er-hood of toil.
in, con-trol, in-spire Our Broth-er-hood of men. A-men.

354

WINDSOR. 11. 10. 11. 10

JOHN GREENLEAF WHITTIER, 1807–1892   JOSEPH BARNBY, 1838–1896

1. O broth - er man, fold to thy heart thy broth - er;
2. For he whom Je - sus loved has tru - ly spo - ken,—
3. Fol - low with rev - erent steps the great ex - am - ple

Where pit - y dwells, the peace of God is there;
The ho - lier wor - ship which he deigns to bless
Of him whose ho - ly work was 'do - ing good';

To wor - ship right - ly is to love each oth - er,
Re - stores the lost, and binds the spir - it bro - ken,
So shall the wide earth seem our Fa - ther's tem - ple,

Each smile a hymn, each kind - ly deed a prayer.
And feeds the wid - ow and the fa - ther - less.
Each lov - ing life a psalm of grat - i - tude. A - men.

281

355

ST. THOMAS. S. M.

WILLIAM PIERSON MERRILL, 1911

AARON WILLIAMS, 1763

1. Rise up, O men of God! Have done with less - er things;
2. Rise up, O men of God! His king - dom tar - ries long:
3. Rise up, O men of God! The Church for you doth wait,
4. Lift high the cross of Christ! Tread where his feet have trod:

Give heart and soul and mind and strength To serve the King of kings.
Bring in the day of broth - er - hood And end the night of wrong.
Her strength un - e - qual to her task; Rise up, and make her great!
As broth - ers of the Son of Man Rise up, O men of God! A - men.

356

HOLY TRINITY. C. M.

CHARLES KINGSLEY, 1871

JOSEPH BARNBY, 1861

1. From thee all skill and sci - ence flow, All pit - y, care and love,
2. And part them, Lord, to each and all, As each and all shall need,
3. And hast - en, Lord, that per - fect day When pain and death shall cease,
4. When ev - er blue the sky shall gleam, And ev - er green the sod,

All calm and cour - age, faith and hope;—O pour them from a - bove.
To rise like in - cense, each to thee, In no - ble thought and deed.
And thy just rule shall fill the earth With health and light and peace;
And man's rude work de - face no more The Par - a - dise of God. A - men.

357

GARDEN CITY. S. M.

EDWARD ROWLAND SILL, 1867

HORATIO W. PARKER, 1890

1. Send down thy truth, O God! Too long the shad-ows frown,
2. Send down thy spir-it free, Till wil-der-ness and town
3. Send down thy love, thy life, Our less-er lives to crown,
4. Send down thy peace, O Lord! Earth's bit-ter voic-es drown

Too long the dark-ened way we've trod, Thy truth, O Lord, send down!
One tem-ple for thy wor-ship be, Thy spir-it, O send down!
And cleanse them of their hate and strife, Thy liv-ing love send down!
In one deep o-cean of ac-cord, Thy peace, O God, send down! A-men.

Music copyrighted by Horatio W. Parker. Used by permission

358

FESTAL SONG S. M.

JOHN JOHNS, 1837

WILLIAM H. WALTER, 1894

1. Come, king-dom of our God, Sweet reign of light and love! Shed
2. O-ver our spir-its first Ex-tend thy heal-ing reign; There
3. Come, king-dom of our God, And make the broad earth thine! Stretch
4. Soon may all tribes be blest With fruit from life's glad tree; And

peace, and hope, and joy a-broad, And wis-dom from a-bove.
raise and quench the sa-cred thirst That nev-er pains a-gain.
o'er her lands and isles the rod That flowers with grace di-vine.
in its shade like broth-ers rest, Sons of one fam-i-ly. A-men.

The Reign of Righteousness

359

LANCASHIRE. 7. 6. 7. 6. D.

GILBERT K. CHESTERTON (1874——)

HENRY SMART, 1867

1. O God of earth and al - tar, Bow down and hear our cry,
2. From all that ter - ror teach - es, From lies of tongue and pen,
3. Tie in a liv - ing teth - er The priest and prince and thrall,

Our earth - ly rul - ers fal - ter, Our peo - ple drift and die;
From all the eas - y speech - es That com - fort cru - el men,
Bind all our lives to - geth - er, Smite us and save us all;

The walls of gold en - tomb us, The swords of scorn di - vide,
From sale and prof - a - na - tion Of hon - or and the sword,
In ire and ex - ul - ta - tion A - flame with faith, and free,

Take not thy thun - der from us, But take a - way our pride.
From sleep and from dam - na - tion, De - liv - er us, good Lord.
Lift up a liv - ing na - tion, A sin - gle sword to thee. A-men.

360

SAVOY CHAPEL. 7. 6. 8. 6. D.

John Hay, 1891, altered

J. Baptiste Calkin, 1827-1905

1. Not in dumb res-ig-na-tion We lift our hands on high;
2. When ty-rant feet are tram-pling Up-on the com-mon weal,
3. Thy will! It strength-ens weak-ness, It bids the strong be just;

Not like the nerve-less fa-tal-ist Con-tent to trust and die:
Thou dost not bid us bend and writhe Be-neath the i-ron heel.
No lip to fawn, no hand to beg, No brow to seek the dust.

Our faith springs like the ea - gle, Who soars to meet the sun,
In thy name we as-sert our right By sword or tongue or pen,
Wher-ev-er man op-press-es man Be-neath thy lib-eral sun,

And cries ex-ult-ing un-to thee, O Lord, thy will be done!
And oft a peo-ple's wrath may flash Thy mes-sage un-to men.
O Lord, be there, thine arm made bare, Thy right-eous will be done! A-men.

The Reign of Righteousness

361

AUSTRIA. 8. 7. 8. 7. D.

ARTHUR CLEVELAND COXE, 1840

FRANZ JOSEPH HAYDN, 1797

1. We are liv-ing, we are dwell-ing In a grand and aw-ful time,
2. Worlds are charging, heaven be-hold-ing; Thou hast but an hour to fight;

In an age on a-ges tell-ing; To be liv-ing is sub-lime.
Now, the blaz-oned cross un-fold-ing, On, right on-ward for the right!

Hark! the wak-ing up of na-tions, Gog and Ma-gog to the fray;
On! let all the soul with-in you For the truth's sake go a-broad!

Hark! what soundeth is cre-a-tion Groan-ing for the lat-ter day.
Strike! let ev-ery nerve and sin-ew Tell on a-ges, tell for God. A-men.

Justice and Freedom

362

ABBOTT. 8.7.8.7.8.7.

HENRY SCOTT HOLLAND, 1902

CHARLES S. YERBURY, 1908

1. Judge e - ter - nal, throned in splen - dor, Lord of lords and
2. Still the wea - ry folk are pin - ing For the hour that
3. Crown, O God, thine own en - deav - or; Cleave our dark - ness

King of kings With thy liv - ing fire of judg - ment
brings re - lease, And the cit - y's crowd - ed clan - gor
with thy sword; Feed the faint and hun - gry peo - ple

Purge this land of bit - ter things; Sol - ace all its
Cries a - loud for sin to cease; And the home - stead
With the rich - ness of thy word; Cleanse the bod - y

wide do - min - ion With the heal - ing of thy wings.
and the wood - land Plead in si - lence for their peace.
of this na - tion Through the glo - ry of the Lord. A - men.

The Reign of Righteousness

363

ARTHUR'S SEAT. 6. 6. 6. 6. 8. 8.

GEORGE T. COSTER, 1900

Arranged from
JOHN GOSS, 1874

1. March on, O soul, with strength! Like those strong men of old Who 'gainst enthroned wrong Stood confident and bold; Who, thrust in prison or cast to flame, Still made their glory in the Name.

2. The sons of fathers we By whom our faith is taught To fear no ill, to fight The holy fight they fought: Heroic warriors, ne'er from Christ By any lure or guile enticed.

3. March on, O soul, with strength! As strong the battle rolls! 'Gainst lies and lusts and wrongs, Let courage rule our souls; In keenest strife, Lord, may we stand, Upheld and strengthened by thy hand.

4. Not long the conflict: soon The holy war shall cease, Faith's warfare ended,— won The home of endless peace; Look up! the victor's crown at length: March on, O soul, march on, with strength! A-men.

Justice and Freedom

364

ST. GEORGE'S, WINDSOR. 7. 7. 7. 7. D.

JAMES RUSSELL LOWELL, 1819–1891

GEORGE J. ELVEY, 1858

1. Men, whose boast it is that ye Come of fa - thers brave and free,
2. Is true free-dom but to break Fet - ters for our own dear sake,
3. They are slaves who fear to speak For the fall - en and the weak;

If there breathe on earth a slave, Are ye tru - ly free and brave?
And with leath - ern hearts for - get That we owe man - kind a debt?
They are slaves who will not choose Ha - tred, scoff - ing, and a - buse,

If ye do not feel the chain When it works a broth-er's pain,
No! true free-dom is to share All the chains our broth-ers wear,
Rath - er than in si - lence shrink From the truth they needs must think;

Are ye not base slaves in-deed, Slaves un-wor-thy to be freed?
And, with heart and hand, to be Ear-nest to make oth-ers free.
They are slaves who dare not be In the right with two or three. A-men.

The Reign of Righteousness

365

ALL SAINTS. C. M. D.

Ozora S. Davis, 1909

Henry S. Cutler, 1872

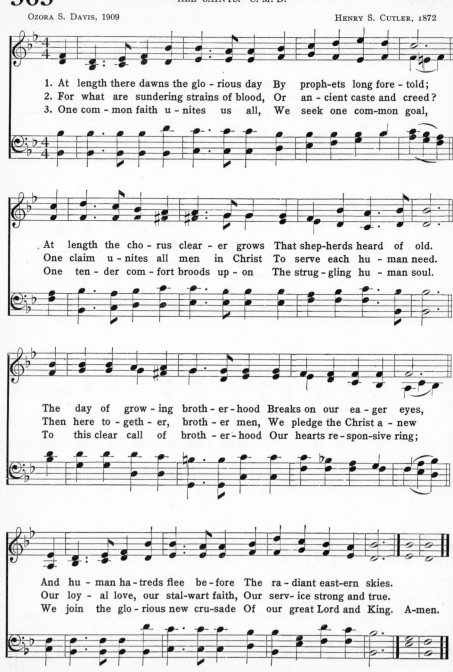

1. At length there dawns the glo - rious day By proph-ets long fore - told;
2. For what are sundering strains of blood, Or an - cient caste and creed?
3. One com - mon faith u - nites us all, We seek one com-mon goal,

At length the cho - rus clear - er grows That shep-herds heard of old.
One claim u - nites all men in Christ To serve each hu - man need.
One ten - der com - fort broods up - on The strug - gling hu - man soul.

The day of grow - ing broth - er - hood Breaks on our ea - ger eyes,
Then here to - geth - er, broth - er men, We pledge the Christ a - new
To this clear call of broth - er - hood Our hearts re - spon-sive ring;

And hu - man ha - treds flee be - fore The ra - diant east-ern skies.
Our loy - al love, our stal-wart faith, Our serv- ice strong and true.
We join the glo - rious new cru-sade Of our great Lord and King. A-men.

Justice and Freedom

366

ST. LEONARD. C. M. D.

JOHN HAYNES HOLMES, 1910

HENRY HILES, 1867

1. O God, whose law from age to age No chance or change can know,
2. The winds, thy faith-ful mes-sen-gers, Are guid-ed by thy hand,
3. Thy ho-ly pur-pose moves be-fore The na-tions on their way,
4. Dear Fa-ther, we would learn to trust The do-ing of thy will,

Whose love for-ev-er more a-bides, While ae-ons come and go;
Thy min-is-ters, the flames of fire, O-bey thy stern com-mand;
And leads the stum-bling hosts of men From dark-ness in-to day.
And in thy per-fect law of love Our doubts and fears would still.

From all the strife of earth-ly life To thine em-brace we flee,
The seas re-sound with-in the bound Where thy do-min-ion reigns,
No cap-tain's sword—no prophet's word—But thy great mer-cy prove;
Help us to know, in joy or woe, Thy ways are al-ways best.

And 'mid our crowd-ing doubts and fears Would put our trust in thee.
And wheel-ing plan-ets seek the paths Thy might-y will or-dains.
No clime or kin-dred but at-test Thy Prov-i-dence of love.
And we, thy chil-dren ev-er-more, By thy great goodness blest. A-men.

The Reign of Righteousness

367

CASSIDY. 10. 10. 10. 10.

THEODORE PARKER, 1846

HUBERT P. MAIN, 1895

1. O thou great Friend to all the sons of men, Who once ap-peared in
2. We look to thee; thy truth is still the light Which guides the na-tions,
3. Yes, thou art still the life; thou art the way The ho-liest know,—light,

hum-blest guise be-low, Sin to re-buke, to break the cap-tive's
grop-ing on their way, Stum-bling and fall-ing in dis-as-trous
life, and way of heaven; And they who dear-est hope and deep-est

chain, And call thy breth-ren forth from want and woe.
night, Yet hop-ing ev-er for the per-fect day.
pray, Toil by the light, life, way, which thou hast given. A-men.

Copyright, 1896, by Hubert P. Main

368

SARDIS. 8. 8. 8. 7.

PERCY DEARMER, 1906

Arranged from
BEETHOVEN, 1770–1827

1. Fa-ther, who on man doth show-er Gifts of plen-ty from thy dow-er,
2. Give pure hap-pi-ness in lei-sure, Tem-per-ance in ev-ery pleas-ure,
3. Lift from this and ev-ery na-tion All that brings us deg-ra-da-tion;
4. Be with us, thy strength sup-ply-ing, That with en-er-gy un-dy-ing,
5. Thou who art our Cap-tain ev-er Lead us on to great en-deav-or;

292

Justice and Freedom

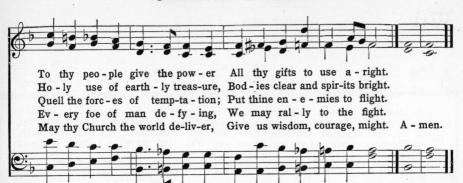

To thy peo-ple give the pow-er All thy gifts to use a-right.
Ho-ly use of earth-ly treas-ure, Bod-ies clear and spir-its bright.
Quell the forc-es of temp-ta-tion; Put thine en-e-mies to flight.
Ev-ery foe of man de-fy-ing, We may ral-ly to the fight.
May thy Church the world de-liv-er, Give us wisdom, courage, might. A-men.

369

MIRFIELD. C. M.

William G. Tarrant, 1892

Arthur Cottman, 1872

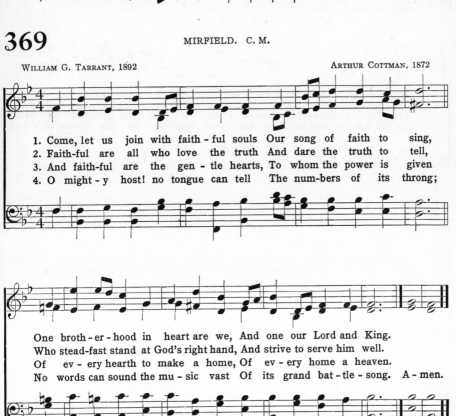

1. Come, let us join with faith-ful souls Our song of faith to sing,
2. Faith-ful are all who love the truth And dare the truth to tell,
3. And faith-ful are the gen-tle hearts, To whom the power is given
4. O might-y host! no tongue can tell The num-bers of its throng;

One broth-er-hood in heart are we, And one our Lord and King.
Who stead-fast stand at God's right hand, And strive to serve him well.
Of ev-ery hearth to make a home, Of ev-ery home a heaven.
No words can sound the mu-sic vast Of its grand bat-tle-song. A-men.

5 From step to step it wins its way
   Against a world of sin;
Part of the battle-field is won,
   And part is yet to win.

6 O Lord of hosts, our faith renew,
   And grant us, in thy love,
To sing the songs of victory
   With faithful souls above.

The Reign of Righteousness

TON-Y BOTEL. 8. 7. 8. 7. D.

JAMES RUSSELL LOWELL, 1845   Welsh Hymn Melody

UNISON

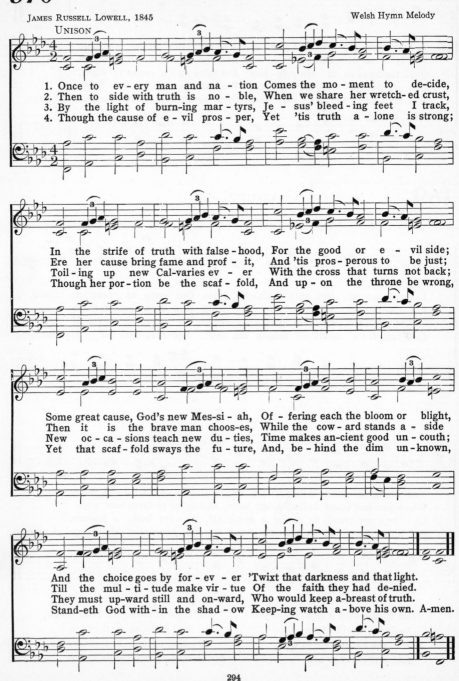

1. Once to ev-ery man and na - tion Comes the mo - ment to de-cide,
2. Then to side with truth is no - ble, When we share her wretch-ed crust,
3. By the light of burn-ing mar - tyrs, Je - sus' bleed - ing feet I track,
4. Though the cause of e - vil pros - per, Yet 'tis truth a - lone is strong;

In the strife of truth with false-hood, For the good or e - vil side;
Ere her cause bring fame and prof - it, And 'tis pros- perous to be just;
Toil - ing up new Cal-varies ev - er With the cross that turns not back;
Though her por - tion be the scaf - fold, And up - on the throne be wrong,

Some great cause, God's new Mes-si - ah, Of - fering each the bloom or blight,
Then it is the brave man choos-es, While the cow - ard stands a - side
New oc - ca - sions teach new du - ties, Time makes an-cient good un - couth;
Yet that scaf-fold sways the fu - ture, And, be - hind the dim un -known,

And the choice goes by for - ev - er 'Twixt that darkness and that light.
Till the mul - ti - tude make vir - tue Of the faith they had de-nied.
They must up-ward still and on-ward, Who would keep a-breast of truth.
Stand-eth God with-in the shad - ow Keep-ing watch a - bove his own. A-men.

371

DANIA. 6. 5. 6. 5. D. With refrain

FREDERICK L. HOSMER, (1840 ——)

FRANK G. ILSLEY, 1831-1887

1. For-ward through the a - ges, In un - bro-ken line, Move the faith-ful
2. Wid - er grows the king - dom, Reign of love and light; For it we must
3. Not a - lone we con - quer, Not a - lone we fall; In each loss or

spir - its At the call di - vine, Gifts in dif-fering meas-ure, Hearts of
la - bor, Till our faith is sight. Proph-ets have proclaimed it, Mar - tyrs
tri - umph Lose or tri - umph all. Bound by God's far pur - pose In one

one ac - cord, Man - i - fold the serv - ice, One the sure re - ward.
tes - ti - fied, Po - ets sung its glo - ry, He - roes for it died.
liv - ing whole, Move we on to-geth - er To the shin-ing goal.

Refrain

For - ward through the a - ges, In un - bro - ken line,

Move the faith - ful spir - its At the call di - vine. A - men.

372

JESU DILECTISSIME. 7. 6. 7. 6. D.

MINOT JUDSON SAVAGE, (1841 ——)

ROBERT H. McCARTNEY, 1844–1895

1. The God that to the fa - thers Re - vealed his ho - ly will
2. 'Twas but far off, in vis - ion, The fa - thers' eyes could see
3. With trust in God's free spir - it, The ev - er - broad-ening ray

Has not the world for - sak - en, He's with the chil - dren still.
The glo - ry of the king - dom, The bet - ter time to be.
Of truth that shines to guide us A - long our for - ward way,

Then en - vy not the twi - light That glim-mered on their way;
To - day we see ful - fill - ing The dreams they dreamt of old;
Let us to - day be faith - ful As were the brave of old,

Look up and see the dawn - ing That broad-ens in - to day.
While near-er, ev - er near - er, Rolls on the age of gold.
Till we, their work com - plet - ing, Bring in the age of gold! A - men.

Social Progress

373

LANCASHIRE. 7.6.7.6.D.

ERNEST W. SHURTLEFF, 1888

HENRY SMART, 1836

1. Lead on, O King E-ter-nal, The day of march has come;
2. Lead on, O King E-ter-nal, Till sin's fierce war shall cease,
3. Lead on, O King E-ter-nal, We fol-low, not with fears,

Hence-forth in fields of con-quest Thy tents shall be our home:
And ho-li-ness shall whis-per The sweet A-men of peace;
For glad-ness breaks like morn-ing Wher-e'er thy face ap-pears:

Through days of prep-a-ra-tion Thy grace has made us strong,
For not with swords loud clash-ing, Nor roll of stir-ring drums;
Thy cross is lift-ed o'er us; We jour-ney in its light;

And now, O King E-ter-nal, We lift our bat-tle song.
With deeds of love and mer-cy, The heaven-ly king-dom comes.
The crown a-waits the con-quest; Lead on, O God of might. A-men.

374

WEBB. 7. 6. 7. 6. D.

JAMES MONTGOMERY, 1821

GEORGE J. WEBB, 1837

1. Hail to the Lord's A - noint - ed, Great Da - vid's great - er Son!
2. He shall come down like show - ers Up - on the fruit - ful earth,
3. Kings shall fall down be - fore him, And gold and in - cense bring;
4. O'er ev - ery foe vic - to - rious, He on his throne shall rest;

Hail, in the time ap - point - ed, His reign on earth be - gun!
And joy and hope, like flow - ers, Spring in his path to birth:
All na - tions shall a - dore him, His praise all peo - ple sing;
From age to age more glo - rious, All - bless - ing, and all - blessed.

He comes to break op - press - ion, To set the cap - tive free,
Be - fore him on the moun - tains Shall peace, the her - ald, go;
For him shall prayer un - ceas - ing And dai - ly vows as - cend;
The tide of time shall nev - er His cov - e - nant re - move;

To take a - way trans - gress - ion, And rule in e - qui - ty.
And right - eous - ness in foun - tains From hill to val - ley flow.
His king - dom still in - creas - ing, A king - dom with - out end.
His name shall stand for - ev - er, His change - less name of Love. A - men.

Social Progress

375

YORKSHIRE. 10. 10. 10. 10. 10. 10.

JOHN W. CHADWICK, 1864

JOHN WAINWRIGHT, 1760

1. E - ter - nal Rul - er of the cease-less round Of cir - cling plan - ets
2. We are of thee, the chil - dren of thy love, The broth - ers of thy
3. We would be one in ha - tred of all wrong, One in our love of
4. O clothe us with thy heaven - ly ar - mor, Lord,— Thy trust - y shield, thy

sing - ing on their way, Guide of the na - tions from the night pro - found
well - be - lov - ed Son; De - scend, O Ho - ly Spir - it, like a dove,
all things sweet and fair, One with the joy that break - eth in - to song,
sword of love di - vine: Our in - spi - ra - tion be thy con-stant word;

In - to the glo - ry of the per - fect day, Rule in our hearts that
In - to our hearts that we may be as one,— As one with thee, to
One with the grief that trem-bles in - to prayer, One in the power that
We ask no vic - to - ries that are not thine: Give or with - hold, let

we may ev - er be Guid - ed, and strengthened, and up - held by thee.
whom we ev - er tend, As one with him, our Broth-er and our Friend.
makes thy children free To fol - low truth, and thus to fol - low thee.
pain or pleas-ure be, E - nough to know that we are serv - ing thee. A-men.

299

The Reign of Righteousness

376

COMMONWEALTH. 7. 6. 7. 6. 8. 8. 8. 5.

EBENEZER ELLIOTT, 1781–1849

JOSIAH BOOTH (1852——)

1. When wilt thou save the peo - ple? O God of mer - cy, when?
2. Shall crime bring crime for - ev - er Strength aid - ing still the strong?
3. When wilt thou save the peo - ple? O God of mer - cy, when?

Not kings and lords, but na - tions! Not thrones and crowns, but men!
Is it thy will, O Fa - ther, That man shall toil for wrong?
The peo - ple, Lord, the peo - ple, Not thrones and crowns, but men!

Flowers of thy heart, O God, are they; Let them not pass, like weeds, a - way,
'No,' say thy mountains; 'No,' thy skies; Man's cloud-ed sun shall bright-ly rise,
God save the peo - ple; thine they are, Thy chil - dren, as thy an - gels fair;

Their her - i - tage a sun - less day, God save the peo - ple!
And songs be heard in-stead of sighs; God save the peo - ple!
From vice, op-pres-sion, and de-spair, God save the peo - ple! A - men.

World Peace and Fellowship

377

RUSSIAN HYMN. 11. 10. 11. 9.

HENRY F. CHORLEY, 1842
JOHN ELLERTON, 1870

ALEXIS T. LWOFF, 1833

1. God the All - ter - ri - ble! King, who or - dain - est
2. God the All - mer - ci - ful! earth hath for - sak - en
3. God the All - right-eous One! man hath de - fied thee;
4. God the All - wise! by the fire of thy chas -tening,
5. So shall thy chil - dren, with thank - ful de - vo - tion,

Thun - der thy clar - ion, the light - ning thy sword;
The ways of bless - ed - ness, slight - ed thy word;
Yet to e - ter - ni - ty stand - eth thy word,
Earth shall to free - dom and truth be re - stored;
Praise him who saved them from per - il and sword,

Show forth thy pit - y on high where thou reign - est,
Bid not thy wrath in its ter - rors a - wak - en;
False - hood and wrong shall not tar - ry be - side thee;
Through the thick dark - ness thy king - dom is hasten - ing;
Sing - ing in cho - rus from o - cean to o - cean,

Give to us peace in our time, O Lord.
Give to us peace in our time, O Lord.
Give to us peace in our time, O Lord.
Thou wilt give peace in thy time, O Lord.
Peace to the na - tions, and praise to the Lord. A - men.

301

378

BRYANT. 8. 6. 8. 6. 8. 8.

JOHN HAMPDEN GURNEY, 1802–1862

WALTER G. ALCOCK, 1862

1. Thro' cen - tu - ries of sin and woe Hath streamed the crim - son flood, While man, in con - cert with the foe, Hath shed his broth - er's blood. Now lift thy ban - ner, Prince of Peace, And let the cru - el war - cry cease.

2. In vain, 'mid clam - ors loud and rude, Thy serv - ants seek re - pose, See, day by day, the strife re - newed, And breth - ren turned to foes: Then lift thy ban - ner, Prince of Peace, Make wrongs a - mong thy sub - jects cease.

3. Still to the heavens the weak will pour Their loud un - ans - wered cry; Still wealth doth heap its se - cret store, And want for - got - ten lie. Lift high thy ban - ner, Prince of Peace, Let ha - tred die, and love in - crease.

4. Thy gos - pel, Lord, is grace and love; O send it all a - broad, Till ev - ery heart sub - mis - sive prove, And bless the reign - ing God. Come, lift thy ban - ner, Prince of Peace, And give the wear - y world re - lease. A - men.

World Peace and Brotherhood

379

BLESSED HOME. 6. 6. 6. 6. D.

FREDERICK L. HOSMER, 1905

JOHN STAINER, 1875

1. Thy king - dom come, O Lord, Wide - cir - cling as the sun;
2. Speed, speed the longed - for time Fore - told by rap - tured seers—

Ful - fil of old thy word, And make the na - tions one;—
The proph - e - cy sub - lime, The hope of all the years;—

One in the bond of peace, The ser - vice glad and free Of
Till rise at last, to span Its firm foun - da - tions broad, The

truth and right - eous - ness, Of love and eq - ui - ty.
com - mon - wealth of man, The cit - y of our God. A - men.

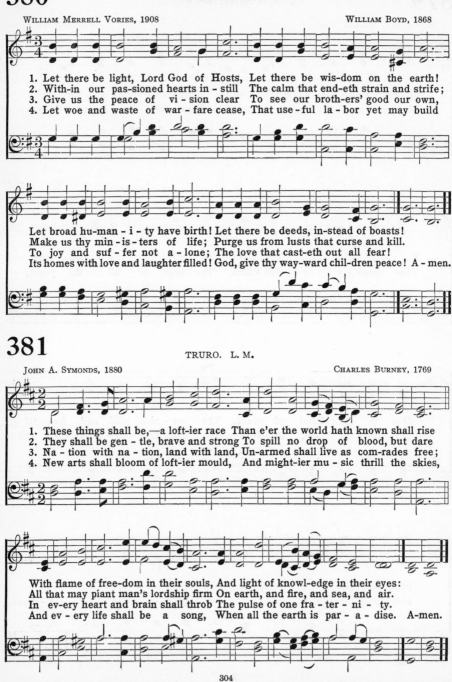

380

PENTECOST. L. M.

WILLIAM MERRELL VORIES, 1908

WILLIAM BOYD, 1868

1. Let there be light, Lord God of Hosts, Let there be wis-dom on the earth!
2. With-in our pas-sioned hearts in - still The calm that end-eth strain and strife;
3. Give us the peace of vi - sion clear To see our broth-ers' good our own,
4. Let woe and waste of war - fare cease, That use - ful la - bor yet may build

Let broad hu-man - i - ty have birth! Let there be deeds, in-stead of boasts!
Make us thy min - is - ters of life; Purge us from lusts that curse and kill.
To joy and suf - fer not a - lone; The love that cast-eth out all fear!
Its homes with love and laughter filled! God, give thy way-ward chil-dren peace! A - men.

381

TRURO. L. M.

JOHN A. SYMONDS, 1880

CHARLES BURNEY, 1769

1. These things shall be,—a loft-ier race Than e'er the world hath known shall rise
2. They shall be gen - tle, brave and strong To spill no drop of blood, but dare
3. Na - tion with na - tion, land with land, Un-armed shall live as com-rades free;
4. New arts shall bloom of loft-ier mould, And might-ier mu - sic thrill the skies,

With flame of free-dom in their souls, And light of knowl-edge in their eyes:
All that may plant man's lordship firm On earth, and fire, and sea, and air.
In ev-ery heart and brain shall throb The pulse of one fra - ter - ni - ty.
And ev - ery life shall be a song, When all the earth is par - a - dise. A-men.

382

HESPERUS. L. M.

Henry W. Baker, 1861

Henry W. Baker, 1868

1. O God of love, O King of peace, Make wars throughout the world to cease;
2. Re-mem-ber, Lord, thy works of old, The won-ders that our fa-thers told;
3. Whom shall we trust but thee, O Lord? Where rest but on thy faith-ful word?
4. Where saints and angels dwell a-bove, All hearts are knit in ho-ly love;

The wrath of sin-ful man restrain, Give peace, O God, give peace a-gain!
Remember not our sin's dark stain, Give peace, O God, give peace a-gain!
None ev-er called on thee in vain, Give peace, O God, give peace a-gain!
O bind us in that heavenly chain! Give peace, O God, give peace a-gain! A-men.

383

ST. PETER. C. M.

John Oxenham, 1908

Alexander R. Reinagle, 1826

1. In Christ there is no East nor West, In him no South nor North;
2. In him shall true hearts ev-ery-where Their high com-mun-ion find;
3. Join hands then, broth-ers of the faith, What-e'er your race may be.
4. In Christ now meet both East and West, In him meet South and North;

But one great fel-low-ship of love Throughout the whole wide earth.
His serv-ice is the gold-en cord Close-bind-ing all man-kind.
Who serves my Fa-ther as a son Is sure-ly kin to me.
All Christ-ly souls are one in him Throughout the whole wide earth. A-men.

384

PENITENTIA. 10. 10. 10. 10.

GEORGE MATHESON, 1890

EDWARD DEARLE, 1874

1. Gath - er us in, thou Love, that fill - est all;
2. Gath - er us in: we wor - ship on - ly thee;
3. Thine is the mys - tic life great In - dia craves;
4. Thine is the Ro - man's strength with - out his pride;
5. Some seek a Fa - ther in the heavens a - bove;

Gath - er our ri - val faiths with - in thy fold;
In va - ried names we stretch a com - mon hand;
Thine is the Par - see's sin - de - stroy - ing beam;
Thine is the Greek's glad world with - out its graves;
Some ask a hu - man im - age to a - dore;

Rend each man's tem - ple - veil, and bid it fall,
In di - verse forms a com - mon soul we see;
Thine is the Bud - dhist's rest from toss - ing waves;
Thine is Ju - de - a's law with love be - side,
Some crave a spir - it vast as life and love;

That we may know that thou hast been of old.
In man - y ships we seek one spir - it - land.
Thine is the em - pire of vast Chi - na's dream.
The truth that cen - sures and the grace that saves.
With - in thy man - sions we have all and more. A - men.

World Peace and Fellowship

385

SALVE DOMINE. 7. 6. 7. 6. D.

JOHN S. B. MONSELL, 1863

LAWRENCE W. WATSON, 1909

1. Light of the world, we hail thee, Flush-ing the east-ern skies;
2. Light of the world, thy beau - ty Steals in - to ev - ery heart,
3. Light of the world, be - fore thee Our spir - its pros - trate fall!;
4. Light of the world, il - lu - mine This dark-ened earth of thine,

Nev - er shall dark-ness veil thee A - gain from hu - man eyes;
And glo - ri - fies with du - ty Life's poor - est, hum - blest part;
We wor-ship, we a - dore thee, Thou light, the life of all;
Till ev - ery-thing that's hu - man Be filled with the di - vine;

Too long, a - las, with-hold-en, Now spread from shore to shore;
Thou rob - est in thy splen - dor The sim - plest ways of men,
With thee is no for - get - ting Of all thine hand hath made;
Till ev - ery tongue and na - tion, From sin's do - min - ion free,

Thy light, so glad and gold - en, Shall set on earth no more.
And help - est them to ren - der Light back to thee a - gain.
Thy ris - ing hath no set - ting, Thy sun - shine hath no shade.
Rise in the new cre - a - tion Which springs from love and thee. A - men.

386

HANFORD. 8. 8. 8. 4.

GEORGE T. COSTER, 1864

ARTHUR S. SULLIVAN, 1874

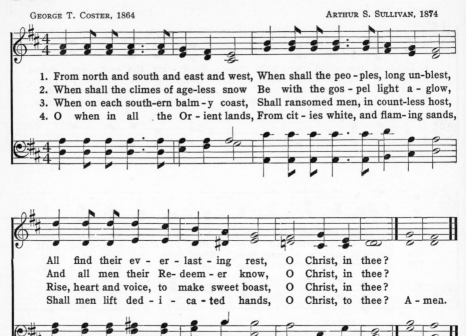

1. From north and south and east and west, When shall the peo-ples, long un-blest,
2. When shall the climes of age-less snow Be with the gos-pel light a-glow,
3. When on each south-ern balm-y coast, Shall ransomed men, in count-less host,
4. O when in all the Or-ient lands, From cit-ies white, and flam-ing sands,

All find their ev-er-last-ing rest, O Christ, in thee?
And all men their Re-deem-er know, O Christ, in thee?
Rise, heart and voice, to make sweet boast, O Christ, in thee?
Shall men lift ded-i-ca-ted hands, O Christ, to thee? A-men.

5 O when shall heathen darkness roll
Away in light, from pole to pole,
And endless day by every soul
Be found in thee?

6 Bring, Lord, the long-predicted hour,
The ages' diadem and flower,
When all shall find their refuge, tower,
And home in thee!

387

ALSTONE. L. M.

JAMES MONTGOMERY, 1823

CHRISTOPHER E. WILLING, 1868

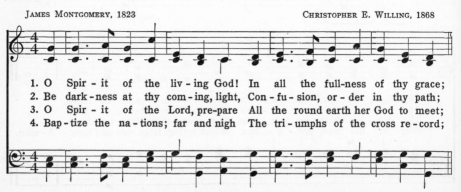

1. O Spir-it of the liv-ing God! In all the full-ness of thy grace;
2. Be dark-ness at thy com-ing, light, Con-fu-sion, or-der in thy path;
3. O Spir-it of the Lord, pre-pare All the round earth her God to meet;
4. Bap-tize the na-tions; far and nigh The tri-umphs of the cross re-cord;

Wher-e'er the foot of man hath trod, De-scend up-on our wait-ing race.
Souls without strength inspire with might; Bid mer-cy tri-umph o-ver wrath.
Breathe thou abroad like morning air Till hearts of stone be-gin to beat.
The name of Je-sus glo-ri-fy Till ev-ery kindred calls him Lord. A-men.

388   WALTHAM. L. M.

GEORGE W. DOANE, 1848   JOHN B. CALKIN, 1872

1. Fling out the ban-ner! let it float Sky-ward and sea-ward, high and wide;
2. Fling out the ban-ner! an-gels bend In anx-ious si-lence o'er the sign,
3. Fling out the ban-ner! hea-then lands Shall see from far the glo-rious sight,
4. Fling out the ban-ner! sin-sick souls That sink and per-ish in the strife,
5. Fling out the ban-ner! wide and high, Sea-ward and sky-ward, let it shine.

The sun that lights its shin-ing folds, The cross on which the Saviour died.
And vain-ly seek to com-pre-hend The won-der of the love di-vine.
And na-tions, crowd-ing to be born, Bap-tize their spir-its in its light.
Shall touch in faith its ra-diant hem, And spring im-mor-tal in-to life.
Nor skill, nor might, nor mer-it ours; We con-quer on-ly in that sign. A-men.

The Christian Kingdom

389

PRESBYTER. C. M. D.

JAMES MONTGOMERY, 1843

WALTER O. WILKINSON, 1895

1. Lift up your heads, ye gates of brass, Ye bars of i - ron, yield,
2. A ho - ly war those ser-vants wage: Mys - te - rious - ly at strife,
3. Though few and small and weak your bands, Strong in your Cap-tain's strength
4. O fear not, faint not, halt not now; Quit you like men, be strong!

And let the King of glo - ry pass; The cross is in the field:
The powers of heaven and hell en - gage For more than death or life.
Go to the con - quest of all lands; All must be his at length;
To Christ shall all the na - tions bow, And sing with you this song,—

That ban - ner, bright - er than the star That leads the train of night,
Ye ar - mies of the liv - ing God, His sac - ra - men - tal host,
Those spoils at his vic - to - rious feet You shall re - joice to lay,
'Up - lift - ed are the gates of brass, The bars of i - ron yield;

Shines on their march, and guides from far His ser-vants to the fight.
Where hal-lowed footsteps nev - er trod Take your ap-point - ed post.
And lay your-selves, as tro-phies meet, In his great judg-ment-day.
Be - hold the King of glo - ry pass; The cross hath won the field!' A - men.

390

WESLEY. 11. 10. 11. 10.

Thomas Hastings, 1832

Lowell Mason, 1830

1. Hail to the bright - ness of Zi - on's glad morn - ing,
2. Hail to the bright - ness of Zi - on's glad morn - ing,
3. Lo, in the des - ert rich flow - ers are spring - ing,
4. See, from all lands, from the isles of the o - cean,

Joy to the lands that in dark - ness have lain;
Long by the proph - ets of Is - rael fore - told;
Streams ev - er co - pious are glid - ing a - long;
Praise to Je - ho - vah as - cend - ing on high;

Hushed be the ac - cents of sor - row and mourn - ing,
Hail to the mil - lions from bond - age re - turn - ing,
Loud from the moun - tain - tops ech - oes are ring - ing,
Fall'n are the en - gines of war and com - mo - tion,

Zi - on in tri - umph be - gins her mild reign.
Gen - tiles and Jews the blest vis - ion be - hold.
Wastes rise in ver - dure and min - gle in song.
Shouts of sal - va - tion are rend - ing the sky. A - men.

The Christian Kingdom

391

WEBB. 7. 6. 7. 6. D.

SAMUEL F. SMITH, 1832

GEORGE J. WEBB, 1830

1. The morn-ing light is break-ing, The dark-ness dis-ap-pears;
2. See hea-then na-tions bend-ing Be-fore the God we love,
3. Blest riv-er of sal-va-tion, Pur-sue thy on-ward way;

The sons of earth are wak-ing To pen-i-ten-tial tears;
And thou-sand hearts as-cend-ing In grat-i-tude a-bove:
Flow thou to ev-ery na-tion, Nor in thy rich-ness stay:

Each breeze that sweeps the o-cean Brings tid-ings from a-far,
While sin-ners, now con-fess-ing, The gos-pel call o-bey,
Stay not till all the low-ly, Tri-um-phant reach their home;

Of na-tions in com-mo-tion, Pre-pared for Zi-on's war.
And seek the Sav-iour's bless-ing, A na-tion in a day.
Stay not till all the ho-ly Pro-claim, 'The Lord is come!' A-men.

Foreign Missions

392

MISSIONARY HYMN. 7. 6. 7. 6. D.

REGINALD HEBER, 1819

LOWELL MASON, 1823

1. From Green-land's i - cy moun-tains, From In - dia's cor - al strand,
2. What though the spi - cy breez - es Blow soft o'er Cey - lon's isle;
3. Can we, whose souls are light - ed With wis - dom from on high,
4. Waft, waft, ye winds, his sto - ry, And you, ye wa - ters, roll,

Where Af - ric's sun - ny fount - ains Roll down their gold - en sand,
Though ev - ery pros - pect pleas - es, And on - ly man is vile:
Can we to men be - night - ed The lamp of life de - ny?
Till, like a sea of glo - ry, It spreads from pole to pole;

From many an an - cient riv - er, From many a palm - y plain,
In vain with lav - ish kind - ness The gifts of God are strown;
Sal - va - tion! O sal - va - tion! The joy - ful sound pro - claim,
Till o'er our ran-somed na - ture The Lamb for sin - ners slain,

They call us to de - liv - er Their land from er - ror's chain.
The hea-then in his blind-ness Bows down to wood and stone.
Till each re - mot - est na - tion Has learned Mes - si - ah's name.
Re - deem- er, King, Cre - a - tor, In bliss re - turns to reign. A - men.

313

393

ITALIAN HYMN. 6. 6. 4. 6. 6. 6. 4.

SAMUEL WOLCOTT, 1869

FELICE GIARDINI, 1769

1. Christ for the world we sing; The world to Christ we bring,
2. Christ for the world we sing; The world to Christ we bring,
3. Christ for the world we sing; The world to Christ we bring,
4. Christ for the world we sing; The world to Christ we bring,

With lov - ing zeal; The poor and them that mourn, The faint and
With fer - vent prayer; The way - ward and the lost, By rest - less
With one ac - cord; With us the work to share, With us re-
With joy - ful song; The new - born souls, whose days, Re - claimed from

o - ver-borne; Sin - sick and sor - row-worn, Whom Christ doth heal.
pas-sions tossed, Re-deemed, at count-less cost, From dark de - spair.
proach to dare, With us the cross to bear, For Christ, our Lord.
er - ror's ways, In-spired with hope and praise, To Christ be - long. A - men.

394

ELMHURST. 8. 8. 8. 6.

MRS. MERRILL E. GATES, 1889

EDWIN D. DREWETT, 1887

1. Send thou, O Lord, to ev - ery place Swift mes - sen-gers be - fore thy face,
2. Send men whose eyes have seen the King, Men in whose ears his sweet words ring;
3. To bring good news to souls in sin; The bruised and broken hearts to win;
4. Gird each one with the Spir-it's sword, The sword of thine own deathless word;

The her-alds of thy wondrous grace, Where thou, thyself, wilt come.
Send such thy lost ones home to bring; Send them where thou wilt come.
In ev-ery place to bring them in; Where thou, thyself, wilt come.
And make them conqu'rors, conqu'ring Lord, Where thou, thyself, wilt come. A-men.

395

DORT. 6. 6. 4. 6. 6. 6. 4.

JOHN MARRIOTT, 1813   LOWELL MASON, 1832

1. Thou, whose al-might-y word Cha-os and dark-ness heard,
2. Thou, who didst come to bring On thy re-deem-ing wing
3. Spir-it of truth and love, Life-giv-ing, ho-ly Dove,

And took their flight; Hear us, we hum-bly pray, And, where the
Heal-ing and sight, Health to the sick in mind, Sight to the
Speed forth thy flight; Move on the wa-ter's face Bear-ing the

gos-pel day Sheds not its glo-rious ray, Let there be light!
in-ly blind, O now, to all man-kind, Let there be light!
lamp of grace, And, in earth's dark-est place, Let there be light! A-men.

396

PURPOSE. P. M.

ARTHUR C. AINGER, 1894

EMILY S. PERKINS, 1921

1. — God is work-ing his pur-pose out, as year suc-ceeds to
2. From ut-most East to ut-most West, where-'er man's foot hath
3. — March we forth in the strength of God, with the ban-ner of Christ un-
4. All we can do is noth-ing worth, un-less God bless the

year: — — God is work-ing his pur-pose out, and the
trod, By the mouth of man-y mes-sen-gers goes
furled, That the light of the glo-ri-ous Gos-pel of truth may
deed, — — Vain-ly we hope for the har-vest till God

time is draw-ing near. — Near-er and near-er draws the time,
forth the voice of God. Give ear to me, ye con-ti-nents,
shine through-out the world. — Fight we the fight with sor-row and sin
gives life to the seed; Yet near-er and near-er draws the time,

the time that shall sure-ly be, When the earth shall be filled with the
ye isles, give ear to me, That the earth shall be filled with the
to set their cap-tives free, That the earth shall be filled with the
the time that shall sure-ly be, When the earth shall be filled with the

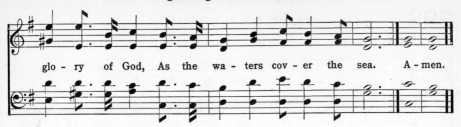

glo - ry of God, As the wa - ters cov - er the sea. A - men.

397

DUKE STREET. L. M.

Isaac Watts, 1719

John Hatton, (——— 1793)

1. Je - sus shall reign wher - e'er the sun Does his suc - ces - sive
2. For him shall end - less prayer be made, And prais - es throng to
3. Peo - ple and realms of ev - ery tongue Dwell on his love with
4. Bless - ings a - bound wher - e'er he reigns; The pris - oner leaps to
5. Let ev - ery crea - ture rise and bring Pe - cu - liar hon - ors

jour - neys run, His king - dom spread from shore to shore,
crown his head; His name, like sweet per - fume, shall rise
sweet - est song, And in - fant voi - ces shall pro - claim
lose his chains, The wea - ry find e - ter - nal rest,
to our King; An - gels de - scend with songs a - gain,

Till moons shall wax and wane no more.
With ev - ery morn - ing sac - ri - fice;
Their ear - ly bless - ings on his name.
And all the sons of want are blest.
And earth re - peat the loud A - men! A - men.

The Christian Kingdom

398

TIDINGS. 11. 10. 11. 10. With Refrain.

MARY A. THOMSON, 1870

JAMES WALCH, 1876

1. O Zi - on, haste, thy mis - sion high ful - fill - ing,
2. Be - hold how man - y thou - sands still are ly - ing,
3. Pro - claim to ev - ery peo - ple, tongue, and na - tion,
4. Give of thy sons to bear the mes - sage glo - rious;
5. He comes a - gain: O Zi - on, ere thou meet him,

To tell to all the world that God is Light; That he who
Bound in the dark - some pris - on - house of sin, With none to
That God, in whom they live and move, is Love: Tell how he
Give of thy wealth to speed them on their way; Pour out thy
Make known to ev - ery heart his sav - ing grace; Let none whom

made all na - tions is not will - ing One soul should per - ish,
tell them of the Sav-iour's dy - ing, Or of the life he
stooped to save his lost cre - a - tion, And died on earth that
soul for them in prayer vic - to - rious; And all thou spend-est
he hath ran - somed fail to greet him, Through thy neg - lect, un -

Refrain

lost in shades of night.
died for them to win.
man might live a - bove. } Pub - lish glad ti - dings, ti - dings of peace,
Je - sus will re - pay.
fit to see his face.

Foreign Missions

Ti - dings of Je - sus, re - demp-tion and re - lease. A - men.

399   MISSIONARY CHANT. L. M.

Bourne H. Draper, 1803   Charles H. C. Zeuner, 1832

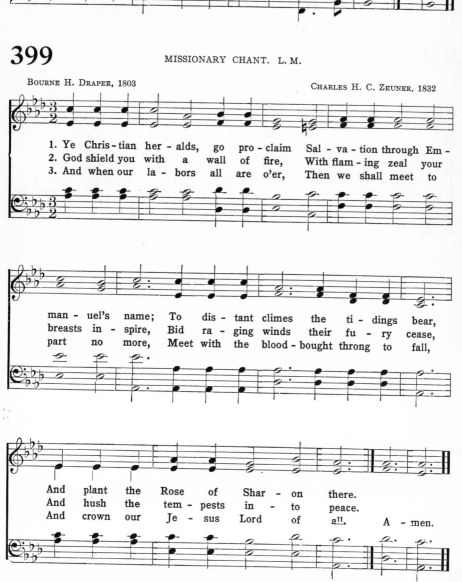

1. Ye Chris - tian her - alds, go pro - claim Sal - va - tion through Em -
2. God shield you with a wall of fire, With flam - ing zeal your
3. And when our la - bors all are o'er, Then we shall meet to

man - uel's name; To dis - tant climes the ti - dings bear,
breasts in - spire, Bid ra - ging winds their fu - ry cease,
part no more, Meet with the blood - bought throng to fall,

And plant the Rose of Shar - on there.
And hush the tem - pests in - to peace.
And crown our Je - sus Lord of all. A - men.

The Christian Kingdom

400

RUSSIAN HYMN. 10. 10. 10. 10.

ALEXANDER POPE, 1712

ALEXIS T. LWOFF, 1833

1. Rise, crowned with light, im - pe - rial Sa - lem, rise!
2. See a long race thy spa - cious courts a - dorn:
3. See bar - barous na - tions at thy gates at - tend,
4. The seas shall waste, the skies to smoke de - cay,

Ex - alt thy tower - ing head and lift thine eyes!
See fu - ture sons, and daugh - ters yet un - born,
Walk in thy light, and in thy tem - ple bend:
Rocks fall to dust, and moun - tains melt a - way;

See heaven its spark - ling por - tals wide dis - play,
In crowd - ing ranks on ev - ery side a - rise,
See thy bright al - tars thronged with pros - trate kings,
But fixed his word, his sav - ing power re - mains;

And break up - on thee in a flood of day.
De - mand - ing life, im - pa - tient for the skies.
While ev - ery land its joy - ous trib - ute brings.
Thy realms shall last, thine own Mes - si - ah reigns. A - men.

401

NATIONAL HYMN. 10. 10. 10. 10.

Laura S. Copenhaver

George W. Warren, 1892

Trumpets, before each verse.

1. Her-alds of Christ who bear the King's com-
2. Through des-ert ways, dark fen and deep mo-
3. Where once the twist-ing trail in dark-ness
4. Lord, give us faith and strength the road to

mands, Im-mor-tal tid-ings in your mor-tal hands,
rass, Through jun-gles, slug-gish seas, and mountain pass,
wound Let march-ing feet and joy-ous song re-sound,
build, To see the prom-ise of the day ful-filled,

Pass on and car-ry swift the news ye bring,
Build ye the road, and fal-ter not, nor stay,
Where burn the fun-eral pyres, and cen-sers swing,
When war shall be no more and strife shall cease

Make straight, make straight the high-way of the King.
Pre-pare a-cross the earth the King's high-way.
Make straight, make straight the high-way of the King.
Up-on the high-way of the Prince of Peace. A-men.

The Christian Kingdom

402

TOULON. 10. 10. 10. 10.

W. RUSSELL BOWIE, 1913

LOUIS BOURGEOIS, 1543

1. God of the Na - tions, who from dawn of days
2. Thine an - cient might did break the Pha - raoh's boast,
3. Thy hand hast led a - cross the hun - gry sea
4. Then, for thy grace to grow in broth - er - hood,

Hast led thy peo - ple in their wid - ening ways,
Thou wast the shield for Is - rael's march - ing host,
The ea - ger peo - ples flock - ing to be free,
For hearts a - flame to serve thy des - tined good,

Through whose deep pur - pose stran - ger thou - sands stand
And, all the a - ges through, past crum - bling throne
And from the breeds of earth, thy si - lent sway
For faith, and will to win what faith shall see,

Here in the bor - ders of our prom - ised land;
And bro - ken fet - ter, thou hast brought thine own.
Fash - ions the Na - tion of the broaden - ing day.
God of thy peo - ple, hear us cry to thee. A - men.

Words copyright, 1914, by Survey Associates

322

403

GARFIRTH. 7. 6. 7. 6. D.

Robert Murray, 1880

Robert P. Stewart, 1868

1. From o - cean un - to o - cean Our land shall own thee Lord,
2. O Christ, for thine own glo - ry, And for our coun-try's weal,
3. Where er - ror smites with blind - ness, En - slaves and leads a - stray,
4. Our Sav - iour King, de - fend us, And guide where we should go;

And, filled with true de - vo - tion, O - bey thy sover-eign word.
We hum - bly plead be - fore thee, Thy - self in us re - veal;
Do thou in lov - ing - kind - ness Pro - claim thy gos - pel day,
Forth with thy mes-sage send us, Thy love and light to show,

Our prai - ries and our moun - tains, Our for - ests and each field,
And may we know, Lord Je - sus, The touch of thy dear hand,
Till all the tribes and rac - es That dwell in this fair land,
Till, fired with true de - vo - tion En - kind - led by thy word,

Our riv - ers, lakes, and foun-tains To thee shall trib - ute yield.
And, healed of our dis - eas - es, The tempter's power with-stand.
A - dorned with Chris-tian grac - es, With - in thy courts shall stand.
From o - cean un - to o - cean Our land shall own thee Lord. A - men.

The Christian Kingdom

404

ALL HALLOWS. 7. 6. 7. 6. D.

Anonymous

GEORGE CLEMENT MARTIN, 1892

UNISON

1. The land we love is call - ing From plain and moun-tain height,
2. The soul-starved moun-tain high -lands, The need of coun-try - side,
3. Oh pil - grims of the morn - ing, Stand in your ra - diant might,

Her val - iant sons and daugh - ters To lift her bea - con light.
The cit - y's creep-ing dark - ness Where sin and fear a - bide,
Splen-did with faith tri - umph - ant, Touched by the liv - ing Light,

From coast to coast the an - swer Comes ring - ing strong and free,
Shall see the march-ing thou - sands That hear the plead - ing call,
Join hands a - cross the na - tion From toss - ing sea to sea,

HARMONY

A - mer - i - ca, A - mer - i - ca, We bring our lives to thee.
A - mer - i - ca, A - mer - i - ca, We bring to thee our all,
Oh, God may our A - mer - i - ca Bring all her life to thee. A - men.

405

SALVE DOMINE. 7. 6. 7. 6. D.

FREDERICK L. HOSMER, 1884

LAWRENCE W. WATSON, 1909

1. 'O beau - ti - ful, my coun - try!' Be thine a no - bler care
2. For thee our fa - thers suf - fered; For thee they toiled and prayed;
3. O beau - ti - ful, our coun - try! Round thee in love we draw;

Than all thy wealth of com - merce, Thy har - vests wav - ing fair;
Up - on thy ho - ly al - tar Their will - ing lives they laid.
Thine is the grace of free - dom, The ma - jes - ty of law.

Be it thy pride to lift up The man - hood of the poor;
Thou hast no com - mon birth - right, Grand mem - ories on thee shine;
Be right - eous - ness thy scep - ter, Jus - tice thy di - a - dem;

Be thou to the op - press - ed Fair free - dom's o - pen door!
The blood of pil - grim na - tions Com - min - gled flows in thine.
And on thy shin - ing fore - head Be peace the crown - ing gem! A - men.

406

GREENLAND. 7. 6. 7. 6. D.

JOHN HAYNES HOLMES (1879 ——)

J. MICHAEL HAYDN, 1737–1806

1. A - mer - i - ca tri - umph - ant! Brave land of pi - o - neers!
2. A - mer - i - ca tri - umph - ant! Dear home-land of the free!
3. A - mer - i - ca tri - umph - ant! Grasp firm thy sword and shield!
4. A - mer - i - ca, A - mer - i-ca! Tri - umph-ant thou shalt be!

On moun-tain peak and prai - rie Their wind-ing trail ap - pears.
Thy sons have fought and fall - en, To win re - lease for thee.
Not yet have all thy foe - men Been driv - en from the field.
Thy hills and vales shall ech - o The shouts of lib - er - ty.

The wil - der - ness is plant - ed; The des - erts bloom and sing;
They broke the chains of em - pire; They smote the wrongs of state;
They lurk by forge and mar - ket, They hide in mine and mill;
Thy bards shall sing thy glo - ry, Thy proph - ets tell thy praise,

On coast and plain the cit - ies Their smok-y ban - ners fling.
And lies of law and cus - tom They blast-ed with their hate.
And bold with greed of con - quest, They flout thy bless - ed will!
And all thy sons and daugh-ters Ac - claim thy gold - en days. A - men.

By permission of the Author

407

MATERNA. C. M. D.

KATHERINE LEE BATES, 1893, Revised 1910

SAMUEL A. WARD, 1882

1. O beau - ti - ful for spa - cious skies, For am - ber waves of grain,
2. O beau - ti - ful for pil - grim feet, Whose stern, impassioned stress
3. O beau - ti - ful for he - roes proved In lib - er - at - ing strife,
4. O beau - ti - ful for pa - triot dream That sees be - yond the years

For pur - ple moun-tain maj - es - ties A - bove the fruit - ed plain!
A thor - ough-fare for free - dom beat A - cross the wil - der - ness!
Who more than self their coun - try loved, And mer - cy more than life!
Thine al - a - bas - ter cit - ies gleam, Un-dimmed by hu - man tears!

A - mer - i - ca! A - mer - i - ca! God shed his grace on thee,
A - mer - i - ca! A - mer - i - ca! God mend thine ev - ery flaw,
A - mer - i - ca! A - mer - i - ca! May God thy gold re - fine,
A - mer - i - ca! A - mer - i - ca! God shed his grace on thee,

And crown thy good with broth-er-hood From sea to shin - ing sea!
Con - firm thy soul in self - con-trol, Thy lib - er - ty in law!
Till all suc - cess be no - ble-ness, And ev - ery gain di - vine!
And crown thy good with broth-er-hood From sea to shin - ing sea! A - men.

The Christian Kingdom

408

PRESBYTER. C. M. D.

Henry van Dyke, 1912

Walter O. Wilkinson, 1895

UNISON

1. O Lord our God, thy might-y hand Hath made our coun-try free;
2. The strength of ev-ery state in-crease In Un-ion's gold-en chain;
3. O suf-fer not her feet to stray; But guide her un-taught might,
4. Through all the wait-ing land pro-claim Thy gos-pel of good-will;

From all her broad and hap-py land May wor-ship rise to thee;
Her thou-sand cit-ies fill with peace, Her mil-lion fields with grain.
That she may walk in peace-ful day, And lead the world in light.
And may the joy of Je-sus' name In ev-ery bos-om thrill.

Ful-fill the prom-ise of her youth, Her lib-er-ty de-fend;
The vir-tues of her min-gled blood In one new peo-ple blend;
Bring down the proud, lift up the poor, Un-e-qual ways a-mend;
O'er hill and vale, from sea to sea, Thy ho-ly reign ex-tend;

By law and or-der, love and truth, A-mer-i-ca be-friend!
By u-ni-ty and broth-er-hood, A-mer-i-ca be-friend!
By jus-tice, na-tion-wide and sure, A-mer-i-ca be-friend!
By faith and hope and char-i-ty, A-mer-i-ca be-friend! A-men.

409

ALL SAINTS. C. M. D.

ALLEN EASTMAN CROSS, 1918

HENRY S. CUTLER, 1872

1. A - mer - i - ca, A - mer - i - ca, The shouts of war shall cease;
2. What though its stones were laid in tears, Its pil - lars red with wrong,
3. A - mer - i - ca, A - mer - i - ca, Ring out the glad re - frain!

The glo - ry dawns! the day is come Of vic - to - ry and peace!
Its walls shall rise through pa - tient years To soar - ing spires of song!
Sa - lute the flag—sa - lute the dead That have not died in vain!

And now up - on a lar - ger plan We'll build the com - mon good,
For on this house shall faith at - tend With joy on air - y wing,
O glo - ry! glo - ry to thy plan To build the com - mon good,

The tem - ple of the love of man, The House of Broth - er - hood!
And flam - ing loy - al - ty as - cend To God, the on - ly King!
The tem - ple of the rights of man, The House of Broth - er - hood! A - men.

410

BATTLE HYMN OF THE REPUBLIC. Irregular.

JULIA WARD HOWE, 1862

WILLIAM STEFFE, 1852

1. Mine eyes have seen the glo - ry of the com - ing of the Lord;
2. I have seen him in the watch-fires of a hun - dred cir - cling camps;
3. He has sound - ed forth the trum - pet that shall nev - er call re - treat;
4. In the beau - ty of the lil - ies Christ was born a - cross the sea,

He is tramp - ling out the vin - tage where the grapes of wrath are stored;
They have build - ed him an al - tar in the eve - ning dews and damps;
He is sift - ing out the hearts of men be - fore his judg-ment seat;
With a glo - ry in his bos - om that trans - fig - ures you and me;

He hath loosed the fate - ful light-ning of his ter - ri - ble swift sword;
I can read his right - eous sen - tence by the dim and flar - ing lamps,
O be swift, my soul, to an - swer him; be ju - bi - lant, my feet!
As he died to make men ho - ly, let us die to make men free!

Refrain

His truth is march - ing on.
His day is march - ing on.
Our God is march - ing on.
While God is march - ing on.

Glo - ry! glo - ry! Hal - le - lu - jah!

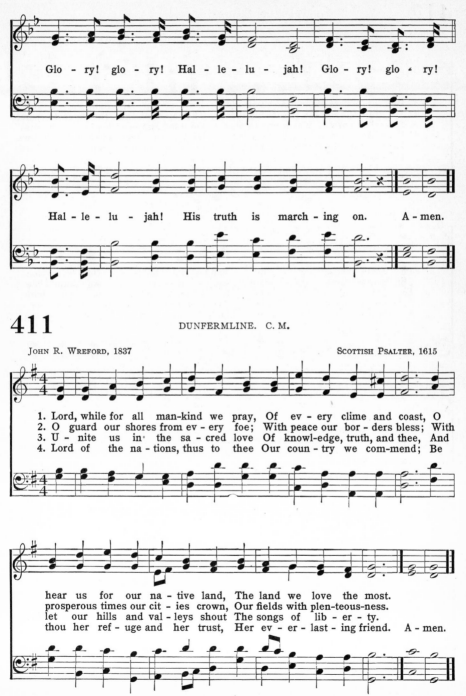

Glo - ry! glo - ry! Hal - le - lu - jah! Glo - ry! glo ~ ry!

Hal - le - lu - jah! His truth is march - ing on. A - men.

411

DUNFERMLINE. C. M.

John R. Wreford, 1837

Scottish Psalter, 1615

1. Lord, while for all man-kind we pray, Of ev - ery clime and coast, O
2. O guard our shores from ev - ery foe; With peace our bor - ders bless; With
3. U - nite us in the sa - cred love Of knowl-edge, truth, and thee, And
4. Lord of the na - tions, thus to thee Our coun - try we com-mend; Be

hear us for our na - tive land, The land we love the most.
prosperous times our cit - ies crown, Our fields with plen-teous-ness.
let our hills and val - leys shout The songs of lib - er - ty.
thou her ref - uge and her trust, Her ev - er - last - ing friend. A - men.

The Christian Kingdom

GOWER'S RECESSIONAL. 8. 8. 8. 8. 8. 8.

RUDYARD KIPLING, 1897

JOHN H. GOWER, 1903

UNISON

1. God of our fa-thers, known of old, Lord of our far - flung bat - tle line,
2. The tu-mult and the shout-ing dies; The cap-tains and the kings de - part;
3. Far-called our na - vies melt a - way, On dune and head-land sinks the fire;
4. If drunk with sight of power we loose Wild tongues that have not thee in awe,
5. For hea-then heart that puts her trust In reek - ing tube and i - ron shard;

HARMONY

Be - neath whose aw - ful hand we hold Do - min - ion
Still stands thine an - cient sac - ri - fice, An hum - ble
Lo, all our pomp of yes - ter - day Is one with
Such boast - ing as the Gen - tiles use Or less - er
All val - iant dust that builds on dust, And, guard - ing,

o - ver palm and pine: Lord God of hosts, be with us
and a con - trite heart: Lord God of hosts, be with us
Nin - e - veh and Tyre! Judge of the na - tions, spare us
breeds with - out the law: Lord God of hosts, be with us
calls not thee to guard; For fran - tic boast and fool - ish

yet, Lest we for - get, lest we for - get.
yet, Lest we for - get, lest we for - get.
yet, Lest we for - get, lest we for - get.
yet, Lest we for - get, lest we for - get.
word, Thy mer - cy on thy peo - ple, Lord! A - men.

413

LEST WE FORGET. 8. 8. 8. 8. 8. 8.

JOHN OXENHAM, 1915

G. B. BLANCHARD, (1856——)

1. Lord God of hosts, whose might - y hand Do - min - ion holds on
2. For those who weak and bro - ken lie In wear - i - ness and
3. For those to whom the call shall come, We pray thy ten - der
4. For those who min - is - ter and heal, And spend them-selves, their

sea and land, In peace and war thy will we see Shap -
a - go - ny, Great Heal - er, to their beds of pain Come,
wel - come home, The toil, the bit - ter - ness, all past, We
skill, their zeal; Re - new their hearts with Christ - like faith, And

ing the larg - er lib - er - ty; Na - tions may rise and
touch and make them whole a - gain. O hear a peo - ple's
trust them to thy love at last. O hear a peo - ple's
guard them from dis - ease and death: And in thine own good

na - tions fall, Thy changeless pur - pose rules them all.
prayers, and bless Thy ser - vants in their hour of stress!
prayers for all Who, no - bly striv - ing, no - bly fall!
time, Lord, send Thy peace on earth till time shall end. A - men.

The Christian Kingdom

414

NATIONAL HYMN. 10. 10. 10. 10.

DANIEL C. ROBERTS, 1876

GEORGE W. WARREN, 1892

Trumpets, before each verse

1. God of our fa - thers, whose al - might - y
2. Thy love di - vine hath led us in the
3. From war's a - larms, from dead - ly pes - ti -
4. Re - fresh thy peo - ple on their toil - some

hand Leads forth in beau - ty all the star - ry band
past, In this free land by thee our lot is cast;
lence, Be thy strong arm our ev - er sure de - fense;
way, Lead us from night to nev - er - end - ing day;

Of shin - ing worlds in splen - dor through the skies,
Be thou our rul - er, guard - ian, guide and stay,
Thy true re - lig - ion in our hearts in - crease,
Fill all our lives with love and grace di - vine,

Our grate - ful songs be - fore thy throne a - rise.
Thy word our law, thy paths our cho - sen way.
Thy boun - teous good - ness nour - ish us in peace.
And glo - ry, laud and praise be ev - er thine. A - men.

The Nation

415

AMERICA. 6. 6. 4. 6. 6. 6. 4.

SAMUEL F. SMITH, 1832   HENRY CAREY, 1740

1. My coun - try, 'tis of thee, Sweet land of lib - er - ty,
2. My na - tive coun - try, thee, Land of the no - ble free,
3. Let mu - sic swell the breeze, And ring from all the trees
4. Our fa - thers' God, to thee, Au - thor of lib - er - ty,

Of thee I sing; Land where my fa - thers died, Land of the
Thy name I love; I love thy rocks and rills, Thy woods and
Sweet free - dom's song; Let mor - tal tongues a - wake; Let all that
To thee we sing; Long may our land be bright With free - dom's

pil - grims' pride, From ev - ery moun-tain side Let free-dom ring!
tem-pled hills; My heart with rap-ture thrills, Like that a - bove.
breathe partake; Let rocks their si-lence break, The sound pro - long.
ho - ly light; Pro - tect us by thy might, Great God, our King. A - men.

416

AMERICA

1 God bless our native land,
Firm may she ever stand
    Through storm and night!
When the wild tempests rave,
Ruler of wind and wave,
Do thou our country save,
    By thy great might!

2 For her our prayers shall rise,
To God above the skies,
    On him we wait;
Thou who art ever nigh,

Guarding with watchful eye,
To thee aloud we cry,
    God save the state!

3 Lord of all truth and right,
In whom alone is might,
    On thee we call!
And may the nations see
That men should brothers be,
And form one family!
    God save us all!

SIEGFRIED A. MAHLMANN, 1815
Translated by CHARLES T. BROOKS, 1833. JOHN S. DWIGHT, 1844

The Christian Kingdom

417

STAR-SPANGLED BANNER. Irregular

Francis Scott Key, 1814

John Stafford Smith, 1780

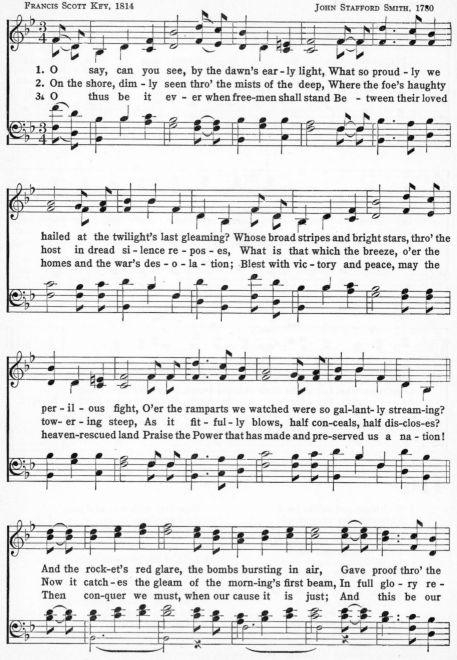

1. O say, can you see, by the dawn's ear-ly light, What so proud-ly we
2. On the shore, dim-ly seen thro' the mists of the deep, Where the foe's haughty
3. O thus be it ev-er when free-men shall stand Be-tween their loved

hailed at the twilight's last gleaming? Whose broad stripes and bright stars, thro' the
host in dread si-lence re-pos-es, What is that which the breeze, o'er the
homes and the war's des-o-la-tion; Blest with vic-tory and peace, may the

per-il-ous fight, O'er the ramparts we watched were so gal-lant-ly stream-ing?
tow-er-ing steep, As it fit-ful-ly blows, half con-ceals, half dis-clos-es?
heaven-rescued land Praise the Power that has made and pre-served us a na-tion!

And the rock-et's red glare, the bombs bursting in air, Gave proof thro' the
Now it catch-es the gleam of the morn-ing's first beam, In full glo-ry re-
Then con-quer we must, when our cause it is just; And this be our

The Nation

Refrain

night that our flag was still there. O say, does that Star-span-gled
flect-ed now shines on the stream; 'Tis the Star-span-gled Ban-ner: O
mot-to: 'In God is our trust!' And the Star-span-gled Ban-ner in

Ban-ner yet wave O'er the land of the free and the home of the brave?
long may it wave O'er the land of the free and the home of the brave!
tri-umph shall wave O'er the land of the free and the home of the brave.

418

CLAIRVAUX. C. M.

IRVING MAURER, 1912

RICHARD FRANCIS LLOYD

1. O God, hear thou the na-tion's prayer, We lift our cause to thee:
2. Give us to build our cit-ies pure, Sal-va-tion throned a-bove;
3. Give us to guide the a-lien feet; To teach the broth-er's way;
4. May vis-ions call and faith en-flame, And ban-ish lust and greed:

We wage the ho-ly war of Christ; We fight to make man free.
To shel-ter low-ly homes from ill, And tune our mills with love.
To save our moth-er-hood from need; To guard our chil-dren's play.
Make thou A-mer-i-ca to be A land of soul-ful deed. A-men.

The Christian Kingdom

419

DUKE STREET. L. M.

LEONARD BACON, 1833

JOHN HATTON (−1793)

1. O God, be-neath thy guid-ing hand, Our ex-iled
2. Thou heard'st, well pleased, the song, the prayer: Thy bless-ing
3. Laws, free-dom, truth, and faith in God Came with those
4. And here thy name, O God of love, Their child-ren's

fa-thers crossed the sea; And when they trod the win-try
came; and still its power Shall on-ward, through all a-ges,
ex-iles o'er the waves; And where their pil-grim feet have
child-ren shall a-dore, Till these e-ter-nal hills re-

strand, With prayer and psalm they wor-shipped thee.
bear The mem-ory of that ho-ly hour.
trod, The God they trust-ed guards their graves.
move, And spring a-dorns the earth no more. A-men.

420

TRURO. L. M.

ALLEN EASTMAN CROSS, 1920

CHARLES BURNEY, 1769

1. More light shall break from out thy word For pil-grim fol-lowers of the gleam,
2. What might-y hopes are in our care, What ho-ly dreams of broth-er-hood;
3. Wild roars the blast, the storm is high! A-bove the storm are shin-ing still
4. The an-cient stars, the an-cient faith, De-fend us till our voyage is done—

Till, led by thy free spir - it, Lord, We see and share the pil - grim dream!
God of our Fa-thers, help us dare Their passion for the com-mon good!
The lights by which we live and die; Our peace is ev - er in thy will!
A- cross the floods of fear and death The May-flower still is sail-ing on! A-men.

Copyrighted by Allen Eastman Cross. Used by permission

421   SPANISH HYMN. 7. 7. 7. 7. 7. 7.

Arranged by
BENJAMIN CARR, 1826

FRANCES M. OWEN, about 1872

1. When thy sol - diers take their swords, When they speak the sol - emn words,
2. When the world's sharp strife is nigh, When they hear the bat - tle - cry,
3. When their hearts are lift - ed high With suc - cess or vic - to - ry,
4. When the vows that they have made, When the prayers that they have prayed,
5. Through life's con-flict guard us all, Or if wound - ed some should fall

When they kneel be - fore thee here, Feel - ing thee, their Fa - ther, near;
When they rush in - to the fight, Know- ing not temp - ta - tion's might;
When they feel the conqueror's pride; Lest they grow self - sat - is - fied,
Shall be fad - ing from their hearts; When their first warm faith de - parts;
Ere the vic - to - ry be won, For the sake of Christ, thy Son,

These thy chil-dren, Lord, de-fend; To their help thy spir - it send.
These thy chil-dren, Lord, de-fend; To their zeal thy wis-dom lend.
These thy chil-dren, Lord, de-fend; Teach their souls to thee to bend.
These thy chil-dren, Lord, de-fend; Keep them faith-ful to the end.
These thy chil-dren, Lord, de-fend; And in death thy com-fort lend. A - men.

339

The Christian Kingdom

422

MORWELLHAM. 8. 6. 8. 6. 8. 6.

W. Russell Bowie, 1909

Charles H. Steggall, 1826-1905

1. O Ho - ly Cit - y seen of John, Where Christ the
2. Hark, how from men whose lives are held More cheap than
3. Give us, O God, the strength to build The Cit - y
4. Al - read - y in the mind of God That Cit - y

Lamb doth reign, With - in whose four - square walls shall come
mer - chan - dise, From wom - en strug - gling sore for bread,
that hath stood Too long a dream, whose laws are love,
ris - eth fair,— Lo, how its splen - dor chal - len - ges

No night, nor need, nor pain, And where the tears are
From lit - tle chil - dren's cries, There swells the sob - bing
Whose ways are broth - er - hood, And where the sun that
The souls that great - ly dare,— Yea, bids us seize the

wiped from eyes That shall not weep a - gain!
hu - man plaint That bids thy walls a - rise!
shin - eth is God's grace for hu - man good.
whole of life And build its glo - ry there! A - men.

423

ST. GERMANS. 6. 6. 6. 6. 6. 6.

FRANCIS T. PALGRAVE, 1867

FREDERICK C. MAKER, (1844——)

1. O thou not made with hands,
   Not throned a-bove the skies,
   Nor walled with shin-ing walls,
   Nor framed with stones of price,
   More bright than gold or gem,
   God's own Je-ru-sa-lem!

2. Wher-e'er the gen-tle heart
   Finds cour-age from a-bove,
   Wher-e'er the heart for-sook
   Warms with the breath of love,
   Where faith bids fear de-part,
   Cit-y of God, thou art.

3. Thou art wher-e'er the proud
   In hum-ble-ness melts down,
   Where self it-self yields up,
   Where mar-tyrs win their crown,
   Where faith-ful souls pos-sess
   Them-selves in per-fect peace.

4. Where in life's com-mon ways
   With cheer-ful feet we go,
   When in his steps we tread
   Who trod the way of woe,
   Where he is in the heart,
   Cit-y of God, thou art.

5. Not throned a-bove the skies,
   Nor gold-en-walled a-far,
   But where Christ's two or three
   In his name gath-ered are,
   Be in the midst of them,
   God's own Je-ru-sa-lem. A-men.

424

GARDINER. L. M.

Frank Mason North, 1903

William Gardiner's
Sacred Melodies, 1815

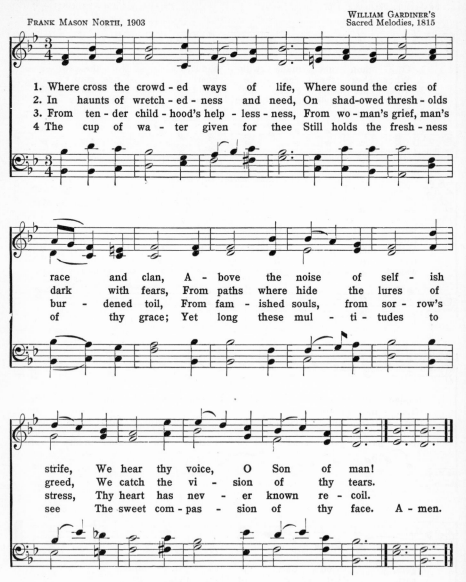

1. Where cross the crowd-ed ways of life, Where sound the cries of
2. In haunts of wretch-ed-ness and need, On shad-owed thresh-olds
3. From ten-der child-hood's help-less-ness, From wo-man's grief, man's
4. The cup of wa-ter given for thee Still holds the fresh-ness

race and clan, A-bove the noise of self-ish
dark with fears, From paths where hide the lures of
bur-dened toil, From fam-ished souls, from sor-row's
of thy grace; Yet long these mul-ti-tudes to

strife, We hear thy voice, O Son of man!
greed, We catch the vi-sion of thy tears.
stress, Thy heart has nev-er known re-coil.
see The sweet com-pas-sion of thy face. A-men.

5 O Master, from the mountain side,
  Make haste to heal these hearts of pain;
  Among these restless throngs abide,
  O tread the city's streets again.

6 Till sons of men shall learn thy love,
  And follow where thy feet have trod;
  Till glorious from thy heaven above,
  Shall come the City of our God.

The Community

425

BEECHER. 8. 7. 8. 7. D.

FELIX ADLER, 1878

JOHN ZUNDEL, 1870

1. Hail the glo-rious Gold-en Cit-y, Pic-tured by the seers of old!
2. We are build-ers of that cit-y; All our joys and all our groans
3. And the work that we have build-ed, Oft with bleed-ing hands and tears,

Ev-er-last-ing light shines o'er it, Won-drous tales of it are told:
Help to rear its shin-ing ram-parts; All our lives are build-ing stones:
Oft in er-ror, oft in an-guish, Will not per-ish with our years:

On-ly right-eous men and wom-en Dwell with-in its gleam-ing wall;
Wheth-er hum-ble or ex-alt-ed, All are called to task di-vine;
It will live and shine trans-fig-ured In the fin-al reign of Right;

Wrong is ban-ished from its bor-ders, Jus-tice reigns su-preme o'er all.
All must aid a-like to car-ry For-ward one sub-lime de-sign.
It will pass in-to the splen-dors Of the Cit-y of the Light. A-men.

426

ROTTERDAM. 7. 6. 8. 6. D.

WILLIAM GEORGE TARRANT (1853——)

BERTHOLD TOURS, 1875

1. The fa - thers built this cit - y In a - ges long a - go,
2. Yet still the cit - y stand - eth, A hive of toil - ing men,
3. Let all the peo - ple praise thee Give all thy sav - ing health,
4. A com - mon - weal of broth - ers, U - nit - ed, great and small;

And, bus - y in its bus - y streets, They hur - ried to and fro;
And mo-ther's love makes hap - py home For chil - dren now as then;
Or vain the la - borer's strong right arm And vain the mer-chant's wealth.
Up - on our ban - ner bla-zoned be The char - ter, 'Each for all!'

The chil - dren played a - round them And sang the songs of yore,
O God of a - ges, help us Such cit - i - zens to be
Send forth thy light to ban - ish The shad - ows and the shame,
Nor let us cease from bat - tle, Nor wea - ry sheathe the sword,

Till, one by one, they fell a - sleep, To work and play no more.
That chil-dren's chil-dren here may sing The songs of lib - er - ty.
Till all the civ - ic vir - tues shine A - round our cit - y's name.
Un - til this cit - y is be - come The cit - y of the Lord. A - men.

The Home

427 WINDSOR. 11. 10. 11. 10.

CARL J. P. SPITTA, 1833.
Translated by SARAH BORTHWICK FINDLATER, 1853

JOSEPH BARNBY, (1838-1896)

1. O hap-py home, where thou art loved the dear-est,
2. O hap-py home, where each one serves thee, low-ly,
3. O hap-py home, where thou art not for-got-ten
4. Un-til at last, when earth's day's work is end-ed

Thou lov-ing Friend, and Sav-iour of our race,
What-ev-er his ap-point-ed work may be,
When joy is o-ver-flow-ing, full, and free;
All meet thee in the bless-ed home a-bove,

And where a-mong the guests there nev-er com-eth
Till ev-ery com-mon task seems great and ho-ly,
O hap-py home, where ev-ery wound-ed spir-it,
From whence thou cam-est, where thou hast as-cend-ed,

One who can hold such high and hon-ored place.
When it is done, O Lord, as un-to thee.
Is brought, Phy-si-cian, Com-fort-er, to thee.
Thy ev-er-last-ing home of peace and love. A-men.

428

HOLLEY. L. M.

OLIVER WENDELL HOLMES, 1869

GEORGE HEWS, 1835

1. Thou gra - cious Power, whose mer - cy lends The light of
2. For all the bless - ings life has brought, For all its
3. The noon - tide sun - shine of the past, These brief, bright
4. We thank thee, Fa - ther; let thy grace Our lov - ing

home, the smile of friends, Our fam - ilies in thine
sor - rowing hours have taught, For all we mourn, for
mo - ments fad - ing fast, The stars that gild our
cir - cles still em - brace, Thy mer - cy shed its

arms en - fold As thou didst keep thy folk of old.
all we keep, The hands we clasp, the loved that sleep,
dark - ening years, The twi - light ray from ho - lier spheres.
heav - enly store, Thy peace be with us ev - er - more. A-men.

429

MAHON. 8. 7. 8. 7.

Anonymous

C. EDGAR KNOWLES

1. Up to me sweet child-hood look-eth, Heart and mind and soul a - wake;
2. In their young hearts, soft and ten-der, Guide my hand good seed to sow,
3. Fa - ther, or - der all my foot-steps; So di - rect my dai - ly way,
4. Draw us hand in hand to Je - sus, He who child-ren ne'er for - got,

The Home

Teach me of thy ways, O Fa-ther, For sweet childhood's precious sake.
That its blos-som-ing may praise thee Where-so-ev-er they may go.
That in fol-low-ing me, the child-ren May not, stumb-ling, go a-stray.
'Let the lit-tle ones come to me, And do thou for-bid them not.' A-men.

Used by permission

430

BELOIT. L. M.

Norman E. Richardson, 1918
Florence I. Judson-Bradley

Carl G. Reissiger, (1798–1859)

1. My Lord, I do not ask to stand As king or prince of
2. To teach a ten-der voice to pray Two child-ish eyes thy
3. O grant thy pa-tience to im-part Thy ho-ly law, thy
4. As step by step we tread the way, Trust-ing, and con-fi-

high de-gree I on-ly pray that hand in hand
face to see— Two feet to guide in thy straight way
words of truth. Give Lord, thy grace, that my whole heart
dent, and free— A child and I shall, day by day,

A child and I may come to thee.
This fer-vent-ly I ask of thee.
May o-ver-flow with love for youth.
Find sweet com-pan-ion-ship with thee. A-men.

347

The Christian Kingdom

431

REPOSE. 8. 7. 8. 7. 8. 7.

CHRISTIAN BURKE, 1903

JOHN STAINER, 1875

1. Lord of life and King of glo - ry, Who didst deign a
   child to be, Cra - dled on a moth - er's bo - som,
   Throned up - on a moth - er's knee, For the chil - dren
   thou hast giv - en We must an - swer un - to thee.

2. Grant us, then, pure hearts and pa - tient, That in all we
   do or say Lit - tle souls our deeds may cop - y,
   And be nev - er led a - stray; Lit - tle feet our
   steps may fol - low In a safe and nar - row way.

3. When our grow - ing sons and daugh - ters Look on life with
   ea - ger eyes, Grant us then a deep - er in - sight
   And new powers of sac - ri - fice, Hope to trust them,
   faith to guide them, Love that noth - ing good de - nies.

4. May we keep our ho - ly call - ing Stain - less in its
   fair re - nown, That when all the work is o - ver
   And we lay the bur - den down, Then the chil - dren
   thou hast giv - en Still may be our joy and crown. A - men.

Tune copyright, 1897, by Novello, Ewer and Co.

432   ROSEATE HUES. C. M. D.

WASHINGTON GLADDEN, 1897   JOSEPH BARNBY, 1894

1. Be - hold a Sow - er! from a - far   He go - eth forth with might;
2. O Lord of life, to thee we lift   Our hearts in praise for those,
3. Shine forth, O Light, that we may see,   With hearts all un - a - fraid,
4. Light up thy Word, the fet-tered page   From kill - ing bond - age free;

The roll - ing years his fur - rows are,   His seed the grow - ing light;
Thy proph-ets, who have shown thy gift   Of grace that ev - er grows,
The mean - ing and the mys - ter - y   Of things that thou hast made;
Light up our way, lead forth this age   In love's large lib - er - ty.

For all the just his word is sown,   It spring - eth up, al - way;
Of truth that spreads from shore to shore,   Of wis - dom's wid-ening ray,
Shine forth, and let the dark - ling past   Be - neath thy beam grow bright;
O Light of light, with - in us dwell,   Through us thy ra-diance pour,

The ten-der blade is hope's young dawn,   The har-vest, love's new day.
Of light that shin - eth more and more   Un - to thy per - fect day.
Shine forth, and touch the fu - ture vast   With thine un-troub-led light.
That word and life thy truths may tell,   And praise thee ev - er - more.   A-men.

433

ROCKINGHAM. L. M.

FRANCES R. HAVERGAL, 1872

EDWARD MILLER, 1790

1. Lord, speak to me, that I may speak In liv - ing
2. O lead me, Lord, that I may lead The wan - dering
3. O strength - en me, that while I stand Firm on the
4. O teach me, Lord, that I may teach The pre - cious
5. O fill me with thy ful - ness, Lord, Un - til my

ech - oes of thy tone; As thou hast sought, so let me
and the wav - ering feet! O feed me, Lord, that I may
Rock, and strong in thee, I may stretch out a lov - ing
things thou dost im - part; And wing my words, that they may
ver - y heart o'er - flow In kind - ling thought and glow - ing

seek Thy err - ing chil - dren lost and lone.
feed Thy hun - gering ones with man - na sweet!
hand To wrest - lers with the troub - led sea!
reach The hid - den depths of man - y a heart!
word, Thy love to tell, thy praise to show! A - men.

434

DALEHURST, C. M.

M. WOOLSEY STRYKER, 1896

ARTHUR COTTMAN, 1872

1. Al - might - y Lord, with one ac - cord We of - fer thee our youth,
2. Thy cause doth claim our souls by name, Be - cause that we are strong;
3. Let fall on ev - ery col - lege hall The lus - ter of thy cross,
4. Our hearts be ruled, our spir - its schooled A - lone thy will to seek;

And pray that thou would'st give us now The war-fare of the truth.
In all the land, one stead-fast band, May we to Christ be-long.
That love may dare thy work to share And count all else as loss.
And when we find thy bless-ed mind, In-struct our lips to speak. A-men.

435

THANKSGIVING. L. M.

SAMUEL LONGFELLOW, 1874

FRANCIS REGINALD STATHAM, 1844

1. O Life that mak-eth all things new, The bloom-ing
2. From hand to hand the greet-ing flows, From eye to
3. One in the free-dom of the truth, One in the
4. The fre-er step, the full-er breath, The wide ho-

earth, the thoughts of men! Our pil-grim feet, wet with thy dew,
eye the sig-nals run, From heart to heart the bright hope glows;
joy of paths un-trod, One in the soul's per-en-nial youth,
ri-zon's grand-er view, The sense of life that knows no death,

In glad-ness hith-er turn a-gain.
The seek-ers of the Light are one.
One in the larg-er thought of God;
The Life that mak-eth all things new. A-men.

436

BEULAH (HEMY). 6. 6. 6. 6. D.

JOHN ELLERTON, 1881

HENRI F. HEMY, 1818–1888

1. Shine thou up - on us, Lord, True Light of men to - day;
2. Breathe thou up - on us, Lord, Thy Spir - it's liv - ing flame,
3. Speak thou for us, O Lord, In all we say of thee;
4. Live thou with - in us, Lord, Thy mind and will be ours;

And through the writ - ten word Thy ver - y self dis - play;
That so with one ac - cord Our lips may tell thy name;
Ac - cord - ing to thy word Let all our teach - ing be;
Be thou be - loved, a - dored, And served, with all our powers;

That so from hearts which burn With gaz - ing on thy face,
Give thou the hear - ing ear, Fix thou the wan - dering thought,
That all who hear may know Their own true Shep - herd's voice,
That so our lives may teach Thy chil - dren what thou art,

Thy chil - dren all may learn The won - ders of thy grace.
That those we teach may hear The great things thou hast wrought.
Wher - e'er he leads them go, And in his love re - joice.
And plead, by more than speech, For thee with ev - ery heart. A - men.

Schools and Colleges

437

SUMMERFORD. 10. 10. 10. 10.

DENIS WORTMAN, 1884

JOHN T. GRIMLEY, 1887

1. God of the proph - ets! Bless the proph - ets' sons;
2. A - noint them proph - ets! Make their ears at - tend
3. A - noint them priests! Strong in - ter - ces - sors they
4. A - noint them kings! Aye, king - ly kings, O Lord!
5. O might - y age of proph - et - kings, re - turn!

E - li - jah's man - tle o'er E - li - sha cast;
To thy di - vin - est speech; their hearts a - wake
For par - don, and for char - i - ty and peace!
A - noint them with the Spir - it of thy Son!
O truth, O faith, en - rich our ur - gent time!

Each age its sol - emn task may claim but once;
To hu - man need; their lips make el - o - quent
Ah, if with them the world might pass, a - stray,
Theirs, not a jew - eled crown, a blood - stained sword;
Lord Je - sus Christ, a - gain with us so - journ;

Make each one no - bler, strong - er than the last.
To as - sure the right, and ev - ery e - vil break.
In - to the dear Christ's life of sac - ri - fice.
Theirs, by sweet love, for Christ a king - dom won.
A wea - ry world a - waits thy reign sub - lime! A - men.

The Christian Kingdom

438
NOX PRÆCESSIT. C. M.

Samuel Johnson, 1864

J. Baptiste Calkin, 1875

1. City of God, how broad and far   Out-spread thy walls sub-lime!
2. One ho-ly Church, one ar-my strong, One stead-fast, high in-tent,
3. How pure-ly hath thy speech come down From man's prim-e-val youth!
4. How gleam thy watch-fires through the night With nev-er-faint-ing ray!
5. In vain the sur-ge's an-gry shock, In vain the drift-ing sands:

The true thy char-tered free-men are Of ev-ery age and clime.
One work-ing band, one har-vest-song, One King om-nip-o-tent!
How grand-ly hath thine em-pire grown Of free-dom, love and truth!
How rise thy towers, serene and bright, To meet the dawn-ing day!
Un-harmed up-on th' e-ter-nal Rock Th' e-ter-nal Cit-y stands. A-men.

439
HOLY CROSS. C. M.

Samuel Longfellow (1819–1892)

James C. Wade, 1865

1. One ho-ly Church of God ap-pears Through ev-ery age and race,
2. From old-est time, on farth-est shores, Be-neath the pine or palm,
3. Her priests are all God's faith-ful sons, To serve the world raised up;
4. The truth is her pro-phet-ic gift, The soul her sa-cred page;
5. O liv-ing Church, thine er-rand speed, Ful-fil thy task sub-lime;

Un-wast-ed by the lapse of years, Un-changed by changing place.
One Un-seen Pres-ence she a-dores, With si-lence, or with psalm.
The pure in heart her bap-tized ones, Love her com-mun-ion cup.
And feet on mer-cy's er-rands swift, Do make her pil-grim-age.
With bread of life earth's hun-ger feed; Re-deem the e-vil time! A-men.

The Church

440

ST. CATHERINE. L. M. With Refrain

FREDERICK W. FABER, 1849

HENRI F. HEMY and J. G. WALTON, 1874

1. Faith of our fa - thers, liv - ing still In spite of dun - geon,
2. Our fath-ers, chained in pris - ons dark, Were still in heart and
3. Faith of our fa - thers, we will strive To win all na - tions
4. Faith of our fa - thers, we will love Both friend and foe in

fire and sword, O how our hearts beat high with joy
con - science free, And blest would be their chil - dren's fate,
un - to thee; And through the truth that comes from God
all our strife, And preach thee, too, as love knows how,

Refrain

When - e'er we hear that glo - rious word!
Though they, like them, should die for thee:
Man - kind shall then in - deed be free.
By kind - ly words and vir - tuous life.

Faith of our fa - thers,

ho - ly faith, We will be true to thee till death. A - men.

355

The Christian Kingdom

AUSTRIA. 8. 7. 8. 7. D.

John Newton, 1779

Franz Joseph Haydn, 1797

1. Glo - rious things of thee are spo - ken, Zi - on, cit - y of our God;
2. See, the streams of liv - ing wa - ters, Spring-ing from e - ter - nal love,
3. Round each hab - i - ta - tion hov - ering, See the cloud and fire ap - pear

He whose word can - not be bro - ken Formed thee for his own a - bode:
Well sup - ply thy sons and daugh-ters, And all fear of want re - move:
For a glo - ry and a cov - ering, Show - ing that the Lord is near:

On the Rock of A - ges found - ed, What can shake thy sure re - pose?
Who can faint, when such a riv - er Ev - er will their thirst as - suage?
Glo - rious things of thee are spo - ken, Zi - on, cit - y of our God;

With sal - va-tion's walls sur-rounded, Thou may'st smile at all thy foes.
Grace, which, like the Lord the Giv-er, Nev - er fails from age to age.
He whose word can-not be bro - ken, Formed thee for his own a-bode. A - men.

The Church

442

AURELIA. 7. 6. 7. 6. D.

SAMUEL J. STONE, 1866

SAMUEL S. WESLEY, 1864

1. The Church's one foun-da - tion Is Je - sus Christ her Lord;
2. E - lect from ev - ery na - tion, Yet one o'er all the earth,
3. 'Mid toil and trib - u - la - tion, And tu - mult of her war,
4. Yet she on earth hath un - ion With God the Three in One,

She is his new cre - a - tion By wa - ter and the word,
Her char - ter of sal - va - tion One Lord, one faith, one birth;
She waits the con - sum - ma - tion Of peace for - ev - er - more;
And mys - tic sweet com - mun - ion With those whose rest is won;

From heaven he came and sought her To be his ho - ly bride;
One ho - ly name she bless - es, Par - takes one ho - ly food.
Till with the vis - ion glo - rious Her long - ing eyes are blest,
O hap - py ones and ho - ly; Lord, give us grace that we,

With his own blood he bought her, And for her life he died.
And to one hope she press - es, With ev - ery grace en - dued.
And the great church vic - to - rious Shall be the church at rest.
Like them, the meek and low - ly, On high may dwell with thee. A - men.

The Christian Kingdom

443

EIN FESTE BURG. 8. 7. 8. 7. 6. 6. 6. 6. 7.

MARTIN LUTHER, 1529
Translated by FREDERICK H. HEDGE, 1853

MARTIN LUTHER, 1529

1. A might-y for-tress is our God, A bul-wark nev-er fail - ing;
2. Did we in our own strength con-fide, Our striv-ing would be los - ing,
3. And tho' this world, with dev - ils filled, Should threaten to un - do us;
4. That word a - bove all earth - ly powers, No thanks to them, a - bid - eth;

Our help-er he, a - mid the flood Of mor - tal ills pre - vail - ing.
Were not the right man on our side, The man of God's own choos - ing.
We will not fear, for God hath willed His truth to tri - umph through us.
The Spir - it and the gifts are ours Thro' him who with us sid - eth;

For still our an - cient foe Doth seek to work us woe; His craft and power are
Dost ask who that may be? Christ Je - sus, it is he, Lord Sab - a - oth his
The prince of dark-ness grim,—We trem-ble not for him; His rage we can en -
Let goods and kin - dred go, This mor - tal life al - so; The bod - y they may

great; And armed with cruel hate, On earth is not his e - qual.
name, From age to age the same, And he must win the bat - tle.
dure, For lo! his doom is sure, One lit - tle word shall fell him.
kill: God's truth a - bid - eth still, His king-dom is for - ev - er. A-men.

358

The Church

444

CLOISTERS. 11. 11. 11. 5.

MATTHAUS A. VON LOWENSTERN, 1644
Translated by PHILIP PUSEY, 1840

JOSEPH BARNBY, 1875

1. Lord of our life, and God of our sal - va - tion,
2. See round thine ark the hun - gry bil - lows curl - ing;
3. Lord, thou canst help when earth - ly ar - mor fail - eth;
4. Peace in our hearts our e - vil thoughts as - suag - ing,
5. Grant us thy help till back - ward they are driv - en;

Star of our night, and hope of ev - ery na - tion,
See how thy foes their ban - ners are un - furl - ing;
Lord, thou canst save when dead - ly sin as - sail - eth;
Peace in thy Church, where broth - ers are en - gag - ing,
Grant them thy truth that they may be for - giv - en;

Hear and re - ceive thy Church's sup - pli -
Lord, while their darts en - ven - omed they are
Peace, when the world its bus - y war is
Grant peace on earth, and, aft - er we have

ca - tion, Lord God Al - might - y.
hurl - ing, Thou canst pre - serve us.
vail - eth: Grant us thy peace, Lord.
wag - ing; Send us, O Sav - iour.
striv - en, Peace in thy heav - en. A - men.

359

445

DEDHAM. C. M.

William Cullen Bryant, 1820

William Gardiner, 1812

1. O thou, whose own vast tem - ple stands Built o - ver earth and sea,
2. And let the Com - fort - er and Friend, Thy Ho - ly Spir - it, meet
3. May they who err be guid - ed here To find the bet - ter way,
4. May faith grow firm, and love grow warm, And hal - lowed wish - es rise,

Ac - cept the walls that hu - man hands Have raised, O God, to thee.
With those who here in wor - ship bend Be - fore thy mer - cy - seat.
And they who mourn and they who fear Be strengthened as they pray.
While round these peaceful walls the storm Of earth-born passion dies. A - men.

446

ST. ANNE. C. M.

Arthur C. Coxe, 1839

William Croft, 1708

1. O where are kings and em - pires now Of old that went and came?
2. We mark her good - ly bat - tle - ments, And her foun - da - tions strong;
3. For not like king - doms of the world, Thy ho - ly Church, O God!
4. Un - sha - ken as e - ter - nal hills, Im - mov - a - ble she stands,

But, Lord, thy Church is pray - ing yet, A thou-sand years the same.
We hear with - in the sol - emn voice Of her un - end - ing song.
Tho' earthquake shocks are threat'ning her, And tem-pests are a - broad,
A moun - tain that shall fill the earth, A house not made by hands. A - men.

447

STATE STREET. S. M.

TIMOTHY DWIGHT, 1800

JONATHAN C. WOODMAN, 1844

1. I love thy king-dom, Lord, The house of thine a-bode,
2. I love thy church, O God; Her walls be-fore thee stand,
3. For her my tears shall fall, For her my prayers as-cend,
4. Be-yond my high-est joy I prize her heaven-ly ways,
5. Sure as thy truth shall last, To Zi-on shall be given

The church our blest Re-deem-er saved With his own pre-cious blood.
Dear as the ap-ple of thine eye, And grav-en on thy hand.
To her my cares and toils be given Till toils and cares shall end.
Her sweet com-mun-ion, sol-emn vows, Her hymns of love and praise.
The bright-est glo-ries earth can yield, And bright-er bliss of heaven. A-men.

448

BOYLSTON. S. M.

JOHN FAWCETT, 1782

LOWELL MASON, 1832

1. Blest be the tie that binds Our hearts in Chris-tian love:
2. Be-fore our Fa-ther's throne We pour our ar-dent prayers;
3. We share our mu-tual woes, Our mu-tual bur-dens bear,
4. When we a-sun-der part, It gives us in-ward pain;

The fel-low-ship of kin-dred minds Is like to that a-bove.
Our fears, our hopes, our aims, are one, Our com-forts and our cares.
And oft-en for each oth-er flows The sym-pa-thiz-ing tear.
But we shall still be joined in heart, And hope to meet a-gain. A-men.

The Christian Kingdom

449

MAIDSTONE. 8. 7. 8. 7. D.

HENRY F. LYTE, 1834

WALTER B. GILBERT, 1862

1. Pleas- ant are thy courts a - bove, In the land of light and love;
2. Hap - py birds that sing and fly Round thy al - tars, O Most High!
3. Hap - py souls! their prais - es flow Ev - er in this vale of woe;
4. Lord, be mine this prize to win, Guide me through a world of sin;

Pleas- ant are thy courts be - low, In this land of sin and woe.
Hap - pier souls that find a rest In a heaven - ly Fa-ther's breast!
Wa - ters in the des - ert rise, Man - na feeds them from the skies;
Keep me by thy sav - ing grace; Give me at thy side a place.

O, my spir - it longs and faints For the con - verse of thy saints,
Like the wan-dering dove, that found No re - pose on earth a - round,
On they go from strength to strength Till they reach thy throne at length,
Sun and shield a - like thou art; Guide and guard my er - ring heart:

For the bright-ness of thy face, For thy full - ness, God of grace!
They can to their ark re - pair And en - joy it ev - er there.
At thy feet a - dor - ing fall Who hast led them safe thro' all.
Grace and glo - ry flow from thee; Show'r, O show'r them, Lord, on me! A - men.

362

450

VICTORY. 8. 8. 8. With Alleluia

Composite: based on
JOHN GREENLEAF WHITTIER, 1807–1892

Arranged from
PALESTRINA, 1515-1594

1. Thy grace im-part! in time to be Shall one great tem-ple rise to thee,—
2. White flowers of love its walls shall climb, Soft bells of peace shall ring its chime,
3. A sweet-er song shall then be heard, Con-fess-ing, in a world's ac-cord,
4. That song shall swell from shore to shore, One hope, one faith, one love re-store

Thy church our broad hu-man-i-ty. Al - le - lu - ia!
Its days shall all be ho-ly time. Al - le - lu - ia!
The in-ward Christ, the liv-ing Word. Al - le - lu - ia!
The seam-less robe that Je-sus wore. Al - le - lu - ia! A - men.

451

IN MEMORIAM. 8. 8. 8. 4.

GEORGE RAWSON, 1857

FREDERICK C. MAKER, 1876

1. By Christ redeemed, in Christ re-stored, We keep the mem-o-ry a-dored,
2. His bod-y bro-ken in our stead Is here in this me-mo-rial bread,
3. The streams of his dread ag-o-ny, His life-blood shed for us, we see;
4. And thus that dark be-tray-al night With the last ad-vent we u-nite
5. O bless-ed hope! with this e-late Let not your hearts be des-o-late,

And show the death of our dear Lord Un - til he come.
And so our fee-ble love is fed Un - til he come.
The wine shall tell the mys-ter-y Un - til he come.
By one blest chain of lov-ing rite Un - til he come.
But, strong in faith, in pa-tience wait Un - til he come. A - men.

452

LANGRAN. 10. 10. 10. 10.

HORATIUS BONAR, 1855

JAMES LANGRAN, 1862

1. Here, O my Lord, I see thee face to face;
2. Here would I feed up - on the bread of God,
3. This is the hour of ban - quet and of song;

Here would I touch and han - dle things un - seen;
Here drink with thee the roy - al wine of heaven;
This is the heaven - ly ta - ble spread for me:

Here grasp with firm - er hand th'e - ter - nal grace,
Here would I lay a - side each earth - ly load,
Here let me feast, and feast - ing, still pro - long

And all my wea - ri - ness up - on thee lean.
Here taste a - fresh the calm of sin for - given.
The brief, bright hour of fel - low - ship with thee. A - men.

The Lord's Supper.

MORECAMBE. 10. 10. 10. 10.

EDWARD H. BICKERSTETH, 1872

FREDERICK C. ATKINSON, 1880

1. Not wor - thy, Lord, to gath - er up the crumbs
2. I am not wor - thy to be thought thy child,
3. I hear thy voice; thou bidd'st me come and rest;
4. My praise can on - ly breathe it - self in prayer,

With tremb - ling hand, that from thy ta - ble fall,
Nor sit the last and low - est at thy board;
I come, I kneel, I clasp thy pierc - ed feet;
My prayer can on - ly lose it - self in thee;

A wea - ry, heav - y - la - den sin - ner comes
Too long a wan - derer, and too oft be - guiled,
Thou bidd'st me take my place, a wel - come guest,
Dwell thou for - ev - er in my heart, and there,

To plead thy prom - ise and o - bey thy call.
I on - ly ask one rec - on - cil - ing word.
A - mong thy saints, and of thy ban - quet eat.
Lord, let me sup with thee; sup thou with me. A - men.

454

MENDON. L. M.

Bernard of Clairvaux, 1150
Translated by Ray Palmer, 1858

German Melody:
Arranged by Samuel Dyer, 1814

1. Je-sus, thou joy of lov-ing hearts, Thou fount of life, thou
2. Thy truth un-changed hath ev-er stood; Thou sav-est those that
3. We taste thee, O thou liv-ing bread, And long to feast up-
4. Our rest-less spir-its yearn for thee, Wher-e'er our change-ful
5. O Je-sus, ev-er with us stay, Make all our mo-ments

light of men, From the best bliss that earth im-parts,
on thee call; To them that seek thee thou art good,
on thee still; We drink of thee, the foun-tain-head,
lot is cast; Glad when thy gra-cious smile we see,
calm and bright; Chase the dark night of sin a-way,

We turn un-filled to thee a-gain.
To them that find thee all in all.
And thirst our souls from thee to fill.
Blest when our faith can hold thee fast.
Shed o'er the world thy ho-ly light. A-men.

455

MARTYRDOM. C. M.

James Montgomery, 1825

Hugh Wilson, 1825

1. Ac-cord-ing to thy gra-cious word, In meek hu-mil-i-ty,
2. Thy bod-y, bro-ken for my sake, My bread from heaven shall be;
3. Geth-sem-a-ne, can I for-get? Or there thy con-flict see,
4. When to the cross I turn mine eyes, And rest on Cal-va-ry,
5. And when these fail-ing lips grow dumb, And mind and mem-ory flee,

This will I do, my dy-ing Lord, I will re-mem-ber thee.
The cup, thy pre-cious blood, I take, And thus re-mem-ber thee.
Thine a-go-ny and blood-y sweat, And not re-mem-ber thee?
O Lamb of God, my sac-ri-fice, I must re-mem-ber thee.
When thou shalt in thy kingdom come, Then, Lord, re-mem-ber me. A-men.

456   EUCHARISTIC HYMN. 9. 8. 9. 8.

REGINALD HEBER, 1827   JOHN S. B. HODGES, 1868.

1. Bread of the world, in mer - cy bro - ken, Wine of the soul, in
2. Look on the heart by sor - row bro - ken, Look on the tears by

mer - cy shed, By whom the words of life were spo - ken,
sin - ners shed; And be thy feast to us the to - ken,

And in whose death our sins are dead.
That by thy grace our souls are fed. A - men.

The Christian Kingdom

457

LACRYMÆ. 7.7.7.

ROBERT H. BAYNES, 1864

ARTHUR S. SULLIVAN, 1872

1. Je - sus, to thy ta - ble led, Now let ev - ery
2. While in pen - i - tence we kneel, Thy sweet pres - ence
3. While on thy dear cross we gaze, Mourn - ing o'er our
4. When we taste the mys - tic wine, Of thine out - poured
5. From the bonds of sin re - lease, Cold and waver - ing
6. Lead us by thy pierc - ed hand, Till a - round thy

heart be fed With the true and liv - ing bread.
let us feel, All thy won - drous love re - veal.
sin - ful ways, Turn our sad - ness in - to praise.
blood the sign, Fill our hearts with love di - vine.
faith in - crease; Lamb of God, grant us thy peace.
throne we stand In the bright and bet - ter land. A - men.

458

OLMUTZ. S. M.

AARON R. WOLFE, 1858

From GREGORIAN CHANT
Arranged by LOWELL MASON, 1824

1. A part - ing hymn we sing A - round thy ta - ble, Lord;
2. Here have we seen thy face, And felt thy pres - ence here;
3. The pur - chase of thy blood, By sin no long - er led,
4. In self - for - get - ting love Be our com - mun - ion shown,

A - gain our grate - ful trib - ute bring, Our sol - emn vows re - cord.
So may the sa - vor of thy grace In word and life ap - pear.
The path our dear Re - deem - er trod May we re - joic - ing tread.
Un - til we join the church a - bove, And know as we are known. A - men.

459

SCHUMANN. S. M.

Ascribed to
ROBERT SCHUMANN, 1810–1856

WILLIAM WALSHAM HOW, about 1858

1. We give thee but thine own, What-e'er the gift may be: All
2. May we thy boun-ties thus As stew-ards true re-ceive, And
3. O hearts are bruised and dead, And homes are bare and cold, And
4. And we be-lieve thy word, Though dim our faith may be, What-

that we have is thine a-lone, A trust, O Lord, from thee.
glad-ly, as thou bless-est us, To thee our first-fruits give.
lambs for whom the Shep-herd bled Are stray-ing from the fold.
e'er for thine we do, O Lord, We do it un-to thee. A-men.

460

BROCKLESBURY. 8. 7. 8. 7.

WILLIAM A. MUHLENBERG, 1826

CHARLOTTE A. BARNARD, 1868

1. Sav-iour, who thy flock art feed-ing With the shep-herd's kind-est care,
2. Now, these lit-tle ones re-ceiv-ing, Fold them in thy gra-cious arm;
3. Nev-er, from thy pas-ture rov-ing, Let them be the li-on's prey;
4. Then, with-in thy fold e-ter-nal, Let them find a rest-ing place,

All the fee-ble gen-tly lead-ing, While the lambs thy bos-om share.
There, we know, thy word be-liev-ing, On-ly there se-cure from harm.
Let thy ten-der-ness, so lov-ing, Keep them thro' life's dangerous way.
Feed in pas-tures ev-er ver-nal, Drink the riv-ers of thy grace. A-men.

461
SILOAM. C. M.

REGINALD HEBER, 1827

ISAAC WOODBURY, 1842

1. By cool Si - lo - am's sha - dy rill How
2. Lo, such the child whose ear - ly feet The
3. O thou, whose in - fant feet were found With-
4. De - pend - ent on thy boun - teous breath, We

sweet the lil - y grows! How sweet the breath be -
paths of peace have trod; Whose se - cret heart, with
in thy Fa - ther's shrine, Whose years, with change - less
seek thy grace a - lone In child - hood, man - hood,

neath the hill Of Shar - on's dew - y rose!
in - fluence sweet, Is up - ward drawn to God.
vir - tue crowned, Were all a - like di - vine;
age, and death, To keep us still thine own. A - men.

462
ELLINGHAM. 7. 7. 7. 7.

EDWIN P. PARKER, 1890

NATHANIEL S. GODFREY, 1881

1. Lord, as we thy name pro-fess, May our hearts thy love con - fess;
2. Make us res - o - lute to do What thou show-est to be true;
3. May thy yoke be meek - ly worn May thy cross be brave - ly borne;

Words used by permission of Edwin P. Parker

And in all our praise of thee May our lips and lives a - gree.
Make us hate and shun the ill, Loy - al to thy ho - ly will.
Make us pa - tient, gen - tle, kind, Pure in life and heart and mind. A-men.

463   HOWARD. 6. 5. 6. 5. D.

WILLIAM GEORGE TARRANT, 1853–ALONZO P. HOWARD, 1838–1902

1. March-ing with the he - roes, Com-rades of the strong, Lift we hearts and
2. Glo - ry to the he - roes, Who in days of old Trod the path of
3. So we sing the sto - ry Of the brave and true, Till a-mong the

voic - es As we march a - long; O the joy - ful mu - sic
du - ty, Faith-ful, wise, and bold, For the right un - flinch - ing,
he - roes We are he - roes, too; Loy - al to our Cap - tain

All in cho-rus raise! Theirs the song of triumph, Ours the song of praise.
Strong the weak to save, Warriors all and freemen, Fight-ing for the slave.
Like the men of yore, March-ing with the he-roes On-ward, ev-er-more. A-men.

Hymn and Tune Book, 1914. Used by permission

464

SAMUEL. 6. 6. 6. 6. 8. 8.

James D. Burns, 1857

Arthur S. Sullivan, 1874

1. Hushed was the eve - ning hymn, The tem - ple courts were
2. The old man, meek and mild, The priest of Is - rael,
3. O give me Sam - uel's ear,— The o - pen ear, O
4. O give me Sam - uel's heart,— A low - ly heart, that
5. O give me Sam - uel's mind,— A sweet un - mur - muring

dark; The lamp was burn - ing dim Be - fore the
slept; His watch the tem - ple child, The lit - tle
Lord, A - live and quick to hear Each whis - per
waits Where in thy house thou art, Or watch - es
faith, O - be - dient and re - signed To thee in

sa - cred ark; When sud - den - ly a voice di - vine
Le - vite, kept; And what from E - li's sense was sealed
of thy word, Like him to an - swer at thy call,
at thy gates, By day and night, a heart that still
life and death, That I may read with child - like eyes

Rang through the si - lence of the shrine.
The Lord to Han - nah's son re - vealed.
And to o - bey thee first of all!
Moves at the breath - ing of thy will!
Truths that are hid - den from the wise! A - men.

Children and Youth

465

MARION. S. M. With Refrain

EDWARD H. PLUMPTRE, 1865

ARTHUR H. MESSITER, 1883

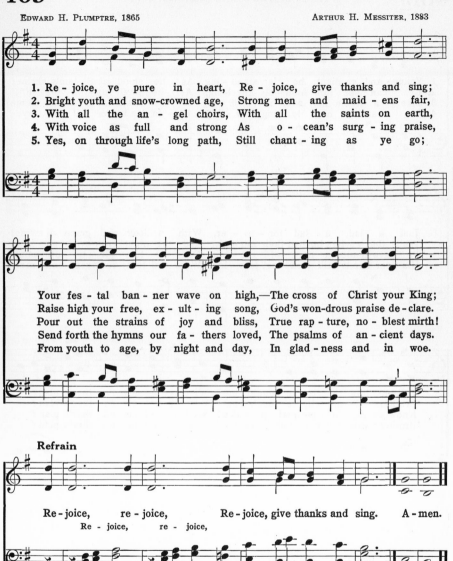

1. Re - joice, ye pure in heart, Re - joice, give thanks and sing;
2. Bright youth and snow-crowned age, Strong men and maid - ens fair,
3. With all the an - gel choirs, With all the saints on earth,
4. With voice as full and strong As o - cean's surg - ing praise,
5. Yes, on through life's long path, Still chant - ing as ye go;

Your fes - tal ban - ner wave on high,—The cross of Christ your King;
Raise high your free, ex - ult - ing song, God's won-drous praise de - clare.
Pour out the strains of joy and bliss, True rap - ture, no - blest mirth!
Send forth the hymns our fa - thers loved, The psalms of an - cient days.
From youth to age, by night and day, In glad - ness and in woe.

Refrain

Re - joice, re - joice, Re - joice, give thanks and sing. A - men.

Re - joice, re - joice,

6 Still lift your standard high,
   Still march in firm array,
  As warriors through the darkness toil
   Till dawns the golden day.

7 At last the march shall end,
   The wearied ones shall rest,
  The pilgrims find their Father's house,
   Jerusalem the blest.

466

A PSALM OF THE SON OF MAN 8. 7. 8. 7. D.

ALLEN EASTMAN CROSS, 1921

LOUIS ADOLPHE COERNE, 1921

1. Young and ra-diant, he is stand-ing As he stood at Sa-lem's shrine;
2. I can see him hum-bly kneel-ing, As he knelt up-on the hill;
3. Like a flame his soul is strik-ing In his wrath at greed and shame;
4. I can see him dy-ing, lov-ing Un-to death on Cal-va-ry;

Just a lad, a lad for-ev-er, With a look and grace di-vine!
While the wa-ters hushed their mu-sic, And the night grew bright and still:
'Ye have made a den of rob-bers Of the tem-ple to his name;
His dear hands still plead-ing, pray-ing, Worn and torn for you and me!

'Tell me, how it is ye sought me? Wist ye not my Fa-ther's plan?
'Brothers, tell me why ye sought me? Wist ye not my Fa-ther's plan?
Know ye not his e-qual jus-tice? Wist ye not my Fa-ther's plan?
'Brothers, will ye scorn and leave me? Wist ye not my Fa-ther's plan?

I must be a-bout his busi-ness, Would I be a Son of Man.'
He must grow in grace and wisdom, Who would be a Son of Man.'
He must bathe his sword in heaven Who would be a Son of Man.'
He must wear a crown of sor-row Who would be a Son of Man.' A-men.

467

GREYSTONE. 7. 6. 7. 6. D. With Refrain

CECIL FRANCES ALEXANDER, 1848

W. R. WAGHORNE, 1906

Refrain

1. All things bright and beau - ti - ful, All crea-tures great and small,

All things wise and won - der - ful, The Lord God made them all. A - men. **Fine**

2. Each lit - tle flower that o - pens, Each lit - tle bird that sings,
3. The cold wind in the win - ter, The pleas - ant sum - mer sun,
4. The tall trees in the green - wood, The mead - ows where we play,
5. He gave us eyes to see them, And lips that we might tell

D. C.

He made their glow - ing col - ors, He made their ti - ny wings.
The ripe fruits in the gar - den,— He made them ev - ery one.
The rush - es by the wa - ter We gath - er ev - ery day;—
How great is God Al - might - y, Who has made all things well.

The Christian Kingdom

468

LULLABY. 6. 5. 6. 5. 6. 5. 6. 6. With Refrain

WILLIAM C. GANNETT, (1840——)

ADAM GEIBEL, (1855——)

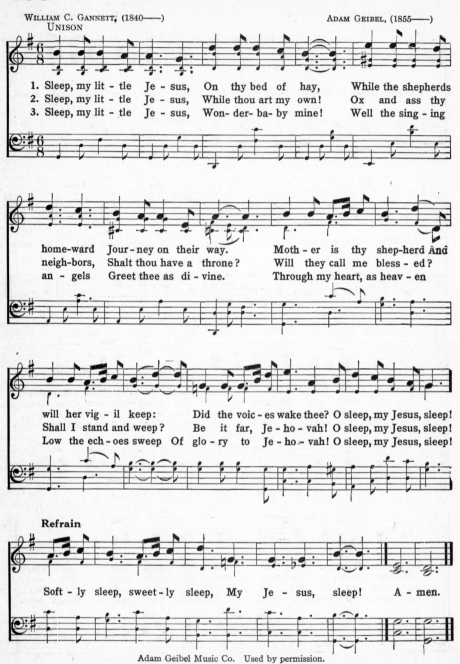

1. Sleep, my lit - tle Je - sus, On thy bed of hay, While the shepherds home-ward Jour - ney on their way. Moth - er is thy shep-herd And will her vig - il keep: Did the voic - es wake thee? O sleep, my Jesus, sleep!

2. Sleep, my lit - tle Je - sus, While thou art my own! Ox and ass thy neigh-bors, Shalt thou have a throne? Will they call me bless - ed? Shall I stand and weep? Be it far, Je - ho - vah! O sleep, my Jesus, sleep!

3. Sleep, my lit - tle Je - sus, Won - der- ba- by mine! Well the sing - ing an - gels Greet thee as di - vine. Through my heart, as heav - en Low the ech - oes sweep Of glo - ry to Je - ho - vah! O sleep, my Jesus, sleep!

Refrain

Soft - ly sleep, sweet - ly sleep, My Je - sus, sleep! A - men.

Adam Geibel Music Co. Used by permission.

469

THE BLESSED NAME. 8. 7. 8. 7. With Refrain

GEORGE W. BETHUNE, 1858

JOSEPH BARNBY, (1838–1896)

1. There is no name so sweet on earth, No name so dear in heav - en,
2. 'Twas Ga - briel first that did pro - claim, To his most bless-ed moth - er,
3. And when he hung up - on the cross, They wrote his name a- bove him,
4. So now up - on his Fa - ther's throne, Al - might - y to re - lease us
5. O Je - sus, by that match-less name, Thy grace shall fail us nev - er;

As that be - fore his won-drous birth To Christ the Sav - iour giv - en.
That name which now and ev - er - more We praise a - bove all oth - er.
That all might see the rea - son we For ev - er - more must love him.
From sin and pains, he ev - er reigns The Prince and Sav - iour Je - sus!
To - day as yes - ter - day the same, Thou art the same for - ev - er.

Refrain

We love to sing a - round our King, And hail him bless - ed Je - sus;

For there's no word ear ev - er heard So dear, so sweet as Je - sus. A-men.

470

STORIES OF JESUS. 8. 4. 8. 4. 5. 4. 5. 4.

W. H. Parker, 1904

F. A. Challinor, 1904

1. Tell me the stories of Jesus I love to hear; Things I would
ask him to tell me If he were here; Scenes by the way-side,
Tales of the sea, Stories of Jesus, Tell them to me.

2. First let me hear how the children Stood round his knee; And I shall
fancy his blessing Resting on me: Words full of kindness,
Deeds full of grace, All in the love-light Of Jesus' face.

3. Into the city I'd follow The children's band, Waving a
branch of the palm-tree High in my hand; One of his heralds,
Yes, I would sing Loudest hosannas! Jesus is King!

4. Tell me, in accents of wonder, How rolled the sea, Tossing the
boat in a tempest On Galilee! And how the Master,
Ready and kind, Chided the billows, And hushed the wind. A-men.

5. Tell how the sparrow that twitters
   On yonder tree,
And the sweet meadow-side lily
   May speak to me—
Give me their message,
   For I would hear
How Jesus taught us
   Our Father's care.

6. Show me that scene in the garden,
   Of bitter pain;
And of the cross where my Saviour
   For me was slain—
Sad ones or bright ones,
   So that they be
Stories of Jesus,
   Tell them to me.

471
CLARION. C. M. D.

Anonymous

GEORGE E. ALVIS, 1890

1. O Je - sus, Prince of life and truth, Be - neath thy ban - ner bright,
2. In ser - ried ranks, with fear - less tread, O Cap - tain of us all,
3. O Je - sus, once a Naz - areth boy, And tempt - ed like as we,

We ded - i - cate our strength and youth To bat - tle for the right;
Thy glo - ry on our ban - ners shed, We ans - wer to thy call;
All in - ward foes help us de - stroy And spot - less all to be.

We give our lives with glad in - tent To serve the world and thee,
And where the fierc - est bat - tles press A - gainst the hosts of sin,
We trust thee for the grace to win The high, vic - to - rious goal,

To die, to suf - fer and be spent To set our broth - ers free.
To res - cue those in dire dis-tress We glad - ly en - ter in.
Where pur - i - ty shall con - quer sin In Christ-like self - con - trol. A - men.

The Christian Kingdom

472

MESSAGE. 10. 8. 8. 7. 7. With Refrain

Colin Sterne, 1896

Adapted from
H. Ernest Nichol, 1896

1. We've a sto - ry to tell to the na - tions That shall
2. We've a song to be sung to the na - tions, That shall
3. We've a mes - sage to give to the na - tions, That shall
4. We've a Sav - iour to show to the na - tions, Who the

turn their hearts to the right, A sto - ry of truth and mer - cy,
lift their hearts to the Lord; A song that shall con - quer e - vil
Lord who reign - eth a - bove, Hath sent us his Son to save us,
path of sor - row has trod, That all of the world's great peo - ples

A sto - ry of peace and light, A sto - ry of peace and light.
And shat - ter the spear and sword, And shat - ter the spear and sword.
And show us that God is love, And show us that God is love.
Might come to the truth of God, Might come to the truth of God!

Refrain

For the darkness shall turn to dawn - ing, And the dawn-ing to noon-day bright,

And Christ's great kingdom shall come on earth, The kingdom of Love and Light. A-men.

473

LYNDE. 5, 6, 6, 4, 6, 6, 6, 4

ELSIE THALHEIMER, 1800

Thuringian Folk Song

1. Thou art my Shep-herd, Car-ing in ev-ery need, Thy lov-ing
2. Or if my way lie Where storms are rag-ing nigh, Noth-ing can

lamb to feed, Trust-ing thee still. In the green pastures low, Where liv-ing
ter-ri-fy, I trust thee still. How can I be a-fraid, While soft-ly

wa-ters flow, Safe by thy side I go, Fear-ing no ill.
on my head Thy ten-der hand is laid; I fear no ill. A-men.

The Christian Kingdom

474

OLD GLORY. Irregular

WILBUR D. NESBIT, 1916

GRACE WILBUR CONANT, 1909

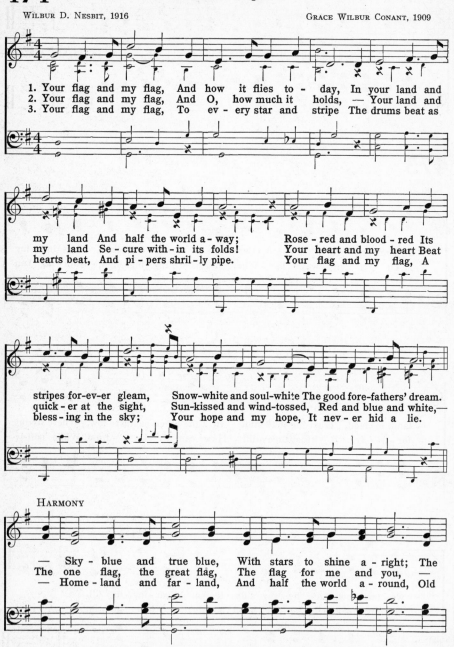

1. Your flag and my flag, And how it flies to-day, In your land and my land And half the world a-way; Rose-red and blood-red Its stripes for-ev-er gleam, Snow-white and soul-white The good fore-fathers' dream. — Sky-blue and true blue, With stars to shine a-right; The

2. Your flag and my flag, And O, how much it holds, — Your land and my land Se-cure with-in its folds! Your heart and my heart Beat quick-er at the sight, Sun-kissed and wind-tossed, Red and blue and white,— The one flag, the great flag, The flag for me and you, —

3. Your flag and my flag, To ev-ery star and stripe The drums beat as hearts beat, And pi-pers shril-ly pipe. Your flag and my flag, A bless-ing in the sky; Your hope and my hope, It nev-er hid a lie. — Home-land and far-land, And half the world a-round, Old

HARMONY

For Those at Sea

glo - ried gui - don of the day, A shel - ter through the night.
Glo - ri - fied all else be - side, The red and white and blue.
Glo - ry hears the great sa - lute And flut - ters to the sound. A - men.

475

MOZART. L. M.

Henry Burton, 1905

From the Kyrie, Twelfth Mass,
by Johann Mozart, 1756–1791

1. O Mak - er of the sea and sky, Whose word the
2. What if thy foot - steps are not known? We know thy
3. Thou bidd'st the north or south wind blow; The lone - ly
4. The sun that lights the home - land dear Spreads the new
5. And so, se - cure from all a - larms, Thy seas be -

storm - y winds ful - fill, On the wide o - cean
way is in the sea; We trace the shad - ow
sea - bird is thy care; And in the clouds which
morn - ing o'er the deep; And in the dark thy
neath, thy skies a - bove, Clasped in the ev - er -

thou art nigh, Bid - ding these hearts of ours be still.
of thy throne, Con - stant a - mid in - con - stan - cy.
come and go, We see thy char - iots ev - ery - where.
stars ap - pear, Keep - ing their watch - es while we sleep.
last - ing arms, We rest in thine un - slum - bering love. A - men.

476

MELITA. 8. 8. 8. 8. 8. 8.

WILLIAM WHITING, 1860

JOHN B. DYKES, 1861

1. E - ter - nal Fa - ther, strong to save, Whose arm doth bind the
2. O Sav - iour, whose al - might - y word The winds and waves sub -
3. O Sa - cred Spir - it, who didst brood Up - on the cha - os
4. O Trin - i - ty of love and power, Our breth - ren shield in

rest - less wave, Who bidd'st the might - y o - cean deep,
mis - sive heard, Who walk - ed'st on the foam - ing deep,
dark and rude, Who bad'st its an - gry tu - mult cease,
dan - ger's hour; From rock and tem - pest, fire and foe,

Its own ap - point - ed lim - its keep; O hear us when we
And calm a - mid its rage didst sleep; O hear us when we
And gav - est light and life and peace; O hear us when we
Pro - tect them where - so - e'er they go, Thus ev - er let there

cry to thee For those in per - il on the sea.
cry to thee For those in per - il on the sea.
cry to thee For those in per - il on the sea.
rise to thee Glad hymns of praise from land and sea. A - men.

The Life Victorious

AMSTERDAM. 7. 6. 7. 6. 7. 7. 7. 6.

ROBERT SEAGRAVE, 1742, altered

JAMES NARES, 1715–1783

1. Rise, my soul, and stretch thy wings, Thy bet - ter por - tion trace;
2. Cease, my soul, O cease to mourn! Press on - ward to the prize;

Rise from tran - si - to - ry things, Toward heaven, thy des - tined place.
Soon the Sav - iour will re - turn, To take thee to the skies.

Sun and moon and stars de - cay, Time shall soon this earth re - move;
There is ev - er - last - ing peace, Rest, en - dur - ing rest, in heaven;

Rise, my soul, and haste a - way To seats pre - pared a - bove.
There will sor - row ev - er cease, And crowns of joy be given. A - men.

The Christian Kingdom

478

BONAR. P. M.

HORATIUS BONAR, 1866

Arranged from
J. BAPTISTE CALKIN, 1867

1. Up - ward where the stars are burn - ing, Si - lent, si - lent in their turn - ing, Round the nev - er chang - ing pole,— Up - ward where the sky is bright - est, Up - ward where the blue is light - est, Lift I now my long - ing soul.

2. Far a - bove that arch of glad - ness, Far be - yond these clouds of sad - ness, Are the man - y man - sions fair. Far from pain and sin and fol - ly, In that pal - ace of the ho - ly, I would find my man - sion there.

3. Where the Lamb on high is seat - ed, By ten thou - sand voic - es greet - ed, Lord of lords, and King of kings! Son of Man! they crown, they crown him, Son of God! they own, they own him; With his name the pal - ace rings.

4. Bless - ing, hon - or, with - out meas - ure, Heaven-ly rich - es, earth - ly treas - ure, Lay we at his bless - ed feet; Poor the praise that now we ren - der, Loud shall be our voic - es yon - der, When be - fore his throne we meet. A - men.

479

O QUANTA QUALIA. 10. 10. 10. 10.

Peter Abelard, 1079–1142
Translated by John Mason Neale, 1854

Ancient Plain-song

1. O what the joy and the glo - ry must be,
2. What are the Mon - arch, his court and his throne?
3. Tru - ly Je - ru - sa - lem name we that shore,
4. There, where no troub - les dis - trac - tion can bring,
5. Low be - fore him with our prais - es we fall,

Those end - less Sab - baths the bless - ed ones see;
What are the peace and the joy that they own?
Vi - sion of peace, that brings joy ev - er - more;
We the sweet an - thems of Zi - on shall sing;
Of whom, and in whom, and through whom are all;

Crown for the val - iant, to wea - ry ones rest;
O that the blest ones, who in it have share,
Wish and ful - fill - ment can sev - ered be ne'er,
While for thy grace, Lord, their voic - es of praise
Of whom, the Fa - ther; and in whom, the Son;

God shall be all, and in all ev - er blest.
All that they feel could as ful - ly de - clare!
Nor the thing prayed for come short of the prayer.
Thy bless - ed peo - ple e - ter - nal - ly raise.
Through whom, the Spir - it, with them ev - er One.

A - men.

480

MATERNA. C. M. D.

Latin. "F. B. P." 1583

Samuel A. Ward, 1882

1. O moth-er dear, Je-ru-sa-lem, When shall I come to thee?
2. No murk-y cloud o'er-shad-ows thee, Nor gloom, nor dark-some night;
3. Thy gar-dens and thy good-ly walks Con-tin-ual-ly are green,
4. Those trees for-ev-er-more bear fruit, And ev-er-more do spring:

When shall my sor-rows have an end? Thy joys when shall I see?
But ev-ery soul shines as the sun; For God him-self gives light.
Where grow such sweet and pleasant flowers As no-where else are seen.
There ev-er-more the an-gels are, And ev-er-more do sing.

O hap-py har-bor of the saints! O sweet and pleas-ant soil!
There lust and lu-cre can-not dwell, There en-vy bears no sway.
Right thro' the streets with sil-ver sound The liv-ing wa-ters flow.
Je-ru-sa-lem, my hap-py home, Would God I were in thee!

In thee no sor-row may be found, No grief, no care, no toil.
There is no hun-ger, heat, nor cold, But pleas-ure ev-ery way.
And on the banks, on eith-er side, The trees of life do grow.
Would God my woes were at an end, Thy joys that I might see! A-men.

481

EWING. 7. 6. 7. 6. D.

Bernard of Cluny, about 1145
Translated by John M. Neale, 1851

Alexander Ewing, 1853

1. Je - ru - sa - lem the gold - en, With milk and hon - ey blest,
2. They stand, those halls of Zi - on, All ju - bi - lant with song,
3. There is the throne of Da - vid; And there, from care re - leased,
4. O sweet and bless - ed coun - try, The home of God's e - lect!

Be - neath thy con - tem - pla - tion Sink heart and voice op - pressed:
And bright with many an an - gel, And all the mar - tyr throng;
The shout of them that tri - umph, The song of them that feast;
O sweet and bless - ed coun - try That ea - ger hearts ex - pect!

I know not, O I know not, What joys a - wait us there,
The Prince is ev - er in them, The day - light is se - rene;
And they, who with their Lead - er, Have con - quered in the fight,
Je - sus, in mer - cy bring us To that dear land of rest,

What ra - dian - cy of glo - ry, What bliss be-yond com - pare!
The pas - tures of the bless - ed Are decked in glo - rious sheen.
For - ev - er and for - ev - er Are clad in robes of white.
Who art, with God the Fa - ther And Spir - it, ev - er blest! A - men.

482

PARADISE. 8. 6. 8. 6. With Refrain

FREDERICK W. FABER, 1862. Altered

JOSEPH BARNBY, 1866

1. O Par - a - dise, O Par - a - dise! Who doth not crave for rest?
2. O Par - a - dise, O Par - a - dise, The world is grow - ing old;
3. O Par - a - dise, O Par - a - dise, We long to sin no more;
4. Lord Je - sus, King of Par - a - dise, O keep us in thy love,

Who would not seek the hap - py land Where they that loved are blest?
Who would not be at rest and free Where love is nev - er cold?
We long to be as pure on earth As on thy spot - less shore;
And guide us to that hap - py land Of per - fect rest a - bove.

Refrain

Where loy - al hearts and true

Where loy - - - al hearts and true Stand ev - er in the light,
loy - al

All rap - ture thro' and thro', In God's most ho - ly sight. A - men.

483

HOMELAND. 7. 6. 7. 6. D.

HUGH R. HAWEIS, 1855

ARTHUR S. SULLIVAN, 1867

1. The Home-land! O the Home-land! The land of souls free-born!
2. My Lord is in the Home-land, With an-gels bright and fair;
3. For loved ones in the Home-land Are wait-ing me to come

No gloom-y night is known there, But aye the fade-less morn: I'm
No sin-ful thing nor e-vil, Can ev-er en-ter there; The
Where nei-ther death nor sor-row In-vade their ho-ly home: O

sigh-ing for that coun-try, My heart is ach-ing here; There
mu-sic of the ran-somed Is ring-ing in my ears, And
dear, dear na-tive coun-try, O rest and peace a-bove! Christ

is no pain in the Home-land To which I'm draw-ing near.
when I think of the Home-land My eyes are wet with tears.
bring us all to the Home-land Of his e-ter-nal love. A-men.

The Christian Kingdom

484

ALFORD. 7. 6. 8. 6. D.

HENRY ALFORD, 1867

JOHN B. DYKES, 1875

1. Ten thou-sand times ten thou-sand In spark-ling rai-ment bright,
2. What rush of al-le-lu-ias Fills all the earth and sky!
3. O then what rap-tured greet-ings On Ca-naan's hap-py shore!
4. Bring near thy great sal-va-tion, Thou Lamb for sin-ners slain;

The ar-mies of the ran-somed saints Throng up the steeps of light:
What ring-ing of a thou-sand harps Be-speaks the tri-umph nigh!
What knit-ting sev-ered friend-ships up, Where part-ings are no more!
Fill up the roll of thine e-lect, Then take thy power and reign:

'Tis fin-ished, all is fin-ished, Their fight with death and sin:
O day, for which cre-a-tion And all its tribes were made;
Then eyes with joy shall spar-kle, That brimmed with tears of late,
Ap-pear, De-sire of na-tions, Thine ex-iles long for home;

Fling o-pen wide the gold-en gates, And let the vic-tors in.
O joy, for all its for-mer woes A thou-sand fold re-paid!
Or-phans no lon-ger fa-ther-less, Nor wid-ows des-o-late.
Show in the heav'n thy prom-ised sign; Thou Prince and Sav-iour, come. A-men.

The Life Victorious

PATMOS. 7. 6. 8. 6. D.

GODFREY THRING, 1886

HENRY J. STORER, 1891

1. I heard a sound of voic - es A - round the great white throne,
2. From ev - ery clime and kin - dred, And na - tions from a - far,
3. I saw the ho - ly cit - y, The New Je - ru - sa - lem,
4. And there no sun was need - ed, Nor moon to shine by night,

With harp - ers harp - ing on their harps To him who sat there - on:
As ser - ried ranks re - turn - ing home In tri - umph from a war:
Come down from heaven, a bride a - dorned With jew - elled di - a - dem.
God's glo - ry did en - light - en all, The Lamb him - self the light;

'Sal - va - tion, glo - ry, hon - or!' I heard the song a - rise,
I heard the saints up - rais - ing, The myr - iad hosts a - mong,
The flood of crys - tal wa - ters Flowed down the gold - en street;
And there his serv - ants serve him, And, life's long bat - tle o'er,

As thro' the courts of heaven it rolled In won - drous har - mo - nies.
In praise of him who died, and lives, Their one glad tri - umph - song.
And na - tions brought their honors there, And laid them at her feet.
Enthroned with him, their Sav - iour, King, They reign for - ev - er - more. A - men.

393

The Christian Kingdom

486

PILGRIMS. 11. 10. 11. 10. With Refrain

FREDERICK W. FABER, 1854

HENRY SMART, 1868

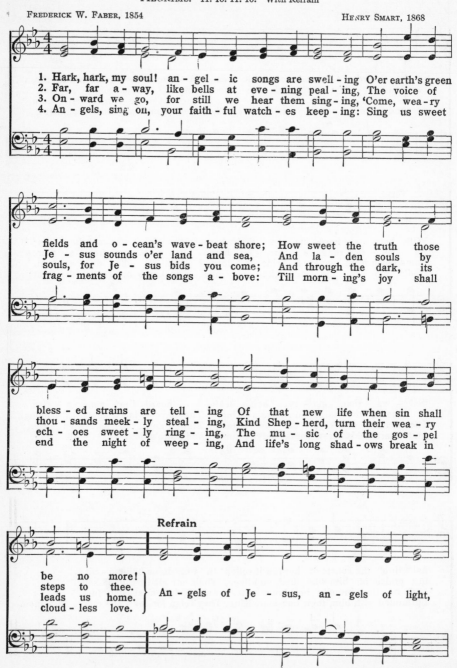

1. Hark, hark, my soul! an-gel-ic songs are swell-ing O'er earth's green
2. Far, far a-way, like bells at eve-ning peal-ing, The voice of
3. On-ward we go, for still we hear them sing-ing, 'Come, wea-ry
4. An-gels, sing on, your faith-ful watch-es keep-ing: Sing us sweet

fields and o-cean's wave-beat shore; How sweet the truth those
Je-sus sounds o'er land and sea, And la-den souls by
souls, for Je-sus bids you come; And through the dark, its
frag-ments of the songs a-bove: Till morn-ing's joy shall

bless-ed strains are tell-ing Of that new life when sin shall
thou-sands meek-ly steal-ing, Kind Shep-herd, turn their wea-ry
ech-oes sweet-ly ring-ing, The mu-sic of the gos-pel
end the night of weep-ing, And life's long shad-ows break in

Refrain

be no more!
steps to thee.
leads us home.
cloud-less love. } An-gels of Je-sus, an-gels of light,

394

The Life Victorious

Sing - ing to wel - come the pil - grims of the night! A - men.

487

TRUST. 11. 10. 11. 6.

JOHN GREENLEAF WHITTIER, 1882

CHARLES E. KETTLE, 1833–1895

1. When on my day of life the night is fall - ing, And, in the
2. Thou, who hast made my home of life so pleas - ant, Leave not its
3. Be near me when all else is from me drift - ing: Earth, sky, home's
4. I have but thee, my Fa - ther! let thy spir - it Be with me
5. Suf - fice it if— my good and ill un - reck - oned, And both for -

winds from un - sunned spa - ces blown, I hear far voic - es
ten - ant when its walls de - cay; O Love di - vine, O
pic - tures, days of shade and shine, And kind - ly fac - es
then to com - fort and up - hold; No gate of pearl, no
given through thine a - bound - ing grace— I find my - self by

out of dark - ness call - ing My feet to paths un - known—
Help - er ev - er pres - ent, Be thou my strength and stay!
to my own up - lift - ing The love which an - swers mine.
branch of palm I mer - it Nor street of shin - ing gold.
hands fa - mil - iar beck - oned Un - to my fit - ting place. A - men.

6 Some humble door among thy many mansions,
　　Some sheltering shade where sin and striving cease,
　And flows forever, through heaven's green expansions,
　　The river of thy peace.

7 There from the music round about me stealing,
　　I fain would learn the new and holy song,
　And find at last, beneath thy trees of healing,
　　The life for which I long.

The Christian Kingdom

488

SARUM. 10. 10. 10. 4.

William Walsham How, 1864   Joseph Barnby, 1869

1. For all the saints who from their la-bors rest,
2. Thou wast their rock, their for - tress, and their might:
3. O may thy sol - diers, faith - ful, true, and bold,
4. O blest com - mun - ion, fel - low - ship di - vine!
5. And when the strife is fierce, the war - fare long,

Who thee by faith be - fore the world con - fessed,
Thou, Lord, their cap - tain in the well - fought fight;
Fight as the saints who no - bly fought of old,
We fee - bly strug - gle, they in glo - ry shine;
Steals on the ear the dis - tant tri - umph - song,

Thy name, O Je - sus, be for - ev - er blest.
Thou, in the dark - ness drear, their one true light.
And win with them the vic - tor's crown of gold.
Yet all are one in thee, for all are thine.
And hearts are brave a - gain, and arms are strong.

Al - le - lu - ia! Al - le - lu - ia! A - men.

6 The golden evening brightens in the west;
  Soon, soon to faithful warriors cometh rest;
  Sweet is the calm of Paradise the blest.   Alleluia!

7 But lo! there breaks a yet more glorious day;
  The saints triumphant rise in bright array;
  The King of Glory passes on his way.   Alleluia!

8 From earth's wide bounds, from ocean's farthest coast,
  Through gates of pearl streams in the countless host,
  Singing to Father, Son, and Holy Ghost, Alleluia!

The Life Victorious

RUTHERFORD. P. M.

ANNE R. COUSIN, 1857

CHRETIEN D'URHAN, 1834

1. The sands of time are sink - ing, The dawn of heav - en breaks,
2. O Christ, he is the foun - tain, The deep, sweet well of love!
3. With mer - cy and with judg - ment My web of time he wove,
4. The bride eyes not her gar - ment, But her dear bride-groom's face;

The sum - mer morn I've sighed for, The fair, sweet morn a - wakes.
The streams on earth I've tast - ed; More deep I'll drink a - bove.
And aye the dews of sor - row Were lus - tered with his love:
I will not gaze at glo - ry, But on my King of grace;

O dark hath been the mid - night, But day - spring is at hand,
There is an o - cean full - ness His mer - cy doth ex - pand,
I'll bless the hand that guid - ed, I'll bless the heart that planned
Not at the crown he giv - eth, But on his pierc - ed hand:

And glo - ry, glo - ry dwell - eth In Em- man- uel's land.
And glo - ry, glo - ry dwell - eth In Em- man- uel's land.
When throned where glo-ry dwell - eth In Em- man- uel's land.
The Lamb is all the glo - ry Of Em- man- uel's land. A - men.

The Christian Kingdom

490

LEOMINSTER. S. M. D.

JAMES MONTGOMERY, 1835

GEORGE W. MARTIN, 1862
Harmonized by ARTHUR S. SULLIVAN, 1874

1. 'For ev - er with the Lord!' A - men, so let it be! Life
2. My Fa - ther's house on high, Home of my soul, how near At
3. 'For - ev - er with the Lord!' Fa - ther, if 'tis thy will, The
4. So when my lat - est breath Shall rend the veil in twain, By

from the dead is in that word, 'Tis im - mor - tal - i - ty. Here
times to faith's fore - see - ing eye Thy gold - en gates ap - pear! Ah!
prom - ise of that faith - ful word E'en here to me ful - fil: Be
death I shall es - cape from death, And life e - ter - nal gain. Know-

in the bod - y pent, Ab - sent from him I roam, Yet
then my spir - it faints To reach the land I love, The
thou at my right hand, Then can I nev - er fail; Up -
ing as I am known, How shall I love that word, And

night - ly pitch my mov - ing tent A day's march near-er home.
bright in - her - i - tance of saints, Je - ru - sa - lem a - bove.
hold thou me, and I shall stand; Fight, and I must pre - vail.
oft re - peat be - fore the throne, 'For - ev - er with the Lord!' A - men.

The Life Victorious

ST. LEONARD. C. M. D.

John White Chadwick, 1876

Henry Hiles, 1868

1. It sing-eth low in ev-ery heart, We hear it each and all,
2. 'Tis hard to take the bur-den up, When these have laid it down;
3. More home-like seems the vast un-known, Since they have en-tered there;

A song of those who an-swer not, How-ev-er we may call:
They bright-ened all the joy of life, They soft-ened ev-ery frown:
To fol-low them were not so hard, Wher-ev-er they may fare;

They throng the si-lence of the breast, We see them as of yore,
But O 'tis good to think of them When we are troub-led sore;
They can-not be where God is not, On an-y sea or shore;

The kind, the brave, the true, the sweet, Who walk with us no more.
Thanks be to God that such have been, Though they are here no more.
What-e'er be-tides, thy love a-bides, Our God, for-ev-er-more. A-men.

492

REST. (BRADBURY). L. M.

MARGARET MACKAY, 1832

WILLIAM B. BRADBURY, 1843

1. A - sleep in Je - sus! bless - ed sleep, From which none
2. A - sleep in Je - sus! O how sweet To be for
3. A - sleep in Je - sus! peace - ful rest, Whose wak - ing
4. A - sleep in Je - sus! O for me May such a
5. A - sleep in Je - sus! far from thee Thy kin - dred

ev - er wake to weep! A calm and un - dis - turbed re -
such a slum - ber meet; With ho - ly con - fi - dence to
is su - preme - ly blest; No fear, no woe, shall dim that
bliss - ful ref - uge be; Se - cure - ly shall my ash - es
and their graves may be; But thine is still a bless - ed

pose, Un - bro - ken by the last of foes.
sing That death hath lost its ven - omed sting.
hour That man - i - fests the Sav - iour's power.
lie, Wait - ing the sum - mons from on high.
sleep, From which none ev - er wake to weep. A - men.

493

AMBROSE. S. M.

PHOEBE CARY, 1852

ROBERT S. AMBROSE, 1876

1. One sweet - ly sol - emn thought Comes to me o'er and o'er;
2. Near - er my Fa - ther's house, Where man - y man - sions be;
3. Near - er the bound of life, Where bur - dens are laid down;
4. But, ly - ing dark be - tween, Wind - ing down thro' the night,
5. Fa - ther, per - fect my trust! Strength-en my power of faith!

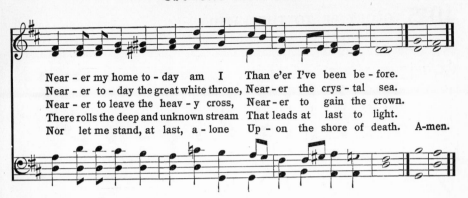

Near - er my home to - day am I Than e'er I've been be - fore.
Near - er to - day the great white throne, Near - er the crys - tal sea.
Near - er to leave the heav - y cross, Near - er to gain the crown.
There rolls the deep and unknown stream That leads at last to light.
Nor let me stand, at last, a - lone Up - on the shore of death. A-men.

494

ARLINGTON. C. M.

ISAAC WATTS, 1707

THOMAS A. ARNE, 1762

1. There is a land of pure de - light, Where saints im-mor - tal reign;
2. There ev - er - last - ing spring a - bides, And nev - er - wither-ing flowers;
3. Sweet fields be - yond the swell - ing flood Stand dressed in liv - ing green;
4. But tim - orous mor - tals start and shrink To cross this nar - row sea;

In - fi - nite day ex - cludes the night, And pleas-ures ban-ish pain.
Death, like a nar - row sea, di - vides This heavenly land from ours.
So to the Jews old Ca - naan stood, While Jordan rolled be-tween.
And ling - er, shivering, on the brink, And fear to launch a - way. A - men.

5 O could we make our doubts remove,
   Those gloomy doubts that rise,
And see the Canaan that we love
   With unbeclouded eyes;

6 Could we but climb where Moses stood,
   And view the landscape o'er,
Not Jordan's stream, nor death's cold flood,
   Should fright us from the shore.

495 GLORY BE TO THE FATHER

GLORIA PATRI

Anonymous—Second Century

Henry W. Greatorex, 1811–1858

Glo-ry be to the Fa-ther, and to the Son, and to the Ho-ly Ghost; As it was in the be-gin-ing, is now and ev-er shall be, world with-out end. A-men, A-men.

496 GLORY BE TO THE FATHER

GLORIA PATRI

Anonymous—Second Century

Old Scottish Chant

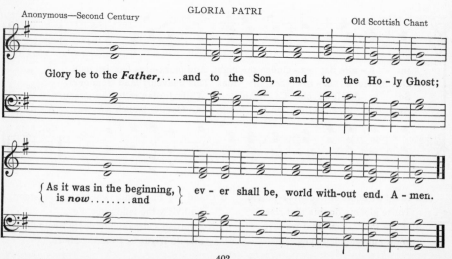

Glory be to the *Father*,....and to the Son, and to the Ho-ly Ghost; { As it was in the beginning, is *now*........and } ev-er shall be, world with-out end. A-men.

497 GLORY BE TO GOD ON HIGH

ANGELIC SONG

A. ARCHANGELSKY
Arranged by RUTHERFORD KINGSLEY

Luke II (14) UNISON

Glo - ry, glo - ry, glo - ry to God, Glo - ry to God in the high - est, Glo - ry, glo - ry, glo - ry to God, Glo - ry to God in the high - est, And on earth peace, and on earth peace, good will towards men, good will towards men. A - - men, A - men, A - men.

498 GLORY BE TO GOD ON HIGH

GLORIA IN EXCELSIS

From the Greek—Second Century   Old Scottish Chant

1. Glory *be to*....... | God on high: | and on *earth* | peace, good will towards men.
2. We praise thee, we } | wor-ship thee: | we glorify thee, we } | thy — great — glory.
   bless *thee*, we } | | give thanks to *thee* |
   | | for }

3. O Lord *God*,...... | heavenly King: | *God* the | Fa-ther Al - - mighty.
4. O Lord, the only } | Je - sus Christ: | O Lord God, Lamb } | Son — of the Father,
   begotten *Son* } | | of *God* } |

5. That takest *away* the...... | sins of the | world: | have *mercy* up- | on — | us.
6. Thou that takest *away* the | sins of the | world; | *re* - - | ceive our | prayer.
7. Thou that sittest at the } | God the | Father: | have *mercy* up- | on — | us.
   right *hand* of } | | | | |

8. For *thou* .... | only art | holy: | . *Thou* | on-ly | art the | Lord.
9. Thou only, O } | Ho - ly | Ghost: | art most *high* } | God the | Fa - | ther.
   Christ, with the } | | in the glory of } | | A-men.

499 MY SOUL DOTH MAGNIFY THE LORD

MAGNIFICAT

Luke I (46–56)   John Randall

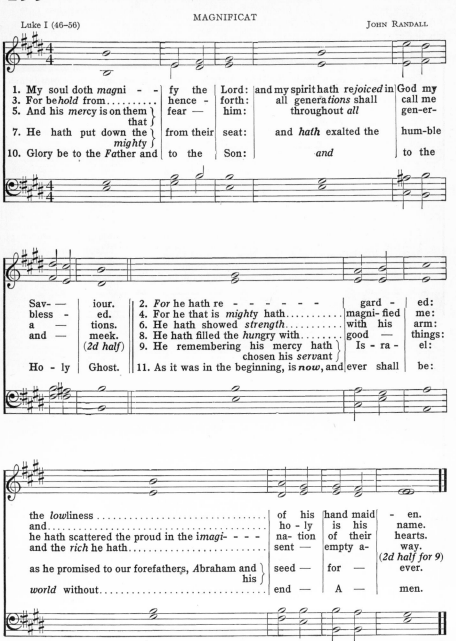

1. My soul doth *magni* - - | fy the | Lord: | and my spirit hath re*joiced* in | God my
3. For be*hold* from.......... | hence - | forth: | all genera*tions* shall | call me
5. And his *mercy* is on them } that | fear — | him: | throughout *all* | gen-er-
7. He hath put down the } *mighty* | from their | seat: | and *hath* exalted the | hum-ble
10. Glory be to the *Father* and | to the } | Son: | ·and | to the

Sav- — | iour.
bless - | ed.
a — | tions.
and — | meek.
 | (2d half)
Ho - ly | Ghost.

2. *For* he hath re - - - - - - | gard - | ed:
4. For he that is *mighty* hath.......... | magni- fied | me:
6. He hath showed *strength*.......... | with his | arm:
8. He hath filled the *hungry* with....... | good — | things:
9. He remembering his mercy hath } chosen his *servant* | Is - ra - | el:
11. As it was in the beginning, is *now*, and | ever shall | be:

the *low*liness............................... | of his | hand maid | - en.
and.. | ho - ly | is his | name.
he hath scattered the proud in the i*magi*- - - | na- tion | of their | hearts.
and the *rich* he hath...................... | sent — | empty a- | way.
 | | | (2d half for 9)
as he promised to our forefathers, Abraham and } his | seed — | for — | ever.
world without............................. | end — | A — | men.

405

Chants, Canticles, Ascriptions

500 CHRIST, OUR PASSOVER

EASTER CHANT

I Cor. V (7–8) Rom. VI (9–11) I Cor. XV (20–22)

Joseph Barnby (1838–1896)

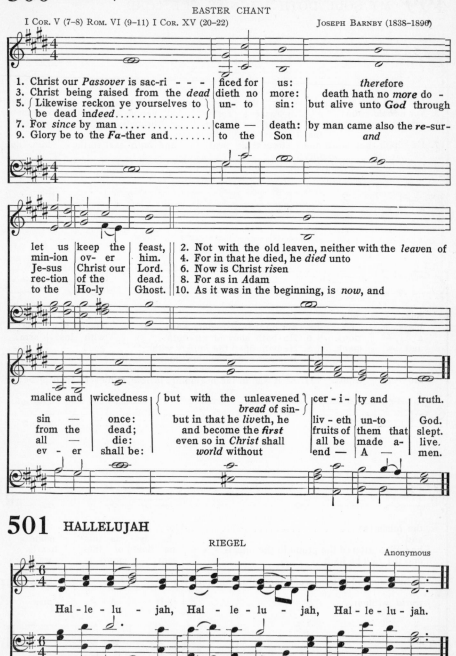

1. Christ our *Passover* is sac-ri - - - | ficed for | us: | *therefore*
3. Christ being raised from the *dead* diet | dieth no | more: | death hath no *more* do -
5. { Likewise reckon ye yourselves to } | un- to | sin: | but alive unto *God* through
   { be dead in*deed* }
7. For *since* by man . . . . came — | death: | by man came also the *re*-sur-
9. Glory be to the *Fa*-ther and . . . . to the | Son | *and*

let us | keep the | feast, | 2. Not with the old leaven, neither with the *leav*en of
min-ion | ov- er | him. | 4. For in that he *died* unto
Je-sus | Christ our | Lord. | 6. Now is Christ *risen*
rec-tion | of the | dead. | 8. For as in *Adam*
to the | Ho-ly | Ghost. | 10. As it was in the beginning, is *now*, and

malice and | wickedness | { but with the unleavened } | cer - i - | ty and | truth.
sin — | once: | { *bread* of sin- } | liv - eth | un-to | God.
from the | dead; | and become the *first* | fruits of | them that | slept.
all | die: | even so in *Christ* shall | all be | made a- | live.
ev - er | shall be: | *world* without | end — | A — | men.

501 HALLELUJAH

RIEGEL

Anonymous

Hal - le - lu - jah, Hal - le - lu - jah, Hal - le - lu - jah.

406

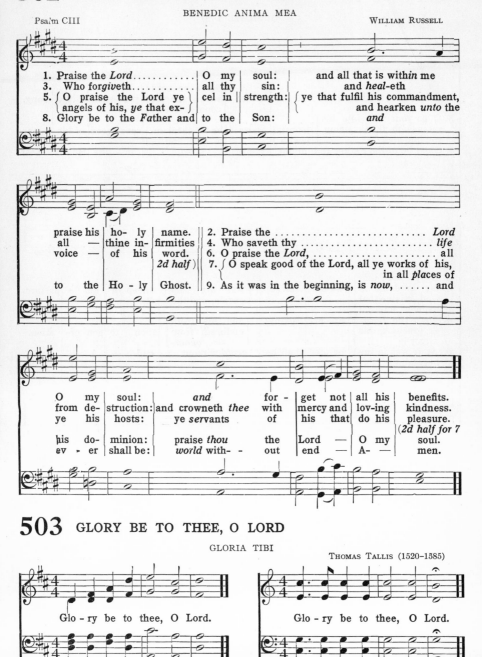

502 PRAISE THE LORD, O MY SOUL

BENEDIC ANIMA MEA

Psalm CIII

WILLIAM RUSSELL

1. Praise the *Lord*............. | O my | soul: | and all that is with*in* me
3. Who for*giveth*............. | all thy | sin: | and *heal*-eth
5. { O praise the Lord ye ‹ angels of his, *ye* that ex- } | cel in ‖ strength: | { ye that fulfil his commandment, and hearken *unto* the
8. Glory be to the *Father* and | to the | Son: | and

praise his | ho - ly | name. ‖ 2. Praise the .... *Lord*
all — | thine in- | firmities ‖ 4. Who saveth thy .... *life*
voice — | of his | word. ‖ 6. O praise the *Lord*, ... all
2d half ‖ 7. { O speak good of the Lord, all ye works of his, in all *places* of
to the | Ho - ly | Ghost. ‖ 9. As it was in the beginning, is *now*, ... and

O my | soul: | *and* | for - | get not | all his | benefits.
from de- | struction: | and crowneth *thee* | with | mercy and | lov-ing | kindness.
ye his | hosts: | ye *servants* | of | his that | do his | pleasure.
(*2d half for 7*
his do- | minion: | praise *thou* | the | Lord — | O my | soul.
ev - er | shall be: | *world* with- - | out | end — | A- — | men.

503 GLORY BE TO THEE, O LORD

GLORIA TIBI

THOMAS TALLIS (1520-1585)

Glo - ry be to thee, O Lord.

Glo - ry be to thee, O Lord.

407

504 O BE JOYFUL IN THE LORD

JUBILATE DEO

Psalm C

JOHN ROBINSON

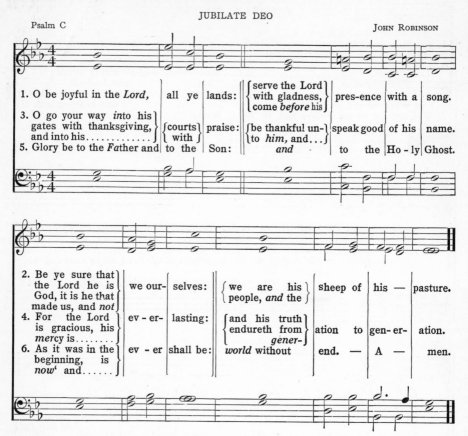

1. O be joyful in the *Lord,* | all ye | lands: | {serve the Lord / with gladness, / come *before* his} | pres-ence | with a | song.

3. O go your way *into* his gates with thanksgiving, / and into his............. | {courts} with | praise: | {be thankful un- / to *him,* and...} | speak good | of his | name.

5. Glory be to the *Father* and | to the | Son: | *and* · | to | the Ho - ly | Ghost.

2. Be ye sure that the Lord he is God, it is he that made us, and *not* | we our- | selves: | {we are his / people, *and* the} | sheep of | his — | pasture.

4. For the Lord is gracious, his *mercy* is........ | ev - er- | lasting: | {and his truth / endureth from / *gener-*} | ation | to gen-er- | ation.

6. As it was in the beginning, is *now'* and...... | ev - er | shall be: | *world* without | end. — | A — | men.

505 OUT OF THE DEPTHS

DE PROFUNDIS

Psalm CXXX

Anonymous

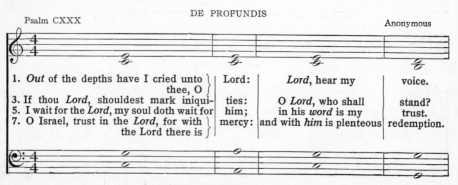

1. *Out* of the depths have I cried unto thee, O | Lord: | *Lord,* hear my | voice.

3. If thou *Lord,* shouldest mark iniqui- | ties: | O *Lord,* who shall | stand?

5. I wait for the *Lord,* my soul doth wait for | him; | in his *word* is my | trust.

7. O Israel, trust in the *Lord,* for with the Lord there is | mercy: | and with *him* is plenteous | redemption.

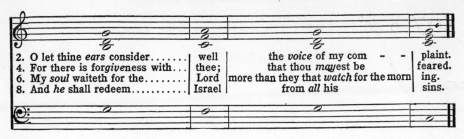

2. O let thine *ears* consider....... | well | the *voice* of my com - - | plaint.
4. For there is for*give*ness with... | thee; | that thou *may*est be | feared.
6. My *soul* waiteth for the........ | Lord | more than they that *watch* for the morn | ing.
8. And *he* shall redeem.......... | Israel | from *all* his | sins.

506 GOD BE MERCIFUL UNTO US

DEUS MISEREATUR

Psalm LXVII

Arranged from
BEETHOVEN, 1770–1827

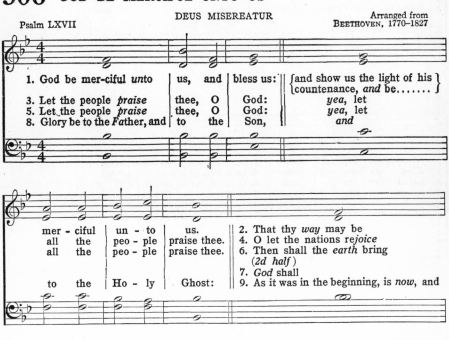

1. God be mer-ci*ful unto* | us, and | bless us: || {and show us the light of his
                                                      {countenance, *and* be....... }
3. Let the people *praise* | thee, O | God: || *yea,* let
5. Let the people *praise* | thee, O | God: || *yea,* let
8. Glory be to the *Father,* and | to the | Son, || *and*

mer - ciful | un - to | us. || 2. That thy *way* may be
all the | peo - ple | praise thee. || 4. O let the nations re*joice*
all the | peo - ple | praise thee. || 6. Then shall the *earth* bring
                                      (*2d half*)
                                      7. *God* shall
to the | Ho - ly | Ghost: || 9. As it was in the beginning, is *now*, and

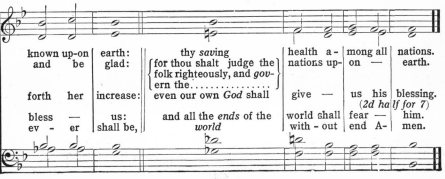

known up-on | earth: || thy *saving* | health a- | mong all | nations.
and be | glad: || {for thou shalt judge the} | nations up- | on — | earth.
                  {folk righteously, and *gov*-}
                  {ern the............... }
forth her | increase: || even our own *God* shall | give — | us his | blessing.
                                                              (*2d ha*lf for 7)
bless — | us: || and all the *ends* of the | world shall | fear — | him.
ev - er | shall be, || *world* | with - out | end A- | men.

409

507 O COME, LET US SING UNTO THE LORD

VENITE

Psalm XCV

WILLIAM BOYCE (1710–1779)

508 BLESSED ARE THE POOR IN SPIRIT

BEATITUDES

Matthew, V (3–12)

George W. Garrett (1834–1897)

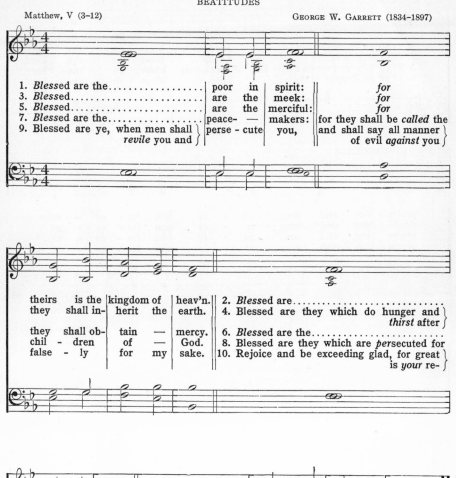

1. *Bless*ed are the.................. poor in spirit: *for*
3. *Bless*ed...................... are the meek: *for*
5. *Bless*ed...................... are the merciful: *for*
7. *Bless*ed are the.............. peace- — makers: for they shall be *called* the
9. Blessed are ye, when men shall ⎱ perse - cute you, and shall say all manner ⎱
      revile you and ⎰ of evil *against* you ⎰

theirs is the kingdom of heav'n. **2.** *Bless*ed are..........................
they shall in- herit the earth. **4.** Blessed are they which do hunger and ⎱
      thirst after ⎰
they shall ob- tain — mercy. **6.** *Bless*ed are the......................
chil - dren of — God. **8.** Blessed are they which are *per*secuted for
false - ly for my sake. **10.** Rejoice and be exceeding glad, for great ⎱
      is *your* re- ⎰

they that mourn: *for* they — shall be comforted.
right - eous- ness: *for* they — shall be filled.
pure in heart: *for* they shall see — God.
righteous-ness sake: *for* theirs is the kingdom of heaven.
ward in heaven: for so persecuted ⎱ prophets which were be - fore you.
      they the ⎰

509 O ALL YE WORKS OF THE LORD

BENEDICITE

1. O all ye Works of the Lord, bless ye the Lord:
2. O ye Angels of the Lord, bless ye the Lord:
3. O ye Waters that be above the Firmament, bless ye the Lord:
4. O all ye Powers of the Lord, bless ye the Lord:

praise him, and mag - ni - fy him for - ev - er.
praise him, and mag - ni - fy him for - ev - er.
praise him, and mag - ni - fy him for - ev - er.
praise him, and mag - ni - fy him for - ev - er.

5. O ye Sun, and Moon, bless ye the Lord:
6. O ye Stars of Heaven, bless ye the Lord:
7. O ye Showers, and Dew, bless ye the Lord:
8. O ye Winds of God, bless ye the Lord:

praise him, and mag - ni - fy him for - ev - er.
praise him, and mag - ni - fy him for - ev - er.
praise him, and mag - ni - fy him for - ev - er.
praise him, and mag - ni - fy him for - ev - er.

Chants, Canticles, Ascriptions

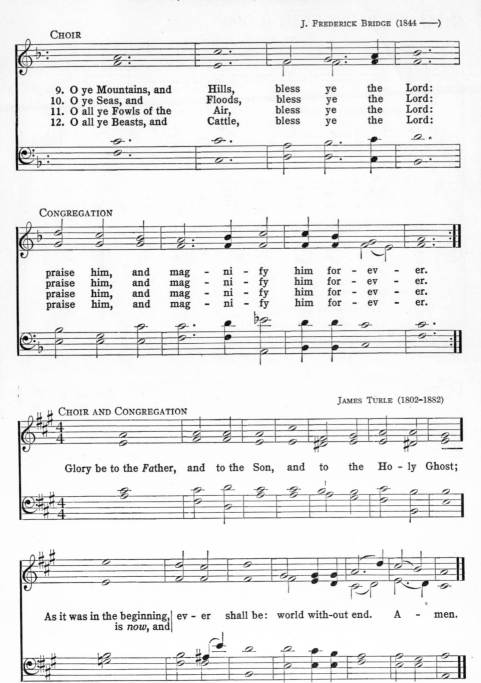

J. FREDERICK BRIDGE (1844 ——)

CHOIR

9. O ye Mountains, and Hills, bless ye the Lord:
10. O ye Seas, and Floods, bless ye the Lord:
11. O all ye Fowls of the Air, bless ye the Lord:
12. O all ye Beasts, and Cattle, bless ye the Lord:

CONGREGATION

praise him, and mag - ni - fy him for - ev - er.
praise him, and mag - ni - fy him for - ev - er.
praise him, and mag - ni - fy him for - ev - er.
praise him, and mag - ni - fy him for - ev - er.

JAMES TURLE (1802–1882)

CHOIR AND CONGREGATION

Glory be to the *Father*, and to the Son, and to the Ho - ly Ghost;

As it was in the beginning, | ev - er shall be: world with-out end. A - men.
          is *now*, and |

413

510 WE PRAISE THEE, O GOD

TE DEUM LAUDAMUS

Anonymous—Fourth Century   Joseph Barnby, 1838–1896

We praise thee, O God: We ac - knowl-edge thee to be the Lord.

All the earth doth wor - ship thee, The Fa - ther ev - er - last-ing.

UNISON READING:

To thee all angels cry aloud;
The heavens, and all the powers therein;
To thee cherubim and seraphim continually do cry,—

SANCTUS

A. S. Cooper

Ho - ly, ho - ly, ho - ly Lord God of Sab - a - oth; Heaven and earth are

full of thy glo - ry, Full of the maj - es - ty of thy glo - ry.

UNISON:

The glorious company of the apostles

The goodly fellowship of the prophets

The noble army of martyrs

Praise thee.

Chants, Canticles, Ascriptions

UNISON:

The holy Church throughout all the world doth acknowledge thee;
The Father of an infinite majesty;
Thine adorable, true and only Son;
Also the Holy Ghost, the Comforter.

TE DEUM LAUDAMUS   JOSEPH BARNBY

Thou art the King of Glo-ry, O Christ;

Thou art the Ev-er-last-ing Son of the Fa-ther

RESPONSIVELY:

When thou tookest upon thee to deliver man,
Thou didst humble thyself to be born of a virgin.
When thou hadst overcome the sharpness of death
Thou didst open the kingdom of heaven to all believers.
Thou sittest at the right hand of God, in the glory of the Father.
We believe that thou shalt come to be our Judge.
We therefore pray thee, help thy servants,
Whom thou hast redeemed with thy precious blood.
Make them to be numbered with thy saints, in glory everlasting.
O Lord, save thy people, and bless thine heritage.
Govern them, and lift them up for ever.
Day by day we magnify thee;
And we worship thy name ever, world without end.
Vouchsafe, O Lord, to keep us this day without sin.

MISERERE MEI   Anonymous

O Lord, have mer-cy up-on us, have mer-cy up-on us.

UNISON:

O Lord, let thy mercy be upon us, as our trust is in thee.
O Lord, in thee have I trusted; let me never be confounded.

415

Chants, Canticles, Ascriptions

511 HOLY, HOLY, HOLY

TER SANCTUS

Anonymous—Second Century
UNISON

W. A. C. CRUICKSHANK

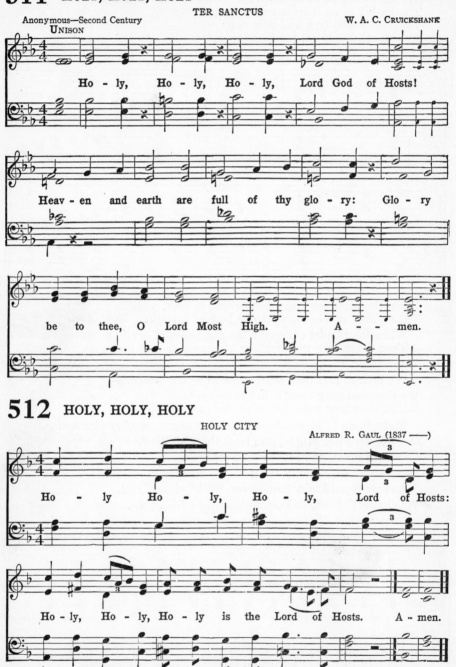

Ho - ly, Ho - ly, Ho - ly, Lord God of Hosts!

Heav - en and earth are full of thy glo - ry: Glo - ry

be to thee, O Lord Most High. A - - men.

512 HOLY, HOLY, HOLY

HOLY CITY

ALFRED R. GAUL (1837 ——)

Ho - ly Ho - ly, Ho - ly, Lord of Hosts:

Ho - ly, Ho - ly, Ho - ly is the Lord of Hosts. A - men.

513 SEND OUT THY LIGHT

LUX FIAT

CHARLES F. GOUNOD (1818–1893)

Send out thy light and thy truth, let them lead me; O let them bring me to thy ho - ly hill. Send out thy light and thy truth, let them lead me; O, let them bring me to thy ho - ly hill. O, let them lead me, O, let them lead me; O, let them bring me to thy ho - ly hill. A - men.

514 THE KINGDOMS OF THIS WORLD

Revelations XI (15)

MESSIAH

Composite—John E. West, 1918
George F. Handel, 1741

The king-doms of this world are be-come the king-doms of our Lord, and of his Christ; and He shall reign for-ev-er and ev-er. Hal-le-lu-jah! Hal-le-lu-jah! A-men.

Copyright, Congregational Union of England and Wales

515 CHRIST, WE DO ALL ADORE THEE

ADORAMUS TE

Theodore Dubois, 1899

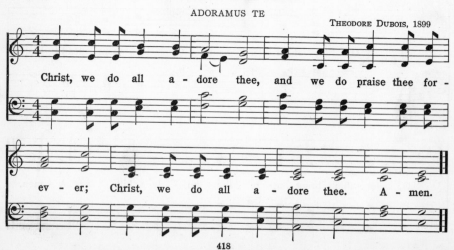

Christ, we do all a-dore thee, and we do praise thee for-ev-er; Christ, we do all a-dore thee. A-men.

516 LIFT UP YOUR HEARTS

SURSUM CORDA

MINISTER:

JOHN CAMIDGE, Arranged

CHOIR AND CONGREGATION

Lift up your hearts

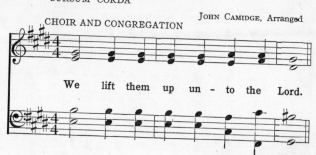

We lift them up un - to the Lord.

O Lord, open thou our eyes.

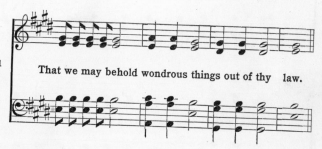

That we may behold wondrous things out of thy law.

O Lord, open thou our lips.

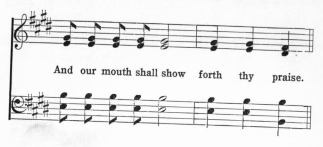

And our mouth shall show forth thy praise.

Praise ye the Lord.

The Lord's name be praised.

517 THE LORD IS IN HIS HOLY TEMPLE

QUAM DILECTA

GEORGE F. ROOT, 1820–1895

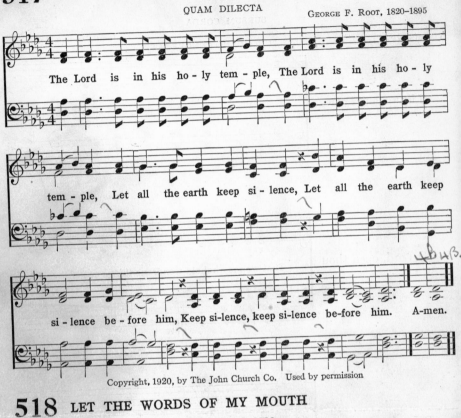

The Lord is in his ho-ly tem-ple, The Lord is in his ho-ly tem-ple, Let all the earth keep si-lence, Let all the earth keep si-lence be-fore him, Keep si-lence, keep si-lence be-fore him. A-men.

Copyright, 1920, by The John Church Co.   Used by permission

518 LET THE WORDS OF MY MOUTH

IN CORDE MEO

ADOLPH BAUMBACH

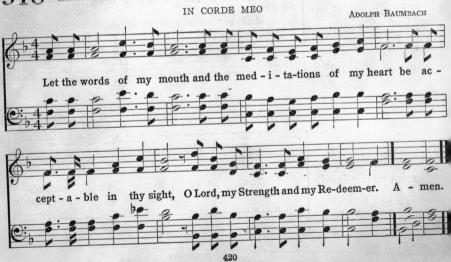

Let the words of my mouth and the med-i-ta-tions of my heart be ac-cept-a-ble in thy sight, O Lord, my Strength and my Re-deem-er. A-men.

But de - liv - er us from e - vil: For thine is the king-dom, The

power, and the glo - ry, For ev - er and ev - er. A - men.

521 O THOU, WHO HEAREST

MORECAMBE. 10. 10. 10. 10.

FREDERICK ATKINSON, 1880

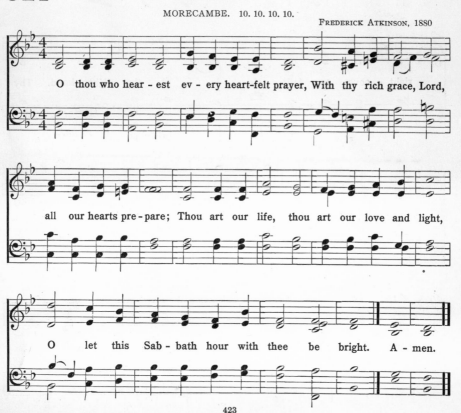

O thou who hear - est ev - er - y heart-felt prayer, With thy rich grace, Lord,

all our hearts pre - pare; Thou art our life, thou art our love and light,

O let this Sab - bath hour with thee be bright. A - men.

522 CAST THY BURDEN UPON THE LORD

BIRMINGHAM

PSALM LV (22) XVI (8)

FELIX MENDELSSOHN, 1846

Cast thy bur-den up-on the Lord, And he shall sus-

tain thee: He nev-er will suf-fer the

right-eous to fall; He is at thy right hand. Thy

mer-cy, Lord, is great, and far a-bove the heav'ns; Let

none be made a-sham-ed, that wait up-on thee.

523 BUT THE LORD IS MINDFUL

DÜSSELDORF

Isaiah XLIX (15)   FELIX MENDELSSOHN, 1836

But the Lord is mind-ful of his own, He re-
mem-bers his chil-dren. A-men.

524 O REST IN THE LORD

WILDERNESS

Psalm XXXVII (1-7)   FELIX MENDELSSOHN, 1846

O rest in the Lord, wait pa-tient-ly for him, and he shall give thee thy
heart's de-sires, and he shall give thee thy heart's de-sires.

525 BLESS THOU THE GIFTS

TALLIS' EVENING HYMN. L. M.

SAMUEL LONGFELLOW, 1886

Arranged from
THOMAS TALLIS, 1567

Bless thou the gifts our hands have bro't: Bless thou the work our hearts have plan'd;

Ours is the faith, the will, the tho't; The rest, O God, is in thy hand. A-men.

526 ALL THINGS COME OF THEE

OFFERINGS

Arranged from
BEETHOVEN

All things *come* of thee, O Lord, and of thine *own* have we . . giv-en thee. A-men.

527 MY GOD, HOW ENDLESS IS THY LOVE

NEWELL. L. M.

ISAAC WATTS, 1719

REUBEN BROOKS, 1897

My God, how end-less is thy love! Thy gifts are ev-ery eve-ning new;

And morning mercies, from a-bove, Gent-ly dis-till, like ear-ly dew. A-men.

528 THE LORD BLESS THEE

PAX VOBISCUM

FREDERICK MAXSON

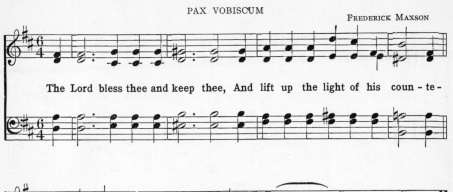

The Lord bless thee and keep thee, And lift up the light of his coun - te -

nance up - on thee, And give thee peace. A - - men.

529 THE SUN IS SINKING FAST

BAKER. P. M.

18th Century
Translated by EDWARD CASWALL, 1858

Anonymous

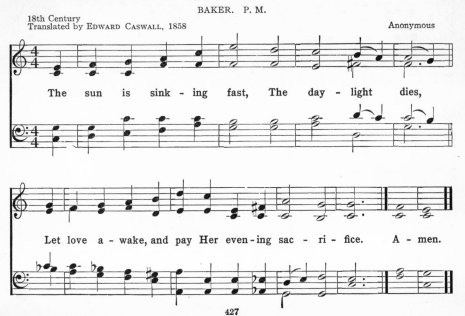

The sun is sink - ing fast, The day - light dies,

Let love a - wake, and pay Her even - ing sac - ri - fice. A - men.

530 FATHER, GIVE THY BENEDICTION

ALLA TRINITA BEATA. 8. 7. 8. 7. D.

SAMUEL LONGFELLOW, 1864

From Laudi Spirituali

Fa - ther, give thy ben - e - dic - tion, Give thy peace be -
Still our minds with truth's con - vic - tion, Calm with trust each

fore we part: Let thy voice with sweet com - mand - ing,
anx - ious heart. Peace which pass - eth un - der - stand - ing

Bid our griefs and strug - gles end:
On our wait - ing spir - its send. A - men.

531 LORD, HAVE MERCY

KYRIE ELEISON

GEORGE J. ELVEY, 1816–1893

Lord, have mer - cy, have mer - cy up - on us,

and in-cline our hearts to keep this law. A-men.

532 THE PEACE WHICH GOD BESTOWS

ELVEY. P. M.

FELICIA D. HEMANS, 1793–1835

GEORGE J. ELVEY, 1816–1893

1. The peace which God be-stows, Which from his pres-ence flows,
2. Ere dai-ly strifes be-gin The war with-out, with-in,

The peace the Fa-ther giv-eth to the Son,
The God of love, in spir-it and in power,

Be known in ev-ery mind, The bro-ken heart to bind,
Now on each bend-ed head His deep-est bless-ings shed,

And bless each trav-eler as he jour-neys on.
And keep us all thro' ev-ery trou-bled hour. A-men.

533 AMENS

Indexes

Index of Authors and Translators

Index of Composers and Sources

Alphabetical Index of Tunes

Alphabetical Index of Tunes

Gloria Tibi, 503
Golden Grove, 209
Gorton, 42
Goss, 99
Gottschalk (Mercy), 181
Gounod, 22
Gower's Recessional, 412
Grace Church, 349
Greenland, 278, 406
Greenwood, 26
Greystone, 467

Hamburg, 154
Hanford, 255, 386
Hankey, 289
Hanover, 3
Harvard, 249
Haven, 183
Haydn, 23
He Leadeth Me 270
Heber, 67
Hermas, 49
Hervey's Litany, 206
Hesperus, 247, 382,
Hinchman, 55
Holy City, 512
Holy Cross, 229, 439
Holy Trinity, 356
Holley, 302, 428
Homeland, 483
Hope, 25
Horton, 199
Howard, 463
Humility, 341
Hursley, 43
Hymn to Joy, 6

Ilkley, 152
Iliff, 286
In Corde, 518
In Memoriam, 451
Innocents, 69, 330
Intercession, New, 221
Italian Hymn, 1, 393

Jam Lucis, 71
Jesu Dilectissime, 332
Jewett, 298
Joy, 120
Jubilate Deo, 504
Just as I am, 202

Kelso, 24
Kirby Bedon, 192, 274
King Edward, 310
Kremser, 3
Kyrie Eleison, 531

Laban, 316
Lacrymae, 457
Lambeth, 77, 190
Lancashire, 160, 359, 373
Land of Rest, 96

Langran, 452
Lanier, 146
Laudes Domini, 20
Leominster, 296, 490
Lest We Forget, 413
Longwood, 9
Lord's Prayer, 520
Louvan, 60
Love's Offering, 338
Lucerna, 193
Lullaby, 468
Lux Beata, 238
Lux Benigna, 267
Lux Fiat, 513
Lynde, 473
Lyndhurst, 236
Lyons, 2

Magnificat, 499
Mahon, 429
Maidstone, 449
Mainzer, 342
Manoah, 10, 80
Margaret, 127
Marion, 465
Marlow, 314
Martyn, 258
Martyrdom, 455
Maryton, 336
Marzo, 144
Materna, 407, 480
Meditation, 157
Melcombe, 28
Melita, 187, 476
Mendebras, 53
Mendelssohn, 114
Mendon, 344, 454
Merrial, 44
Message, 472
Messiah, 514
Miles Lane, 174
Ministry, 347
Mirfield, 325, 369
Miriam, 59
Miserere Nobis, 519
Mission, 327
Missionary Chant, 399
Missionary Hymn, 392
Monkland, 95
Morecambe, 184, 453, 521
More Love to Thee, 290
Morley, 291
Morning Hymn, 18
Morning Star, 124
Morwellham, 422
Mount Calvary, 158
Mozart, 475
Munich, 188

Naomi, 232
National Hymn, 401, 414
Need, 252
Newell, 527

Nicaea, 19
Noel, 93
Nox Praecessit, 261, 438
Nun Danket, 100

Offerings, 526
Old Glory, 474
Old Hundredth, 11
Olive's Brow, 147
Olivet, 220
Olmutz, 458
O Quanta Qualia, 479
Orientis Partibus, 331
Ortonville, 172, 191

Paradise, 482
Park Street, 13
Passion Chorale, 151
Pastor Bonus, 72
Pater Omnium, 89
Patmos, 485
Pax Tecum, 244
Pax Vobiscum, 528
Peek, 307
Penitence, 235
Penitentia, 253, 384
Pentecost, 315, 380
Pilgrims, 486
Pilot, 260
Pleyel's Hymn, 256
Portuguese Hymn, 118, 321
Posen, 78, 280
Presbyter, 389, 408
Purpose, 396

Quam Dilecta, 517
Quem Pastores Laudavere, 205

Radiant Morn, 303
Rathbun, 155
Regent Square, 66, 117
Rejoice, 164
Repose, 431
Rest (Bradbury), 492
Retreat, 223
Richards, 340
Riegel, 501
Rivaulx, 343
Rockingham, 131, 433
Rockingham, New, 194
Roland, 85
Roseate Hues, 432
Rosmore, 125
Rotterdam, 426
Russian Hymn, 377, 400
Ruth, 97
Rutherford, 489

St. Aelred, 139
St. Agnes, 283
St. Andrew, 227, 467
St. Andrew of Crete, 320

442

Alphabetical Index of Tunes

443

Metrical Index of Tunes

Metrical Index of Tunes

Metrical Index of Tunes

Index of Subjects

447

Index of Subjects

Index of Subjects

Index of Subjects

Index of Subjects

Index of First Lines

Index of First Lines

Index of First Lines

Index of First Lines

Index of First Lines